L. S. TONG, J. WEISMAN:
Thermal Analysis of Pressurized Water Reactors

ERRATA

page			
47	Line 2	Slab thickness should read	
			between 1.5 and 6 cm

57 Table 2.2, middle column heading **For** 10 MW **read** 10^4 MW

106 Eq. (2-141) **For** $\mathcal{L}^{-1} \dfrac{T(s)}{\Delta(s)} =$ **read** $\mathcal{L}^{-1} \dfrac{T_c(s)}{\Delta(s)} =$

118 Fig. 3.2 abscissa Min Flow Area/Max Flow Area

127 Line 13 **For** $(4 \, q''/D_e \, G)$ **read** $(4 \, L q''/D_e \, G)$

154 Line 7 **For** functional **read** frictional

186 Line below Eq. (4-14) **For** $U_1(x,y,z) = C$ **read** $U_1(x,y,z) = C_1$

190 Two lines above Eq. (4-40) **For** shown **read** known

206 Eq. (4-87) **For** -4.710 for $x_1 < \chi < x_2$
read -4.710χ for $x_1 < \chi < x_2$

206 Eq. (4-88) **For** -0.653 for $x_2 < \chi$
read -0.653χ for $x_2 < \chi$

207 Line 2 **For** $D_e = 0.245$ to 1.25 **read** $D_e = 0.125$ to 0.6

207 Eq. (4-92) **For** $[P/(1 + 15)]$ **read** $[P/(P + 15)]$

207 Eq. (4-94) **For** $q''_{\text{crit}}/10^6 = K[H' - H)^{1/2}/(H' - H_0)]$
read $q''_{\text{crit}}/10^6 = K[(H' - H)/(H' - H_0)]^{1/2}$

211 Last term of Eq. (4-101) **For** $\left(\dfrac{\rho_v}{\rho_{l \, \text{sat}}}\right)^{0.68}$ **read** $\left(\dfrac{\rho_v}{\rho_{l \, \text{sat}}}\right)^{0.068}$

214 Fig. 4.10 Ordinate should read
HEAT FLUX, Q/A (BTU/HR - FT^2)

240 Table 5-1, footnote a **For** Genna **read** Ginna

273 Eq. (5-58) **For** $q'_2 = \phi/R_2$ **read** $q'_2 = \Theta/R_2$

277 Eq. (5-69) **For** $-\dfrac{\rho FH}{\omega} \dfrac{g}{g_c} + C_4(\omega r - u)^2$
read $-\dfrac{\rho FH}{\omega} \dfrac{g}{g_c} - C_4(\omega r - u)^2$

277 Eq. (5-70) **For** $= -\left\{\left[\dfrac{C'}{\rho}\left(\dfrac{W'}{A'}\right)^1\right]\right\}_R$ **read** $= -\left\{\left[\dfrac{C'}{\rho}\left(\dfrac{W'}{A'}\right)^{n_1}\right]\right\}_R$

Thermal Analysis
of Pressurized
Water Reactors

AR SOCIETY

RGY COMMISSION
(Division of Technical Information)

MONOGRAPH SERIES ON
NUCLEAR SCIENCE AND TECHNOLOGY

JOHN GRAHAM, Series Editor
AMERICAN NUCLEAR SOCIETY

ADVISORY COMMITTEE

Robert W. Dickinson, Atomics International
Gordon E. Hansen, Los Alamos Scientific Laboratory
John Inglima, Consolidated Edison Company
Norman H. Jacobson, American Nuclear Society
Frank E. Jamerson, General Motors Research Laboratory
Lester L. Kintner, U.S. Atomic Energy Commission
John R. Lamarsh, New York University
William E. Loewe, Lawrence Radiation Laboratory
David McCutchan, Westinghouse Astronuclear Laboratory
Jack M. Ravets, Westinghouse Astronuclear Laboratory
Clifford E. Weber, Atomic Energy Commission

MONOGRAPH TITLES AND AUTHORS

Reactor Noise
Joseph A. Thie, Consultant

System Analysis of Nuclear Reactor Dynamics
Lynn E. Weaver, University of Arizona

The Foundations of Nuclear Transport Theory
S. G. Yip and *R. K. Osborn*, University of Michigan

Alkali Metal Handling and Systems Operating Techniques
J. W. Mausteller, F. Tepper, and *S. J. Rodger*,
MSA Research Corporation

Irradiation Effects in Nuclear Fuels
J. A. L. Robertson, Atomic Energy of Canada, Ltd.

Water Coolant Technology of Power Reactors
Paul Cohen, Westinghouse Electric Corporation

Nuclear Reactor Instrumentation (In-Core)
James F. Boland, Argonne National Laboratory

Reactivity Coefficients in Large Fast Reactors
David Okrent and *H. H. Hummel*, Argonne National Laboratory

Nuclear Radiation: Direct Energy Conversion
George H. Miley, University of Illinois

Techniques in Fast Reactor Critical Experiments
W. G. Davey and *W. C. Redman*, Argonne National Laboratory

Thermal Analysis of Pressurized Water Reactors
L. S. Tong, Westinghouse Electric Corporation, and
Joel Weisman, University of Cincinnati

Thermal Analysis of Pressurized Water Reactors

AN AEC MONOGRAPH

L. S. TONG

PWR Systems Division
Nuclear Energy Systems
Westinghouse Electric Corp.
Pittsburgh, Pa.

JOEL WEISMAN

Department of Chemical and Nuclear Engineering
University of Cincinnati
Cincinnati, Ohio

Prepared under the direction of the
American Nuclear Society
for
The Division of Technical Information
United States Atomic Energy Commission

Published by

AMERICAN NUCLEAR SOCIETY

Foreword

This monograph is one of a series developed through the joint efforts of the American Nuclear Society and the Division of Technical Information of the U.S. Atomic Energy Commission. The purpose of the undertaking is to cover very specific areas of nuclear science and technology and thus help to advance the peaceful applications of nuclear energy.

While the monographs are primarily directed toward the operational scientist or engineer concerned with the applications of nuclear energy, they should also be helpful to students of science and engineering who otherwise might have little opportunity to study information within the special area of each monograph.

In looking forward to many dramatic accomplishments in peaceful uses of nuclear energy, the American Nuclear Society is pleased to cooperate with the U.S. Atomic Energy Commission in developing this series of monographs to help reach these achievements.

John Graham
Series Staff Editor
American Nuclear Society

Preface

Pressurized water reactors account for a growing fraction of electric power generating capacity, and the technology of these reactors is now highly developed. The maturity of the industry has brought an increased emphasis on the reliability and economy of nuclear power reactors as thermal machines. The thermal analysis of pressurized water reactors therefore assumes a widening industrial and academic importance.

This work presents the basic principles underlying thermal and hydraulic design of pressurized water reactors. In addition, the empirical data and engineering properties required for design, and not available in conventional handbooks, are given or cited. The book is intended to provide an overview of the entire field for nuclear engineering graduate students and to serve as a general reference for engineers working in the nuclear power industry. It is not intended to be a design manual.

In authoring this work we have endeavored to:

1. concentrate on central station power plants exemplified by existing pressurized water reactors.

2. present modern engineering approaches, such as the use of statistical techniques and optimization methods where appropriate.

3. use information based largely upon design experience.

4. recommend calculation techniques that are general, simple and reliable, but provide references for the detailed treatment of special cases.

5. emphasize the trend of future developments.

All reference material cited is unclassified and available to the public. Some general references that may be of special use are:

C. F. BONILLA, *Nuclear Engineering*, McGraw Hill Book Co., New York (1957).

S. GLASSTONE and M. C. EDLUND, *The Elements of Nuclear Theory*, D. Van Nostrand Co., Princeton, N.J. (1952).

J. R. LAMARSH, *Introduction to Nuclear Reactor Theory*, Addision-Wesley, Reading, Mass. (1966).

M. EL-WAKIL, *Nuclear Power Engineering*, McGraw Hill Book Co., New York (1962).

Reactor Handbook, Vol. I, *Materials*, 2nd ed., C. R. TIPTON, Ed., and Vol. IV, *Engineering*, 2nd ed., S. McLAIN and J. H. MARTINS, Eds., Interscience Publishers, John Wiley & Sons, New York (1964).

T. J. THOMPSON and J. G. BECKERLY, Eds., *The Technology of Nuclear Reactor Safety*, Vol. I, *Reactor Physics and Control*, M.I.T. Press, Cambridge, Mass. (1964).

L. S. Tong
Joel Weisman

July 1970

Contents

Chapter 1 POWER GENERATION

Chapter 2 FUEL ELEMENTS

Chapter 3 HYDRODYNAMICS

Chapter 4 HEAT TRANSFER AND TRANSPORT

Chapter 5 THERMAL AND HYDRAULIC PERFORMANCE OF A REACTOR CORE

Power Generation

A pressurized water reactor (PWR) is a water cooled nuclear reactor under sufficient pressure to prevent net steam generation at the core exit. In this chapter, we briefly delineate the major reactor systems falling under this definition and then describe, from a thermal analyst's viewpoint, the basic power distributions found within these reactors. The purpose of this discussion is to indicate the nature of the phenomena involved and some of the approximations that can be made.

1-1 REACTOR CONFIGURATIONS

1-1.1 Basic Concept

(a) Overall System. In the basic PWR design, the coolant flowing through the core is cooled by heat exchange with a secondary fluid. The overpressure adequate to suppress bulk boiling is maintained by an electrically heated pressurizer. In a typical reactor system[1,2] (Fig. 1.1) the primary coolant is circulated through the reactor core by one or more high pressure pumps; it proceeds to the heat exchanger where steam is generated and is then pumped back to the reactor core inlet. In the secondary system, feedwater is evaporated in the heat exchanger. The saturated steam goes through the turbine where it gives up its energy; it is then condensed in the condenser and returned to the heat exchanger by the boiler feed pumps.

In the commercial reactors being built for central station power, the reactor core, contained in a large pressure vessel with a removable head, is moderated and cooled by light water. Shielding around the vessel maintains low neutron flux levels at the primary loop components, and the reactor vessel, primary loop components, and auxiliaries are located within a structure (Fig. 1.2) that can contain the steam and fission products released in the highly unlikely event of a large break in the primary piping.[3] The primary system coolant in a PWR is completely isolated from the turbine, and this is referred to as an "indirect cycle." In the boiling water reactor (BWR) the steam produced in the core goes directly to the turbine, and this is called a "direct cycle." Thus, the indirect cycle has the advantage

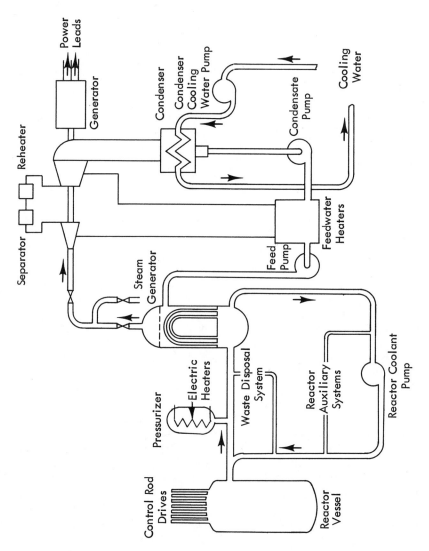

Fig. 1.1 Subcritical pressurized water reactor system. (From Ref. 1.)

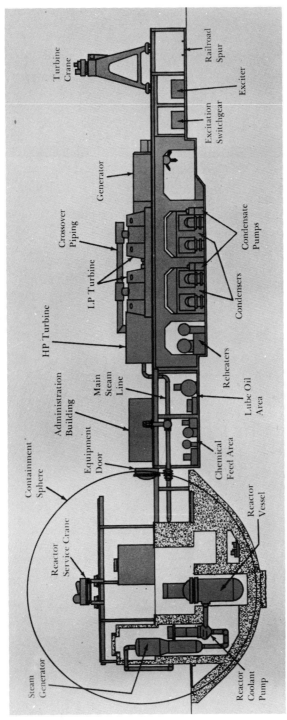

Fig. 1.2 System arrangement for large pressurized water reactor power plant. (From *Westinghouse Engineer*, **25**, 5, 145, 1965.)

of providing a radioactively clean secondary system, but it requires expensive heat exchangers. Such factors as the lower contained volume and simpler control requirements of the PWR compensate for this and make the system economically competitive.

(b) Core Configuration. To date, fuel elements for central station power plants have consisted almost entirely of partly enriched uranium dioxide encapsulated in metal tubes. The tubes are assembled into bundles and cooled by water flowing parallel to their axes. Figure 1.3 shows a horizontal cross section of a typical reactor.[4] The fuel assemblies are placed in a configuration approximating a right circular cylinder; the larger the reactor, the more closely a circular cross section is approached. The assemblies are retained in position by a core baffle attached to the core barrel, which is both the structural support for the baffle and the core support plate

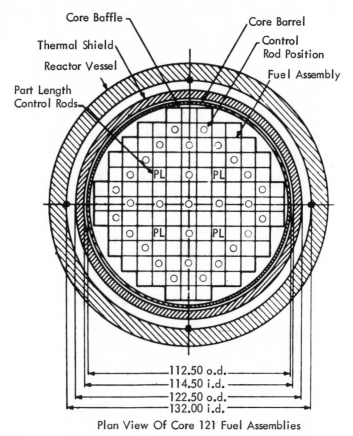

Plan View Of Core 121 Fuel Assemblies

Fig. 1.3   Cross section of the reactor vessel. (From *Proc. American Power Conference*, **30**, 298, 1968.)

upon which the fuel assemblies rest. The core barrel is surrounded by a thicker ring of metal designated as the thermal shield. The shield and the water gaps between the core and vessel thermalize and attenuate the fast neutron flux emanating from the core. In addition, the shield attenuates the gamma flux, and this serves to keep thermal stresses, due to gamma and neutron heating, and total neutron exposure of the reactor vessel within acceptable limits.

The fuel rods are assembled into large square arrays, which are held in position by spring-clips on egg-crate grids spaced about two feet apart along the length of the assembly (Fig. 1.4). Fuel tubes are omitted in a number of locations and are replaced by hollow guide tubes, which provide the structural support needed to tie the assembly together. The top and bottom nozzles are attached to these guide tubes.

The control rods are clusters of absorber rods that fit into the hollow guide tube. Each control rod member of a cluster consists of a sealed stainless-steel tube filled with a neutron absorbing material such as boron carbide or a silver-indium-cadmium alloy. All fuel assemblies are identical, and hence, each has hollow guide tubes, although only a fraction of the assemblies are under control rod positions. The guide tubes that do not contain control rods are fitted with plugging clusters to prevent unnecessary coolant by-pass flow through the empty tubes.

In earlier designs, cruciform shaped control rods, fitted into cutouts at the edges of the fuel assemblies, were used. To prevent large water gaps when the control rods were withdrawn, the rods were fitted with non-absorbing extensions. When the control rods were inserted, the extensions projected below the core, necessitating a longer reactor vessel. The individual water slots left by the newer cluster design are small and rod extensions are not needed.

The vertical reactor vessel cross section (Fig. 1.5) illustrates the structural arrangements and coolant flow path.[5] The core barrel is attached to the lower core support barrel, which is hung from a ledge near the top of the vessel. The upper core support plate and upper control rod shrouds are attached to the upper core support barrel, which fits closely within the lowest support barrel and is supported by it. Both upper and lower core support barrels are designed so they can be removed, but normally the lower support barrel remains in place throughout plant life.

The primary coolant enters through the inlet nozzle and flows downward through the passages between the core barrel and reactor vessel. After turning in the plenum area at the bottom of the pressure vessel, it flows upward through the core and exits through the outlet nozzles via close fitting adapters provided as part of the lower core support barrel.

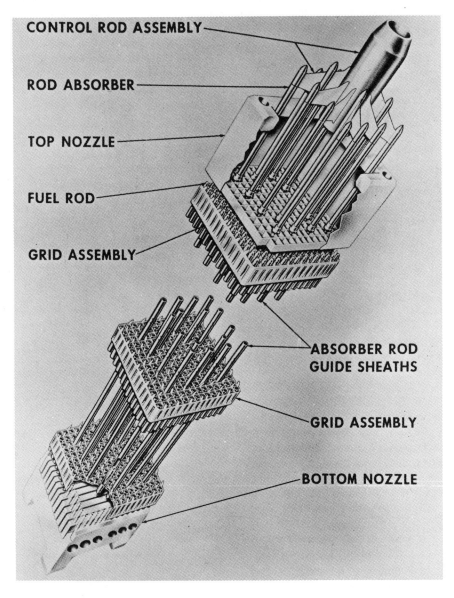

CONTROL ROD ASSEMBLY

ROD ABSORBER

TOP NOZZLE

FUEL ROD

GRID ASSEMBLY

ABSORBER ROD
GUIDE SHEATHS

GRID ASSEMBLY

BOTTOM NOZZLE

Fig. 1.4 Fuel assembly structure. (From *Proc. American Power Conference*, **30**, 298, 1968.)

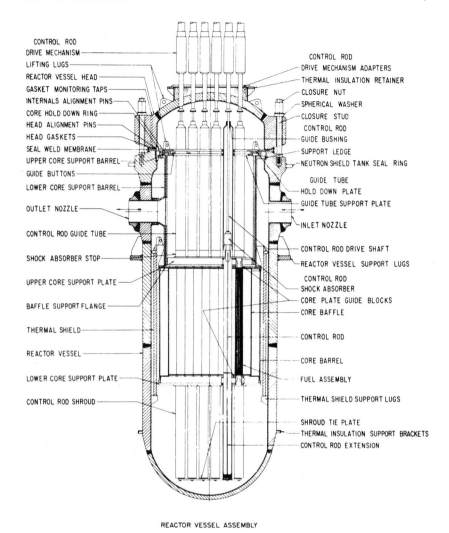

CONTROL ROD
DRIVE MECHANISM
LIFTING LUGS
REACTOR VESSEL HEAD
GASKET MONITORING TAPS
INTERNALS ALIGNMENT PINS
CORE HOLD DOWN RING
HEAD ALIGNMENT PINS
HEAD GASKETS
SEAL WELD MEMBRANE
UPPER CORE SUPPORT BARREL
GUIDE BUTTONS
LOWER CORE SUPPORT BARREL

OUTLET NOZZLE

CONTROL ROD GUIDE TUBE

SHOCK ABSORBER STOP

UPPER CORE SUPPORT PLATE

BAFFLE SUPPORT FLANGE

THERMAL SHIELD

REACTOR VESSEL

LOWER CORE SUPPORT PLATE

CONTROL ROD SHROUD

CONTROL ROD
DRIVE MECHANISM ADAPTERS
THERMAL INSULATION RETAINER
CLOSURE NUT
SPHERICAL WASHER
CLOSURE STUD
CONTROL ROD
GUIDE BUSHING
SUPPORT LEDGE
NEUTRON SHIELD TANK SEAL RING
GUIDE TUBE
HOLD DOWN PLATE
GUIDE TUBE SUPPORT PLATE

INLET NOZZLE

CONTROL ROD DRIVE SHAFT
REACTOR VESSEL SUPPORT LUGS
CONTROL ROD
SHOCK ABSORBER
CORE PLATE GUIDE BLOCKS
CORE BAFFLE

CONTROL ROD

CORE BARREL

FUEL ASSEMBLY

THERMAL SHIELD SUPPORT LUGS

SHROUD TIE PLATE
THERMAL INSULATION SUPPORT BRACKETS
CONTROL ROD EXTENSION

REACTOR VESSEL ASSEMBLY

Fig. 1.5 Vertical cross section on large water moderated PWR. (From *Reactor Handbook*, 2nd ed., Vol. IV, pp. 557–560, Interscience Publishers, New York, 1964.)

(c) Steam Generation. The heat transferred to the secondary fluid is used to generate steam; consequently, the heat exchanger where this occurs is called a steam generator. A number of steam generator configurations have been used, and in all, the primary coolant has been circulated through the tubes and the secondary fluid contained within the shell. The low corrosion rates required to limit primary loop contamination have led to the use of high nickel alloys

for the tubes. Initially, 300 series stainless steel was used exclusively for this purpose, but its sensitivity to stress corrosion has led to the use of Inconel in many more recent units.

Horizontal steam generator units are closest to conventional boiler practice. Single drum or reboiler units (Fig. 1.6), where steam separation takes place in the same drum as the bundle, can be used; however, capacity is limited by the maximum drum size that can be fabricated or shipped and by the achievable circulation ratio. Higher capacity can be obtained by using multiple drum units such as shown in Figs. 1.7 and 1.8. Here, steam is generated in the lower drum containing the tube bundle, and a two-phase mixture flows upward through the risers to the upper drum where the steam is separated. Primary separation takes place at the vortex created in

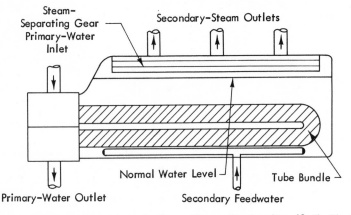

Fig. 1.6   Horizontal U-tube reboiler. (From *Nucleonics*, **19**, 7, 71, 1961.)

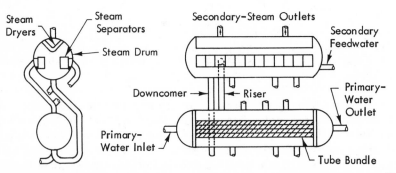

Fig. 1.7   Horizontal straight-tube multiple drum. (From *Nucleonics*, **19**, 7, 71, 1961.)

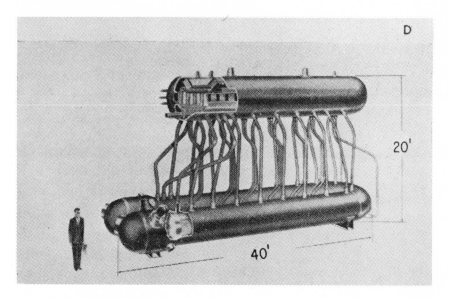

Fig. 1.8 Horizontal U-tube with contour shell and multiple drum. (From
Nucleonics, **19**, *7*, 71, 1961.)

the separators at the entrance to the drum, and the water is returned
to the lower drum via the downcomers.

Unitized vertical steam generators were originally developed to
provide compact, high efficiency units for marine propulsion systems, and nuclear steam generators of this type account for the
majority of the units installed in large central station plants through
1968. All of these units have used a U-tube bundle configuration.

A cross-sectional view of a typical vertical natural recirculation
unit is shown in Fig. 1.9. The two-phase mixture produced in the tube
bundle rises to the primary cyclone separator where the helical
propellor establishes a centrifugal field that produces a free vortex.
The wet steam exists through the central port and enters the
secondary steam separator in the steam drum, while the separated
water flows down through the annular passage around the cyclone
separator. Feedwater is added through a ring just above the tube
bundle, and the subcooled water flows downward in the space between
the tube bundle and shell completing the recirculation loop.

The desire to produce superheated steam has led to the development of the "once through" design. A sectional side view of such a
unit[6] is shown in Fig. 1.10. To provide a comparison of relative size,
the outline of a vertical natural-circulation boiler designed for the
same conditions is superimposed on it. The reactor coolant enters
the "once-through" generator at the upper plenum, flows through

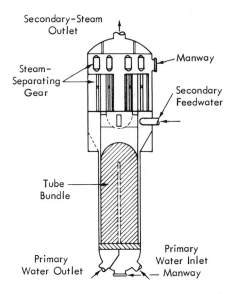

Fig. 1.9   Vertical U-tube single drum.   (From *Nucleonics*, **19**, 7, 7, 1961.)

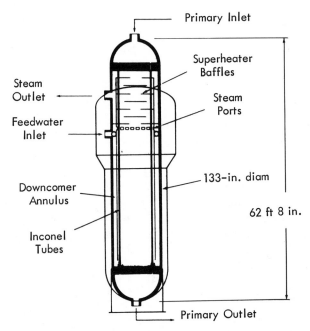

Fig. 1.10 Once-through steam generator; recirculating unit shown in outline.
(From Ref. 6.)

Inconel tubes, and exits from the lower plenum. The entering feedwater is sprayed from an annular ring and mixed with steam bled
from the upper end of the boiler section. The mixture flows down the
annular downcomer and into the tube-bank. No distinct water level is
present since the mixture quality gradually increases to 100% and
superheating starts. The superheater region is baffled to obtain the
cross flow and high velocities needed for efficient heat transfer to
steam. The superheated steam exits through outlet nozzles near the
upper end of the shell.

   (d) The Saturated Steam Turbine Cycle. Large, modern, fossil
fueled steam plants produce steam at pressures near 3200 psig and
temperatures around 1000 to 1050° F. Steam conditions for PWR
power plants are vastly different: The relatively low temperature of
the primary system coolant, coupled with the necessity of providing
an appreciable temperature difference across the heat exchangers,
leads to steam pressures in the range of 400 to 900 psig.
   The majority of the PWR plants produce dry and saturated steam.
The main drawback of a saturated steam cycle is its excessive end-
point moisture (20 to 24%), which leads to blade erosion and blade
efficiency losses that reduce thermal efficiency. Therefore, some
method of moisture removal must be used. Evaporation by constant
temperature throttling reduces the steam pressure and is detrimental
to cycle efficiency; however, the mechanical steam separator has
proved to be efficient and desirable since such moisture separators
both reduce the end-point moisture and improve turbine efficiency.
   The efficiency improvement is enhanced when moisture separation
is combined with reheating. Figure 1.11 shows the general arrangement of the elements of a power generation cycle for a large PWR
using a combination moisture separator, live-steam reheater, which
is placed in the crossover piping between the high and low pressure
turbines. This device, by means of a finned tube heat exchanger, removes moisture and transfers heat from steam bypassed ahead of the
throttle valve to the main stream.
   Since superheat increases the inlet temperature of a steam
turbine and reduces the end point moisture, it improves cycle
efficiency considerably. In a closed cycle, superheating can be
achieved by using either fossil fuel or by the once-through steam
generator previously described. The secondary steam from two
early demonstration power reactors, the Carolina-Virginias Test
Reactor (CVTR) and Indian Point 1, was superheated by fossil fuel;
however, the economics of fossil fired superheat has not proved
attractive, and the more modern plants have used saturated steam or
superheated steam from a nuclear steam generator. Since the
primary heat source is at a relatively low temperature, the amount of
superheat that can be supplied by such a steam generator is low, i.e.,

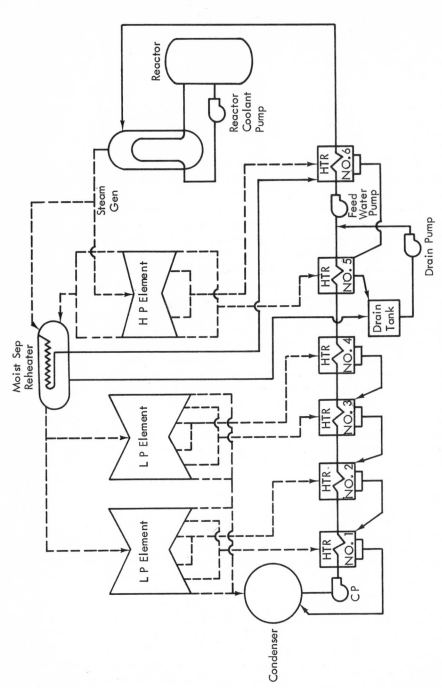

Fig. 1.11 Pressurized water reactor cycle.

of the order of 50°F. The steam cycle followed is thus quite similar to the dry and saturated cycle previously described. Moisture separation or moisture separation plus reheat is still required to prevent excessive end-point moisture.

An extensive discussion of thermodynamic cycles for nuclear power plants is provided by Kalafati,[7] and conventional equipment is described by Artusa.[8]

1-1.2 Other Reactor Concepts

(a) *Compact, Light Water Moderated Reactor Systems.* A compact, low weight system is of paramount importance in plants designed for ship propulsion. One method[9] proposes to achieve this by enclosing the reactor core and steam generator within the same pressure vessel. Coolant flows up through the core and chimney and down through the heat exchangers; it exits through the outer annulus of the double pipes leading to the pumps. The pumps are closely coupled to the reactor but are outside the primary vessel for ease of maintenance. A pressurizer is eliminated by simply maintaining a steam space above the heat exchangers. Since this steam is in equilibrium with water at the average core exit temperature, the quality of the fluid at the hot channel exit is significant.

In meeting the various military requirements, such as those for small plants in remote areas, weight and size may be of even greater importance. Here, highly enriched fuel may be used. Typical of this reactor group is the PM series of power plants that can be transported by air. The fuel elements are hollow tubes, approximately $\frac{1}{2}$ in. in diameter, made up of a highly enriched UO_2-stainless dispersion between stainless-steel claddings. The fuel is cooled by water flowing both inside and outside the fuel tubes. In PM-1,[10] the fuel tubes are assembled into six pie-shaped assemblies and one small central assembly, which are held together by brazed ferrules and end plates.

(b) *Heavy Water Moderated Reactors.* Although natural uranium alone cannot bring a light water moderated reactor to criticality, it is a satisfactory fuel for large reactors moderated and cooled by heavy water. In areas such as Canada, where enrichment facilities are lacking but heavy water and natural uranium are available, attention has turned to this type of reactor.

The simplest design has the moderator and coolant in the same circuit and is similar in many respects to a light water reactor; however, the greater distance (that is, the greater slowing-down length) required to thermalize fission neutrons in heavy water requires a much greater water-to-fuel ratio. One proposed method would achieve this by using fuel elements consisting of concentric rings

with wide spacing between the rings and the fuel elements. Alternately, clusters of cylindrical fuel rods with wide spacing between clusters may be used. The large size cores that result lead to reactor
vessels far larger than those required for a light water plant of the
same rating. For large size plants, vessel sizes and weights are beyond present capabilities; consequently, this concept appears to be
practical only for small- and medium-size plants. The 65-MW(th)
Agesta reactor in Sweden[11] is an example of the fuel cluster design.

Separating the moderating and cooling functions helps circumvent
the difficulties imposed by heavy water's greater slowing down length.
The fuel elements can be grouped into small clusters, each of which
is surrounded by a tube that confines the high pressure coolant. The
pressure tubes are spaced widely to provide enough distance for
neutron moderation between them, and, with appropriate insulation of
the pressure tubes, the moderator outside the tubes can be maintained
at low temperatures. Hence, the moderator can be contained in a
large vessel, or calandria, which is kept at or near atmospheric
pressure. Such thin-walled calandrias can be built in the sizes required by large reactors. Control rods may be placed in the spaces
between pressure tubes so rod drive mechanisms operating at high
pressures are not required.

To maintain good neutron economy, the pressure tube material
must have a low neutron absorption cross section. All of the early
reactors of this type used zirconium alloy pressure tubes, which
meet this requirement while providing a high strength corrosion resistant material. In the Canadian designs, the pressure tubes have
been placed horizontally and have been of the once through type.[12] In
the CVTR,[13] vertical U-tubes were used so that all connections were
made at the calandria top.

(c) Graphite Moderated Reactors. Graphite moderated and light
water cooled reactors have a long history in the production of plutonium, and it is natural that this concept be adapted to power generation by use of higher coolant temperatures. All such reactors built
to date (1968) have maintained an overpressure sufficient to prevent
bulk boiling; hence, they fit our definition of a PWR. The first atomic
power station of the USSR is of this nature. The reactor is encased
in a sealed cylindrical steel jacket filled with graphite bricks pierced
by fuel channels, and an atmosphere of helium or nitrogen is maintained to prevent graphite oxidation. The fuel element design[14] is
rather unusual: The active section of each fuel channel consists of a
graphite cylinder pierced by five tubes. The coolant flows down the
central tube then upward through the passages inside the annular fuel
elements. The fuel elements consist of slightly enriched hollow,
uranium-metal cylinders clad on both sides by thin stainless steel.
The complexity of the fuel element design makes this reactor ill
suited for large central station application.

A large dual-purpose reactor (power and plutonium production) has been erected at the Hanford laboratory of the U.S. Atomic Energy Commission. The reactor, designated the "NPR," consists of a very large rectangular stack of graphite, $33 \times 33 \times 39$ ft, penetrated by about one thousand horizontal pressure tubes.[15] The 2.7-in.-i.d. Zircaloy pressure tubes contain annular fuel elements of uranium metal clad in Zircaloy. If the reactor were converted to power production alone, UO_2 would replace the uranium metal.

Heat is removed from the NPR by six loops, each containing two steam generators. During dual-purpose operation a portion of the low pressure steam proceeds to two turbines and the remainder to 16 dump condensers. For power production only, the dump condensers would be eliminated and higher pressure steam would be generated.

(d) Supercritical Reactors. Reactors using supercritical water substance, or water above the critical pressure, as a reactor coolant have been proposed for future applications. Such systems have the potential advantages of higher efficiency due to higher steam pressure and temperature, higher enthalpy rise through the core, avoidance of limitations imposed by boiling heat transfer, and lower contained energy in the system. Both direct and indirect cycle reactors have been considered. Since no phase change can occur at supercritical pressures, both cycles fall under our definition of a pressurized water reactor.

Supercritical reactors may be of the pressure tube or pressure vessel type. In the SCOTT-R system,[16] the reactor is moderated by heavy water (or graphite) and cooled with light water at supercritical pressure. Each pressure tube contains a fuel assembly of slightly enriched UO_2 in the form of annular rings. A direct cycle, "once through" coolant system, where all the reactor coolant flows directly to the turbine, is used, which eliminates all recirculating equipment in the primary path.

Several pressure vessel concepts have been advanced, the simplest of which is a supercritical indirect-cycle water reactor. In this concept, an indirect-cycle, open lattice, pressurized water reactor is operated at supercritical pressures.

Supercritical reactors require the successful development of a high temperature collapsed-clad fuel element (cladding is so thin that it relies on the fuel for its support). In addition, water chemistry conditions that will suppress radiolysis, control corrosion, and prevent deposition of solids on the fuel must be determined.

1-2 POWER GENERATION AND DISTRIBUTION IN VESSEL TYPE REACTOR CORES

1-2.1 Power Distribution in Unperturbed, Uniformly Loaded Cores

Since light water moderated reactors cannot go critical using entirely natural uranium fuel, the designer has three choices: (a) to utilize fuel elements that all contain slightly enriched fuel; (b) to provide a "spiked core" where highly enriched fuel elements are uniformly dispersed in a matrix of natural uranium elements; and (c) to provide a region of highly enriched fuel surrounded by low enrichment or natural uranium fuel. The last alternative forms the basis of the seed-blanket design. Dispersion of enriched elements among natural uranium fuel results in the power outputs for the enriched rods substantially greater than for the others. It is difficult to provide additional flow to the enriched elements, and they could limit power output. Further, significantly lower fuel costs can be obtained by using slightly enriched fuel in all elements, and this is the common practice for large, central station power plants. No practical reactor design has used a spiked core.

If the fuel elements are dispersed through the core in a uniform manner and the fuel enrichment is uniform throughout, one may roughly approximate the overall neutron behavior by considering the core to be homogeneous. Most light water designs are essentially unreflected; thus, we may consider the unperturbed core as a bare homogeneous reactor. For such a core, an approximation of the neutron flux distribution may be obtained by solution of the wave equation[17]

$$\nabla^2 \phi + B^2 \phi = 0 \quad , \tag{1-1}$$

where ϕ is the thermal neutron flux and B^2 is the geometric buckling. Our boundary conditions for the solution of this equation are that the flux goes to zero at the extrapolated boundaries of the reactor and that it is finite everywhere except at the extrapolated boundaries. The extrapolated boundaries are approximated by adding $0.71 \lambda_{tr}$ (where λ_{tr} is the transport mean free path of a neutron) to the distance from the center line. Thus, for a cylindrical reactor, the extrapolated length L' is

$$L' = L + 1.42 \lambda_{tr} \quad , \tag{1-2}$$

where L is the actual length of the reactor and R', the extrapolated radius, is given by

$$R' = R + 0.71 \lambda_{tr} \quad , \tag{1-3}$$

where R is the actual radius. For large reactors, λ_{tr} is negligible with respect to R and L and may be ignored. The solution for several of the most common geometries are listed in Table 1.1.[18] Under the conditions we have postulated and if the effects of burnup are not significant, power generation is proportional to the thermal neutron flux. Thus, the functions indicated in Table 1.1 provide an overall description of the power distribution.

Table 1.1

THERMAL FLUX DISTRIBUTION IN BARE
HOMOGENEOUS REACTORS

Geometry	Coordinate	Distribution Function
Infinite slab	x	$\cos\left(\dfrac{\pi x}{L'}\right)$
Rectangular parallelepiped	$x, y,$ or z	$\cos\left(\dfrac{\pi x}{L'}\right), \cos\left(\dfrac{\pi y}{L'}\right), \cos\left(\dfrac{\pi z}{L'}\right)$
Sphere	r	$\dfrac{\sin(\pi\, r/R')}{\pi\, r/R'}$
Finite cylinder	r	$J_0(2.405\, r/R')$
	z	$\cos\left(\dfrac{\pi z}{L'}\right)$

Power distribution within a reactor free of control rods is not of academic interest only, and two control systems lead to such a situation for base loaded plants. In the chemical shim control system, boric acid is added to the reactor to compensate for the excess reactivity at the beginning of life, but it is gradually withdrawn as core reactivity declines with lifetime. A similar procedure is used in spectral shift control where the ratio of D_2O to H_2O in the moderator is decreased in response to the change in reactivity with lifetime. Decreasing the amount of D_2O present increases the number of thermal neutrons present in the core, thus increasing reactivity and compensating for the decrease in reactivity due to fuel burnup. At full power, such reactors may be operated with all control rods essentially withdrawn.

The power distribution at the beginning of life, in the uniform, unrodded cylindrical reactor, is approximated closely by a J_0 distribution radially and a cosine distribution axially. Thus, we may write

$$q''' = J_0\left(2.405\, r/R'\right)\cos\left(\frac{\pi z}{L'}\right)q'''_{max}\ ,\qquad (1\text{-}4)$$

where q''' = rate of volumetric heat generation

q'''_{max} = maximum volumetric heat generation at the center of the core

r = radial location

z = axial location (from centerline).

1-2.2 Effect of Fuel Loading

Most of the early pressurized water power reactors were uniformly loaded. In some plants, such as the portable military reactors of the PM series where simplicity of refueling is important, this loading scheme is still followed. For large central station plants, it has the disadvantage that it leads to a high power peaking in the central region of the core. In addition, relatively low average burnups are obtained since even at the end of life the outermost fuel elements have been only moderately burned down. One means of alleviating these difficulties is to use a zone loading scheme where the core is loaded with fuel elements of three or more different enrichments. The most highly enriched fuel elements are placed in the outermost position, and the least enriched are placed in the central region. Since power is approximately proportional to the product of thermal neutron flux and fissionable fuel concentration, the power level in the inner region of the core is lowered and that of the outer region is raised. This power flattening can significantly increase the total power capability of the core. When criticality is no longer possible, the entire core is replaced.

Replacement of the complete core at each refueling leads to a low average core burnup, but this is increased in most fuel cycling schemes by replacing only a portion of the fuel at each refueling. In the simplest of these schemes, the initial core is zone loaded as described above. At the end of the first core life, the most burned fuel from the central core region is removed, the outer regions are moved inward, and fresh fuel is placed in the vacated spaces in the outermost region. The same procedure is followed in all subsequent core loading, so at equilibrium all fuel removed has been through three or more cycles and has a high burnup.

Several variations of this fuel cycling scheme are available, and one significant departure is the so called "Roundelay" method.[19] In the equilibrium cycle, fresh elements are inserted in a uniform distribution throughout the core at each refueling. For example, with Roundelay 3-batch, every third element is replaced and the other elements are left in place. In Fig. 1.12, the fuel elements are numbered in the order in which they might be replaced in the reference core;

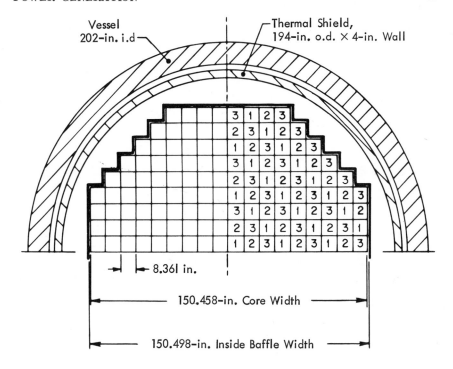

Fig. 1.12 Roundelay fuel cycling scheme. (From Ref. 19.)

during one refueling all No. 1 fuel assemblies would be replaced, and so on. The mixing of the fresh and burned assemblies produces strong coupling between them and permits improved power production form the burned elements.

Figures 1.13 and 1.14 show a typical radial power distribution in equilibrium cores after refueling for three region and Roundelay loaded reactors. The power distributions shown are the ratio of the power at the given point to the average power across the core at that axial location. The marked "ripple" in the Roundelay power distribution results from the significantly different power production from adjacent fuel assemblies with different burnups. In general for both refueling schemes, as burnup proceeds, the peak power decreases from that shown, and the power in the lower power region increases. It should be noted that small changes in fuel assembly placement can significantly affect the peak power. The selection of the exact cycling procedure requires a tedious and involved study.

As noted in Sec. 1-2.1, the nuclear designer may choose a "seed and blanket" design as an alternative to using slightly enriched uranium throughout the core. Such a core consists of one or more relatively small "seed" regions containing highly enriched fuel

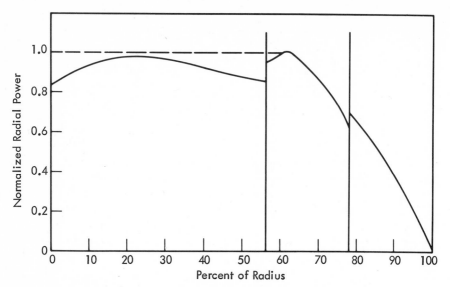

Fig. 1.13 Normalized radial power distribution in a PWR using 3-region batch loading. (From *Nucl. Eng. Design*, **6**, 301, 1967.)

assemblies, and "blanket" regions of natural or low enrichment fuel surrounding the seed regions. The blanket is composed of material whose multiplication factor is less than unity and cannot be made critical by itself. The reactivity of the core is determined primarily by the properties of the seed; thus, control rods are required only in the seed.

The geometry considered initially was that of a cylindrical annular seed with blanket regions both inside and outside. This arrangement, illustrated in Fig. 1.15,[20],[21] was that used in Shippingport Core I. The blanket elements were bundles of zirconium alloy clad cylindrical rods that contained UO_2 pellets fabricated from natural uranium. The seed elements consisted of a series of fuel plates held by Zircaloy alloy boxes, each segmented into four quadrants and the space between the quadrants used for a control rod passage. The fuel plates themselves consisted of an enriched fuel alloy strip sandwiched between two zirconium alloy cover plates and four side strips. In later seeds, a dispersion of UO_2 in Zircaloy replaced the U-Zr alloy fuel.

The power distribution within a seed and blanket reactor is appreciably different than the distribution heretofore considered. In reactors of this type, the infinite multiplication of the annular seed region is greater than unity, while that of the blanket is less than one. The higher fuel content and multiplication factor of the seed result in a higher fast neutron flux in the seed, and in addition, the highly enriched fuel in the seed has a higher thermal absorption cross section than the blanket. This results in a leakage of fast neutrons from the

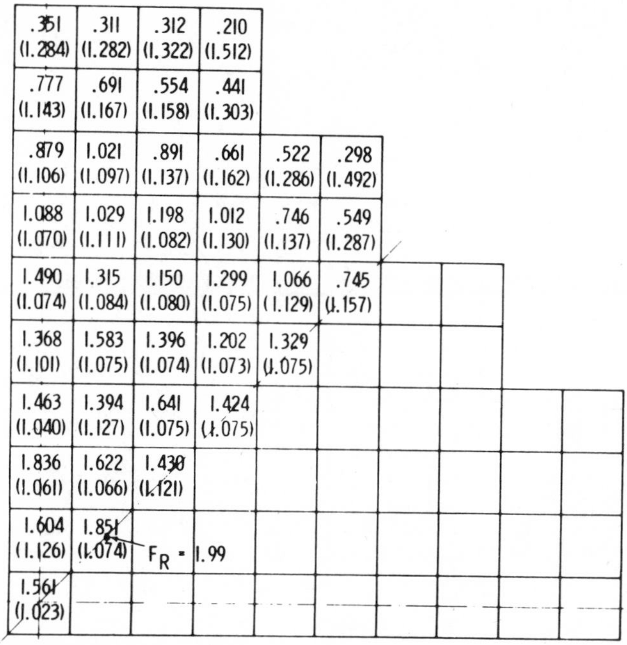

.351 (1.284)	.311 (1.282)	.312 (1.322)	.210 (1.512)		
.777 (1.143)	.691 (1.167)	.554 (1.158)	.441 (1.303)		
.879 (1.106)	1.021 (1.097)	.891 (1.137)	.661 (1.162)	.522 (1.286)	.298 (1.492)
1.088 (1.070)	1.029 (1.111)	1.198 (1.082)	1.012 (1.130)	.746 (1.137)	.549 (1.287)
1.490 (1.074)	1.315 (1.084)	1.150 (1.080)	1.299 (1.075)	1.066 (1.129)	.745 (1.157)
1.368 (1.101)	1.583 (1.075)	1.396 (1.074)	1.202 (1.073)	1.329 (1.075)	
1.463 (1.040)	1.394 (1.127)	1.641 (1.075)	1.424 (1.075)		
1.836 (1.061)	1.622 (1.066)	1.430 (1.121)			
1.604 (1.126)	1.851 (1.074)	F_R = 1.99			
1.561 (1.023)					

FOR EACH ASSEMBLY

Upper number is (average power in assembly)/(average power in core)

Lower number is (maximum power in assembly)/(average power in assembly)

Fig. 1.14 Typical radial power distribution in roundelay loaded reactor. (From Ref. 19.)

seed into the blanket and a leakage of thermal neutrons in the opposite direction.

In the blanket, ^{238}U fast fission produces the power at the beginning of life. As burnup proceeds, the formation of plutonium in the blanket creates new power producing fuel. The leakage of fast neutrons from the seed thus results in power production in a region that cannot by itself maintain a chain reaction. It is economically desirable that as much power as possible be produced in the relatively low-cost natural uranium blanket.

The power division between blanket and seed is one of the important factors in determining the thermal design of a reactor of this type. Radkowsky and Bayard[22] indicate a procedure for obtaining the ratio of blanket-to-seed power at the beginning of life, which gives a ratio of blanket to total power of approximately 0.52 for Shippingport Core I.

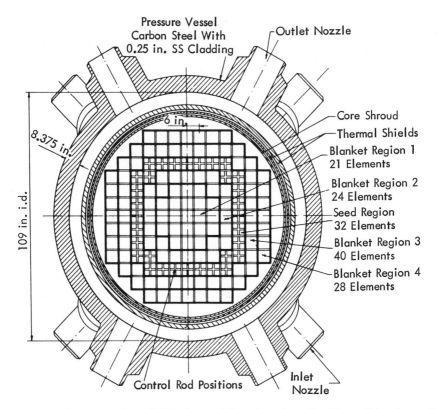

Fig. 1.15 Cross section of Shippingport Reactor, Core 1. (From *Directory of Nuclear Reactors,* Vol. IV, *Power Reactors*, pp. 21-32, 1962.)

The seed power does not decrease as rapidly as the seed volume, and therefore a decrease in seed volume results in increasing the seed power density. Hence, the power sharing tends to be determined by the maximum power density that can be extracted from the seed. Thus, the average power density in the seed may be more than 4 times that of the blanket.[22] Since resonance capture is of no consequence in the seed, it is feasible to use thin fuel elements with high surface area per core volume to attain the high power removal rates required.

On the basis of data from Shippingport, the fraction of total power produced in the blanket increases during the lifetime of any one seed; however, the blanket power drops on the insertion of each successive seed. It dropped from 58% for the first seed to 48% in the average of the fifth seed and to 44% by the tenth seed.

Due to the short radial dimension of the seed, the radial peak to average power ratio in the seed is not far from unity. However, the radial power distribution in the blanket is poor because the neutron flux falls off markedly with distance from the seed. A typical radial power distribution, illustrating the peaking adjacent to an annular seed, is shown in Fig. 1.16.[23] In the example shown, the peak seed to average seed power is 1.15, while the peak to average blanket power is 1.85. During the operating life of a seed, the power distribution is relatively stable, and hence it is feasible to orifice coolant flow to the various positions of the blanket.

Power peaking in the blanket elements adjacent to the seed can be reduced somewhat by the design used in Shippingport Core 2.[20] Here the seed assemblies alternate between two fuel assembly rings; however, the peaking is still considerable, and two-pass coolant flow is

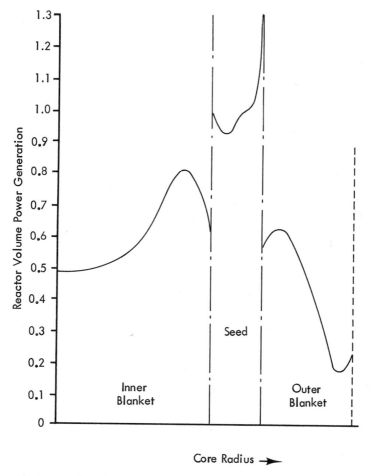

Fig. 1.16 Power distribution in a seed and blanket reactor. (After Ref. 23.)

provided to improve performance. The configuration of the blanket fuel elements was also changed. In Core 2, the blanket fuel elements consist of UO_2 platelets inserted between slotted Zircaloy plates, which are welded together, and the plates are then assembled into a rectangular box. Fuel elements of this design are capable of withstanding burnups considerably in excess of those that can be provided by cylindrical fuel rods.

1-2.3 Effect of Control Rods, Water Slots, and Voids

(a) Effects of Control Rods on Power Distribution. In many reactor designs, all excess reactivity is compensated by the insertion of control rods. The presence of the strongly absorbing material perturbs the flux both axially and radially, but this is not entirely a disadvantage since the rods may be used to improve the radial flux distribution. For example, some or all the rods in the center of the core may be partially inserted at the beginning of life, thereby reducing the peaking of the flux. This effect is illustrated in Fig. 1.17, where it will be observed that the flux goes essentially to zero at the boundaries of the control rods as well as at the extrapolated boundary of the reactor. The flux, and hence the power level in the outer region, is increased concurrently with the decrease in the central region.

The improvement in radial flux distribution attainable by insertion of rods is often more than negated by the change in the axial distribution. The usual situation in a pressurized water reactor, where the

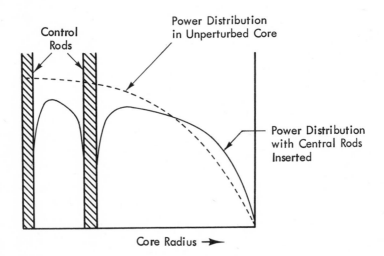

Fig. 1.17 Radial power distribution in a cylindrical reactor with and without control rods.

rods are top entering, is shown in Fig. 1.18. At the beginning of life, the partially inserted rods skew the flux toward the bottom. As the rods are withdrawn, the less burned fuel at the top of core causes the flux to be skewed toward the top at the end of life. As observed in Fig. 1.18, the ratio of peak to average power may be higher than that of unperturbed core.

Power distribution of the type shown in Fig. 1.18 can generally be represented by modifying the usual cosine distribution to the form

$$\phi(l) = (A + Bl) \cos (\alpha_0 l) \quad , \qquad (1\text{-}5)$$

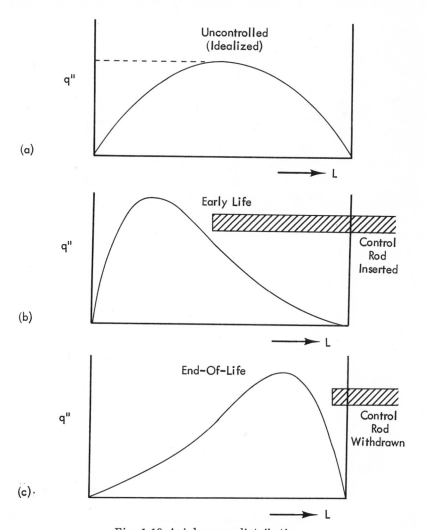

Fig. 1.18 Axial power distribution.

where A, B, and a_0 are constants and l is a dimensionless length coordinate varying from -1 to +1 along the heated length of the core.
Expressions of this form are applicable only if the ratio of peak to
average flux is less than 1.892. The establishment of the constants
and use of expressions of this form are discussed in Sec. 4-2.1.

   *(b) Power Perturbations Due to Structural Material, Water Slots,
and Voids.* No fuel-water lattice is entirely uniform: Additional
structural material is present at all grid locations, in fuel assembly
cans, in the support structure required at the core edges, etc. Since
such material is a neutron absorber without being a moderator or
source, it causes a local decrease in flux and hence in power. The
effect may be small if the material is of low cross section (such as
Zircaloy) but can be substantial if a high cross section material such
as stainless steel is used.

   Of perhaps even more concern to the designer, is the local peaking
due to additional water slots in a light water moderated reactor. Such
spaces result from clearance between fuel assemblies, variations in
lattice dimensions, and slots left by the withdrawal of control rods.
Since the water provides additional moderation, the local thermal
flux, and hence power, increases. This effect is illustrated in Fig.
1.19 for a circular water hole in a low enrichment, stainless-steel-
clad core.[24] Slots of a size that would cause substantially more peaking than that illustrated can easily arise and care is taken to avoid

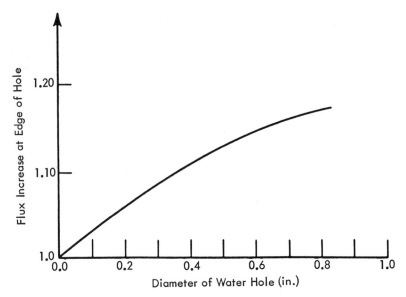

Fig. 1.19 Flux peaking at the edge of a circular water hole. (From *Nucl.
Eng. Design*, **6**, 301, 1967.)

these. For example, where cruciform or Y-shaped control rods are used, followers of a low cross section material can be provided to prevent large water slots from being introduced when the rods are withdrawn.

The creation of a steam void at the exit of the warmest core region is an additional factor that distorts normal flux patterns. In general, replacement of water moderator by steam reduces the core reactivity, and hence flux and power, in the region of the voids. The effect of such voids is particularly significant during transient and accident situations where the coolant enthalpy rises appreciably above its normal value. The power reduction due to void creation can decrease the severity of some situations.

1-2.4 Nuclear Hot-Channel Factors

The thermal designer can readily determine average core parameters from a knowledge of total heat output, core heat transfer data, and flow to the core; however, core performance is not limited by average conditions but by the most severe conditions. It is convenient and useful to define the "hot channel" of the core as that coolant channel or flow path where the core heat flux and enthalpy rise is a maximum. Conditions in the hot channel are defined by several ratios of local conditions to average conditions. These ratios are referred to as "hot-channel factors." Those aspects of the complex nuclear data that are most significant to the thermal designer may be conveyed by three nuclear hot channel factors. We define

F_R^N = Radial Nuclear Factor

$$= \frac{\text{Mean Heat Flux in Hot Channel}}{\text{Mean Heat Flux in Average Channel of Core}} \qquad (1\text{-}6)$$

F_Z^N = Axial Nuclear Factor

$$= \frac{\text{Maximum Heat Flux in Hot Channel}}{\text{Mean Heat Flux in Hot Channel}} \qquad (1\text{-}7)$$

F_Q^N = Nuclear Heat Flux Factor

$$= \frac{\text{Maximum Heat Flux in the Core}}{\text{Mean Heat Flux in the Core}} \cdot \qquad (1\text{-}8)$$

From the above definitions, it immediately follows that

$$F_Q^N = F_Z^N F_R^N \ . \qquad \text{if } F_R = 1 - \text{pin factor} \qquad (1\text{-}9)$$

Some authors define F_Z^N as the highest value that the ratio (maximum channel flux/average flux of given channel) may have, and, when so defined, the maximum of the ratio may not occur in the hot channel. When using reported values of F_Z^N, one should determine the basis for their definition.

The above nuclear factors are defined on the basis of nominal channel dimensions. In computing the limiting heat fluxes and enthalpy rises, consideration must also be given to deviation from nominal dimensions and flow. The procedure used to account for these deviations is discussed in Sec. 5.1.

An estimate of the magnitude of the nuclear hot-channel factors may be obtained by considering a large, bare homogeneous reactor of cylindrical shape. For a uniformly enriched, unpoisoned, unperturbed reactor, we have seen that the heat flux follows a J_0 distribution radially and a cosine distribution axially. Figure 1.20 shows the

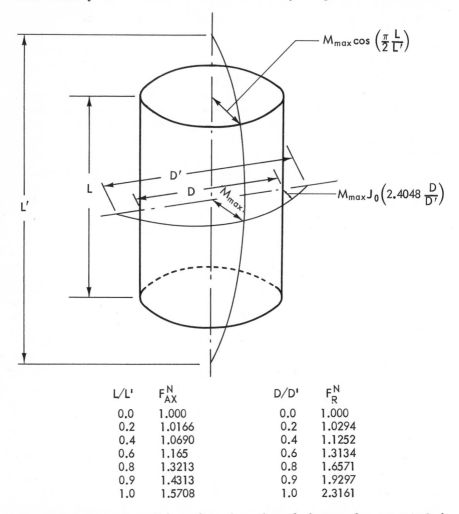

L/L'	F_{AX}^N		D/D'	F_R^N
0.0	1.000		0.0	1.000
0.2	1.0166		0.2	1.0294
0.4	1.0690		0.4	1.1252
0.6	1.165		0.6	1.3134
0.8	1.3213		0.8	1.6571
0.9	1.4313		0.9	1.9297
1.0	1.5708		1.0	2.3161

Fig. 1.20 Axial and radial nuclear hot channel factors for unperturbed cylindrical reactors.

axial and radial nuclear hot-channel factors for such a reactor as a function of the ratios of (actual length)/(actual length + extrapolation length). For large reactors, the extrapolation length becomes negligible, and the values for L/L' and D/D' approach unity. Thus we find that under these idealized conditions $F_0^N = 1.5708 \times 2.3161 = 3.638$. In an actual uniformly loaded core, the overall hot-channel factor would be higher due to such effects as lattice nonuniformities, control rods, changes in fuel and fission product concentration, and coolant property variation. These effects can often be more than compensated by the improvements in F_R^N which can be obtained through nonuniform loading.

For a typical core, Fig. 1.21 illustrates the relative number of fuel elements having radial nuclear hot-channel factors in a given range. The peak radial flux is reached in a very small number of elements (often just one), and the majority of elements have radial factors less than 1.0.

For a "seed and blanket" core, the overall core nuclear hot-channel factor has little meaning in view of the markedly different power generations in the seed and blanket, and it is useful to extend the concept to define hot-channel factors for each region of the core. We can define separate "seed" and "blanket" hot-channel factors by using Eqs. (1-6) through (1-8) with the word "core" replaced by "seed" or "blanket".

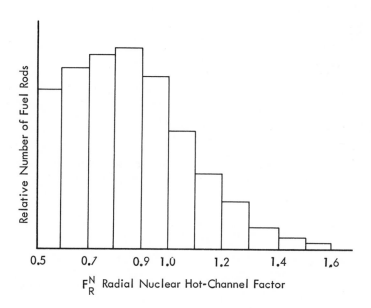

Fig. 1.21 Power census in a typical rodded core.

1-2.5 Heat Generation Within Fuel Elements

It is often assumed that the rate of power generation is essentially constant across the fuel rod. While this is often satisfactory as a first approximation, it is not strictly true. As noted previously, the heat generation in a volume element of fuel of a thermal reactor is essentially proportional to the thermal neutron flux at that point. Since the thermal neutron flux decreases towards the center of the element due to neutron absorption in the fuel, the power generation decreases similarly.

Following the explanation of Ref. (25), we shall consider a unit cell of a uniform rectangular lattice containing cylindrical fuel rods of radius R_0. The problem will be simplified by supposing the square unit cell to be replaced by a circle, radius R_1, having the equivalent area (Fig. 1.22). It will further be assumed that the neutron slowing

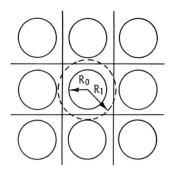

Fig. 1.22 Equivalent cell of fuel rod lattice.

down is constant in the moderator and zero in the fuel. The thermal diffusion equation for monoenergetic neutrons in the fuel rod is then

$$D \nabla^2 \phi - \Sigma_a \phi = 0 \quad , \tag{1-10}$$

when ϕ is the neutron flux at any point in the rod, D the diffusion coefficient, and Σ_a the macroscopic absorption cross section. After dividing by D and replacing Σ_a/D by κ_0^2 we obtain

$$\nabla^2 \phi - \kappa_0^2 \phi = 0 \quad . \tag{1-11}$$

In cylindrical coordinates this becomes

$$\frac{d\phi^2}{dr^2} + \frac{1}{r} \frac{d\phi}{dr} - \kappa_0^2 \phi = 0 \quad . \tag{1-12}$$

Since κ_0^2 is positive, Eq. (1-12) is a modified Bessel equation having the general solution

$$\phi = A I_0 (\kappa_0 r) + A' K_0 (\kappa_0 r) \quad , \tag{1-13}$$

where I_0 and K_0 are zero order, modified Bessel functions of the first and second kind, respectively. The second term may be eliminated since K_0 would require the neutron flux to go to infinity at the axis of the fuel rod. Thus, we obtain for the flux in the rod

$$\phi = A I_0 (\kappa_0 r) \quad . \tag{1-14}$$

The value A may be determined from the boundary condition that $\phi = \phi_{surface}$ at $r = R_0$.

It is also useful to relate the neutron flux at the surface of the fuel rod to the average flux in the fuel with the definition

$$F = \frac{\text{thermal neutron flux at fuel rod surface}}{\text{mean thermal flux in interior of rod}} \quad . \tag{1-15}$$

With the previous assumptions, it may be shown for a cylindrical rod that

$$F = \frac{\kappa_0 R_0}{2} \frac{I_0 (\kappa_0 R_0)}{I_1 (\kappa_0 R_0)} \quad . \tag{1-16}$$

For an infinite slab fuel element, one obtains

$$\phi = \frac{\phi_0 \cosh (\kappa_0 x)}{\cosh (\kappa_0 R_0)} \tag{1-17}$$

and

$$F = \kappa_0 R_0 \coth (\kappa_0 R_0) \quad , \tag{1-18}$$

where

x = distance from the centerline

R_0 = the half thickness of the fuel element

ϕ_0 = the surface flux.

The previous assumption that the power distribution across the fuel rod is directly proportional to the thermal flux is not entirely correct since, as burnup proceeds, the fuel and poison distribution are no longer uniform. In view of the usual uncertainties in flux levels and in physical properties of the fuel elements, consideration of these non uniformities is rarely required. Perhaps more important are the limitations on simple diffusion theory. More exact calculations show that diffusion theory tends to underestimate the flux depression in the fuel.

Most modern computer calculations of flux depression are based on escape probabilities. In particular, the method of Amouyal et al.[26] is widely used. This method is carried out only for the equivalent cell, and the neutron current is taken to be zero at the outer surface of this cell. However, diffusion theory is not assumed to hold within the fuel. Amouyal et al. calculate P_F, the probability that neutrons produced uniformly within the fuel ultimately escape from the fuel. The expression obtained for a cylindrical fuel rod of radius R_0(cm) is

$$\frac{1}{P_F} = 1 + (\Sigma_{aF}/\Sigma_{tF})\{A[1 + \alpha(\Sigma_{sF}/\Sigma_{tF}) + \beta(\Sigma_{sF}/\Sigma_{tF})^2] + R_0\Sigma_{tF}\} \quad , \quad (1\text{-}19)$$

where

$$A = \frac{1 - P_{F0}}{P_{F0}} - R_0\Sigma_{tF}$$

and

P_{F0} = probability that neutron escapes without collision from an infinite cylinder of radius R and macroscopic cross section Σ_{tF} (given by Fig. 1.23)

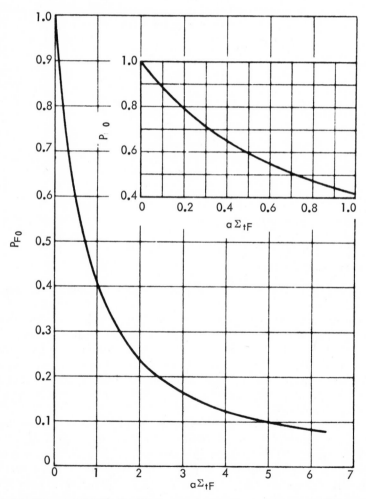

Fig. 1.23 The probability P_{F0} that a neutron escapes without collision from an infinite cylinder of radius a and macroscopic cross section Σ_{tF}. (From *J. Nuclear Energy*, **6**, 79, 1957.)

Σ_{aF} = macroscopic absorption cross section of the fuel, cm^{-1}

Σ_{tF} = total macroscopic cross section of the fuel, cm^{-1}

Σ_{sF} = macroscopic scattering cross section of the fuel, cm^{-1}

α, β = functions of $R_0 \Sigma_{tF}$ plotted in Fig. 1.24.

It may be shown that $1/P_F$ is equivalent to F. Further details on this method are available in Lamarsh.[27]

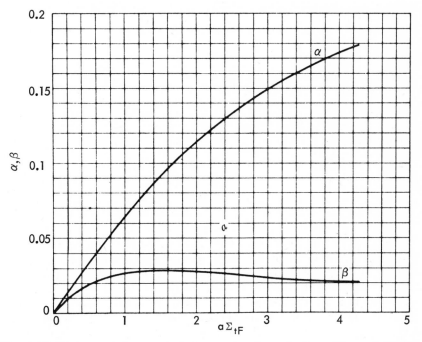

Fig. 1.24 The parameters α and β as a function of $a\Sigma_{tF}$. (From *J. Nuclear Energy*, **6**, 79, 1957.)

1-2.6 Distribution of Power Among Fuel, Moderator, and Structure

In addition to the axial and radial power distributions, the thermal designer must also be concerned with the fraction of heat generated within the fuel elements. Fission energy is released in the form of kinetic energy of fission fragments, neutron kinetic energy, and γ and β rays. The very short range of the fission fragments and β particles ensure that this heat release will take place within the fuel elements.*

---

*Approximately 10% of the β energy is converted to γ as bremsstrahlung and should be treated as γ in the division.

The energy released during neutron thermalization is released to the moderator. The energy released on neutron capture is largely released within the fuel, but a portion of it is released within the reactor structure. The large mass of the fuel produces a substantial self shielding and then most gammas are captured within the fuel. Table 1.2 quantitatively describes the distribution.

Table 1.2

ENERGY BREAKDOWN (MeV/fission) IN A
WATER COOLED REACTOR

Receiver	Time		
	Prompt	Delayed	Total
Fuel Element	Fission Fragment KE 168	β 7	175
Dispersed among fuel, moderator, and structure	Neutron KE 5 γ 7.5	Neutron capture 4 γ 6	22.5
Total	180.5	17	197.5

Five MeV of neutron kinetic energy are absorbed during thermalization. Hence, approximately 2.5% of the fission energy is definitely absorbed by the moderator. This may be taken advantage of in computing the heat which must be transferred by the fuel.

The portion of the gamma and neutron energy absorbed by the moderator and core structure depends on the specific design of the reactor. In a typical PWR design, somewhat less than 1% of the total power is absorbed within the thermal shield, and most of that energy is released by the outer fuel elements. In the central region of the core, the gamma energy is roughly distributed among the core constituents proportionally to their mass. In a uniform lattice core, this leads to the conclusion that essentially all the gammas in the central core region are captured by the fuel elements. In a pressure tube reactor, which has a larger mass of moderator and internal structure, appropriate adjustment should be made.

1-3 POWER GENERATION AND DISTRIBUTION IN PRESSURE TUBE TYPE CORES

1-3.1 Overall Power Distribution

In contrast to light water moderated reactors, the fuel in heavy water or graphite moderated reactors is generally not uniformly distributed throughout the moderator. As previously described (Sec. 1-1.1) the fuel elements in most designs are grouped together in clusters within pressure containing tubes that are dispersed throughout the moderator. Nevertheless, an approximation of the overall distribution of thermal neutron flux, which is adequate for many thermal design purposes, can be obtained by considering the moderator and fuel to be homogeneous. However, we cannot normally consider these reactors to be bare since they are usually surrounded by effective radial reflectors. The effects of such a reflector can be approximately evaluated by consideration of two neutron energy groups—thermal and fast.

For a semi-infinite slab, a sphere, and a cylinder of infinite length, the thermal flux within the core of a uniformly enriched reactor is given by[28]

$$\phi_t = AX + CY \quad , \tag{1-20}$$

where X and Y are functions shown in Table 1.3 for the various geometries.

Table 1.3

SOLUTIONS FOR THERMAL NEUTRON FLUX IN
REFLECTED CORE

	X	Y
Infinite slab	$\cos \mu x$	$\cosh \nu x$
Sphere	$\dfrac{\sin \mu r}{r}$	$\dfrac{\sinh \nu r}{r}$
Infinite cylinder	$J_0(\mu r)$	$I_0(\nu r)$

Notes: μ and ν are properties of the reactor core materials. See Ref. 25 for further discussion.

For thin reflectors, the first term is dominant and the flux distribution differs only slightly from that of an unreflected core. The change in flux pattern produced by a reflector around an infinite cylinder is illustrated in Fig. 1.25.

A somewhat cruder approximation of the behavior of a reflected core can be obtained by considering all neutrons to be thermal. When this is done, the resulting flux distribution equations have the same form as those for a bare core, but the overall dimensions are replaced by effective dimensions. For example, the flux of an unperturbed core is approximated by

$$\phi = \phi_{max}\, J_0\,(2.405r/R_e)\left(\cos\frac{\pi z}{L_e}\right)\ ,\qquad\qquad (1\text{-}21)$$

where

R_e = effective radius of core allowing for radial reflector

L_e = effective length of core allowing for axial reflectors.

Equation (1-21) does not predict the slight rise in core flux that occurs adjacent to the reflector. However, it can provide (see Fig. 1.25) a reasonable estimate of the flux throughout most of the core.

In the common cylindrical core, the large amount of structural material at the ends limits the effectiveness of any axial reflector. A cosine distribution with $L_e \approx L$ is thus often a very good approximation of the axial power variation.

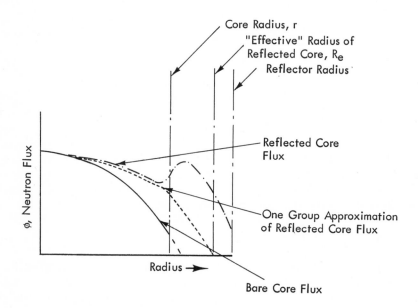

Fig. 1.25 Thermal neutron flux in bare and reflected cylindrical reactors.

1-3.2 Power Generation Within Fuel Clusters

The distance between rods within the pressure tube is generally orders of magnitude smaller than that between pressure tubes, resulting in negligible moderation within the pressure tube in comparison to that obtained between the tubes. As a first approximation, one may therefore ignore the area within the pressure tube as a source of thermal neutrons, and approximate the thermal diffusion equation for thermal neutrons within the pressure tube by a modification of Eq. (1-10). Here we have

$$D_{\mathrm{av}} \nabla^2 \phi - \Sigma a_{\mathrm{av}} \phi = 0 , \qquad (1\text{-}22)$$

where D_{av} and Σa_{av} respectively represent the diffusion coefficient and macroscopic absorption coefficient based on homogenizing the material within the pressure tube. From the development of Sec. 1-2.3, it is seen that this leads to an $I_0(R)$ flux distribution across the fuel cluster. Figure 1.26 illustrates this behavior in the fuel clusters of the heavy water moderated and cooled CVTR.[29]

The flux depression within the fuel assembly, called the "fine flux dip," is superimposed upon the normal radial flux variation across the reactor as a whole. We may then write

$$F_R^N = F_G^N \times F_{R_0}^N , \qquad (1\text{-}23)$$

where

$$F_G^N = \frac{\text{mean flux in the hot fuel rod}}{\text{mean flux in the hot fuel cluster}}$$

$$F_{R_0}^N = \frac{\text{mean flux in the hot fuel cluster}}{\text{mean flux in the average fuel cluster}} .$$

In the design of the CVTR reactor, F_G^N was assigned a value[26] of 1.25.

The thermal flux within a particular fuel rod will vary with the position of the rods in the cluster, and, as one proceeds around a fuel rod, the value of R, the radial distance from the pressure tube center, varies. In addition, for any tube not in the center of the core, there is an overall flux pattern effect on the flux distribution within the cluster. This is illustrated in Fig. 1.27, which shows the circumferential flux variation for the rods in a CVTR fuel assembly. Thus, we can show for any rod that

$$\phi = f(r, \theta) . \qquad (1\text{-}24)$$

To simplify temperature distribution calculation, the distribution for a given rod is often approximated by a function of the form

$$\phi = C_1 + C_2 \, r \cos \theta . \qquad (1\text{-}25)$$

The approximate function is made to fit the actual distribution at the

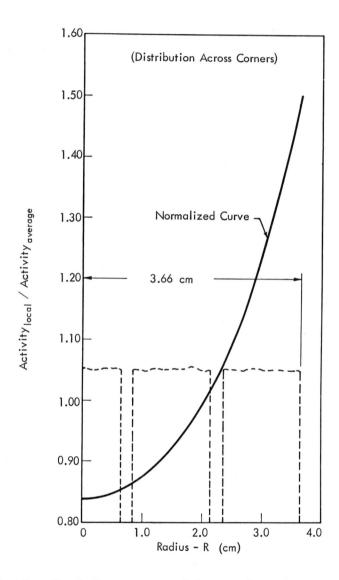

Fig. 1.26 Flux distribution across radial axis of Carolina-Virginia Tube Reactor (CVTR) assembly. (From Ref. 29.)

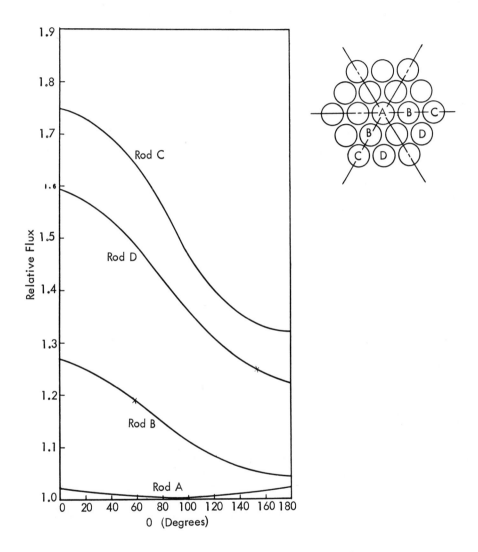

Fig. 1.27 Circumferential variation in flux around fuel rods of Carolina-Virginia Tube Reactor (CVTR) assembly. (From Ref. 29.)

center of the rod and at the point on the circumference having the peak heat flux.[27]

1-4 TRANSIENT POWER GENERATION AND DISTRIBUTION

1-4.1 Power Distribution Following a Load Change

We have previously considered the changes in power distribution due to rod motion occasioned by fuel depletion. In addition to this slow rod movement, one must observe the rapid rod motion in response to a load change. On a load increase, a rod withdrawal must be initiated in order to maintain coolant temperatures, and this results in a spatial change in fission product distribution. The change is of particular importance in the distribution of xenon because of its high yield and cross section (3×10^6 barns). Randall and St. John[30] have pointed out that the changes in xenon distribution during the transient can result in significant power shifts. A typical power shift during a reactivity addition by control rod withdrawal is shown in Fig. 1.28. Immediately after the rod motion, the peak flux shifts upward in the core; it then shifts downward toward its original position.

The time variations of flux at the location of the steady state peak (q_A'') and at the position of the transient peak (q_B'') are given in Fig. 1-28(b), which shows that the transient heat flux may be greater than the final steady state value. This phenomenon must be considered when evaluating nuclear hot-channel factors for nonbase loaded plants. Similar effects may be expected following a local decrease.

1-4.2 Power Generation During Shutdown

(a) *Fission Power Generation.* The rate of power decrease during a reactor shutdown is of concern to the thermal-hydraulic designer since it will affect fuel temperature during accident situations. We shall consider the situation where the reactor is shut down after operating at steady state for an appreciable period. During the steady state operation, the effective multiplication factor k_{eff} must be unity; for start-up, it must be greater than unity; and for shutdown, less than unity. It is useful to define an excess multiplication factor k_{ex} where

$$k_{ex} = k_{eff} - 1 \quad . \tag{1-26}$$

Thus, k_{ex} is positive for a supercritical reactor and negative for a subcritical reactor. If all neutrons may be considered to be emitted promptly at the time of fission, the time behavior of bare thermal reactor is given by

$$\phi\left(\overline{r}, t\right) = \phi_0 \exp(k_{ex} t /l) , \tag{1-27}$$

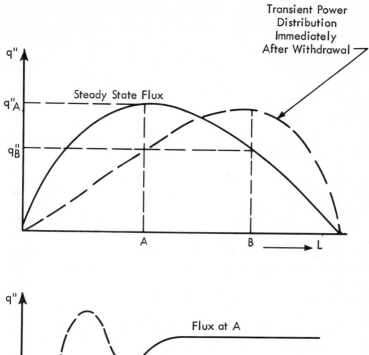

Fig. 1.28 Axial power shift after control rod withdrawal. (From *Nucl. Eng. Design*, **6**, 301, 1967.)

where

ϕ_0 = the steady state neutron flux at $\bar{r}$

t = the time since the power was suddenly changed by k_{ex}

l = the mean lifetime of thermal neutrons.

Equation (1-27) may be considered valid immediately after the change. For longer periods, the effects of the delayed neutron groups must be considered. If the delayed neutrons are approximated by a single group, with a decay constant λ equal to the weighted average for the five groups, one obtains for small reactivity changes

$$\phi = \phi_0 \left\{ \frac{\beta}{\beta - \rho} \exp\left(\frac{\lambda \rho t}{\beta - \rho}\right) - \frac{\rho}{\beta - \rho} \exp\left[-\frac{(\beta - \rho)t}{l}\right] \right\} \quad , \quad (1\text{-}28)$$

where β is the total fraction of delayed neutrons and ρ, the reactivity, is defined as

$$\rho = \frac{k_{ex}}{k_{eff}} \quad . \tag{1-29}$$

The equation is valid only when $(\beta - \rho)$ is positive. Since l will be of the order of magnitude of 10^{-3} sec and λ approximately 0.08 sec^{-1}, the flux during shutdown will be the sum of two positive terms (ρ negative), one of which decreases much more rapidly than the other. The flux, and hence power, initially will decrease rapidly and then fall off slowly in accordance with the first term within the bracket, the subsequent slow decay being due to the effect of the delayed neutrons.

The usual reactor shutdown is brought about by large reductions in reactivity. For this conditions, and considering all five groups of delayed neutrons, the neutron flux is closely approximated by

$$\phi = \phi_0[A_1 \exp(-t\lambda_1) + A_2 \exp(-t\lambda_2) + \text{------} + A_5 \exp(-t\lambda_5)$$

$$+ A_6 \exp(-t/l)] \quad . \tag{1-30}$$

Here the lambdas are the decay constants for the five groups of delayed neutrons. For large reactivity decreases, the rate of flux decay is independent of the reactivity change. Noting the very small value of l and examining the values of λ in Table 1.4,[31] one sees that initially there is a rapid decrease in flux due to the last term but, after a short time, all terms will become negligible except that with the smallest value of λ. The flux will then decay exponentially with a period corresponding to the minimum $1/\lambda$, or about 80 sec.

Table 1.4

DELAYED NEUTRONS IN THERMAL FISSION OF ^{235}U

Mean Life	Decay Constant [λ(sec^{-1})]	Fraction (β_c)
0.62	1.61	0.00084
2.19	0.456	0.0024
6.50	0.151	0.0021
31.7	0.0315	0.0017
80.2	0.0124	0.00026

Based on the foregoing, a good approximation of the fission energy power following a large reactivity decrease is a sudden decrease (prompt jump) followed by a relatively slow exponential decay. The residual power of a light water moderated reactor shutdown following sustained operation at constant power may be approximated, over the time period during which decay heat is important, by

$$P/P_0 = 0.15 \exp(-0.1\,t\,), \qquad (1\text{-}31)$$

where t is in seconds.

(b) Decay Heat. In addition to residual fission energy, there are two other major heat sources:

1. fission product radioactive decay

2. neutron capture product radioactive decay.

Each of these sources must be considered.

Perkins and King[32] and Smith[33] have considered fission product decay heat generation. For the case of a reactor shutdown following infinite period at constant power, their results may be fitted by the expressions

$$P_\beta /P_0 = 0.01\ (t + 1.3)^{-1.21} - 0.55\ (t + 10^5)^{-1.37} \qquad (1\text{-}32)$$

$$P_\gamma/P_0 = 0.01\ (t + 2.9)^{-1.21} - 0.039\ (t + 10^5)^{-1.37}, \qquad (1\text{-}33)$$

where P_β and P_γ represent the β and γ energy respectively and t is again time since shutdown in seconds. The remarks of Sec. 1-2.6 on the distribution of β and γ energy also apply here.

The contribution of neutron capture product decay arises from capture in ^{238}U, control rods, and structure. The contribution of the decay heat generation in the $^{239}U \rightarrow {}^{239}Np \rightarrow {}^{239}Pu$ chain is significant in reactors using slightly enriched fuel but may obviously be ignored when highly enriched fuel is used. This heat product is proportional to the conversion ratio. If a conversion ratio of unity is assumed and the computation of Strominger et al.[34] for decay chains and energy releases is used, one may obtain the following approximate expressions:

$$P_{(\beta+\gamma)} /P_0 = 4 \times 10^{-3}\exp(-4.92 \times 10^{-4}t\,) + 17 \times 10^{-4}\ \exp(-3.4 \times 10^{-6}t).$$
$$(1\text{-}34)$$

The above expression is based on the assumption that half the maximum β energy is emitted in the form of a neutrino and does not contribute to the energy deposition in the core.

The decay heat due to capture in control material will vary greatly depending on the nature of the absorber present in the core during power operation. Decay heat due to silver-indium-cadmium control rods would be more significant than that due to boron-stainless-steel rods. In any case, the capture product decay heat will be substantially less than that due to capture in ^{238}U, but no general expression for this heat generation is available.

The contribution from capture in the structure is small. It is generally satisfactory to ignore this.

If the residual heat generation after several days of shutdown is of interest, the fact that the reactor has operated for a finite time rather than an infinite time becomes important. Obenshain and Foderaro[35] state that the residual heat for a finite time of operation (T_0) may be found by subtracting the value of ($t + T_0$) from the value for infinite operation with a true decay time of t. It should also be noted that for decay times in excess of one minute the contribution of residual fission energy can generally be ignored.

By combining Eqs. (1-30), (1-32), (1-33), and (1-34), one can estimate the total power generation at time t after a reactor shutdown. Figure 1-29 shows the relative power generation for a typical light water moderated reactor,[3] where the heat released to the coolant is appreciably greater than the heat generated, due to the release of heat stored in the fuel. Means for taking this into account are discussed in Sec. 2.3.

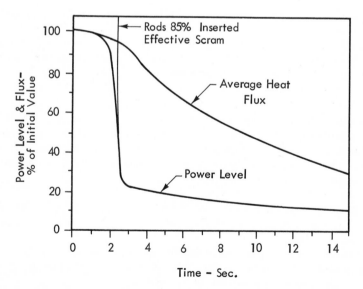

Fig. 1.29 Relative power level and heat flux after a scram. (From *Westinghouse Engineer*, **25**, 5, 145, 1965.)

1-5 HEAT GENERATION IN REACTOR STRUCTURE AND MODERATOR

1-5.1 Structure

Heat is produced in the fuel by absorption of β rays and the kinetic energy of the fission fragments, while outside the fuel, heat is generated primarily by γ-ray absorption. The γ rays come from the γ's released in fission, those released by decaying fission products, or those formed by absorption of neutrons in the core materials.

The variation of the uncollided flux of γ rays ϕ° of a given energy through a slab with a source on one side is given by

$$\phi_i^\circ = S_{a_i} \exp(-\mu_i x) \ , \tag{1-35}$$

where

S_{a_i} = the flux at the surface, MeV/sec cm^2

x = distance from surface, cm

μ_i = attenuation coefficient, cm^{-1}.

The associated heat production is then

$$q_i^\circ = \mu_{a_i} S_{a_i} \exp(-\mu_i x) \ , \tag{1-36}$$

where

μ_{a_i} = energy absorption coefficient, cm^{-1}
q_i° = heat production, MeV/sec cm^2.

When, as in a reactor, we have a source emitting rays of a number of different energies, the total heat production due to the uncollided flux is the sum of the heat production due to each energy level.

$$q_i^\circ = \mu_{a_1} S_{a_1} \exp(-\mu_1 x) + \mu_{a_2} S_{a_2} \exp(-\mu_2 x) + \dots \ . \tag{1-37}$$

The actual heat production is greater than indicated by Eq. (1-37) due to absorption of secondary gammas from Compton scattering. The additional heat production is computed by means of buildup factors B_{a_i} such that the total heat production q is given by

$$q = q_1^\circ B_{a_1} + q_2^\circ B_{a_1} + q_2^\circ B_{a_2} + \dots \ . \tag{1-38}$$

The buildup factors differ for different materials and are a function of μx and the energy level of the γ rays. Rockwell[36] gives a graphical presentation of these.

In a reactor core that has been operating for 100 h or more, the γ-ray energy from both fission and fission products may be assumed to be directly proportional to the local power density. Values for the γ-ray energy production from fission and fission products as well as energy attenuation coefficients are summarized by McClain and Martens.[37] Where the γ flux leaving the core must be determined, the power density near the surface of the core may be used as an approximation since the high self shielding of the core minimizes contributions from other regions.

The variation of neutron flux through a thin slab with a source on one side is of the same form as that for γ rays,

$$\phi = \phi_0 \exp(-\Sigma x) \quad , \tag{1-39}$$

where

ϕ = local neutron flux at x

ϕ_0 = neutron flux at surface of slab

Σ = neutron absorption coefficient, cm^{-1}.

In a structural material consisting of heavy elements, the neutron heat production is due primarily to absorption of gammas produced by neutron interaction with the structure. The heat production q''' due to capture γ rays of a given energy level is therefore directly proportional to the neutron flux and a function of μ_a, x, and total slab thickness. If the neutron flux is given by Eq. (1-39), then

$$q_E''' = K E f(E) \mu_a (\Sigma/\mu) \phi_0 \exp(-\Sigma x)$$
$$\{F_1(\mu x, \Sigma/\mu) + F_1[\mu(L - x), -\Sigma/\mu]\} \quad , \tag{1-40}$$

where

q_E''' = heat production due to capture-γ-ray absorption, W/cm^3

$f(E)$ = fraction of captures producing γ rays of energy E

L = total slab thickness

K = 0.8×10^{-13} Wsec/MeV

μ = linear attenuation coefficient for gammas of energy E, cm^{-1}

μ_a = energy absorption coefficient for gammas of energy E, cm^{-1}

and

$$F_1(b, a) = \int_0^b e^{at} E_1(t) \, dt; \quad E_1(b) = \int_b^\infty \frac{e^{-t}}{t} \, dt \, , \tag{1-41}$$

where b and a are the appropriate arguments required by equation (1-40). The function F_1 may be evaluated from the graphs provided by Rockwell.[38] Equation (1-40) neglects buildup of γ rays due to Compton scattering; therefore, these results should be modified by application of the appropriate buildup factor for thick elements. The total heat generation is then the sum of these values and those obtained from Eq. (1-38).

For steel slab thickness under 1.5 cm, it is usually satisfactory to assume a constant heat production due to neutron absorption. In this

between 1.5 and

range, the buildup factors approximately compensate for the neutron flux attenuation. Furthermore, for slab thickness under 6 cm, heat production due to absorption of capture gammas accounts for less than 2% of the total heat production, and this heat production may be approximated as a constant fraction of the total heat production. It should be noted that in a pressure vessel wall adjacent to a shield tank the neutron flux will begin to rise near the shield tank due to the reflected flux. Here, a better approximation would be a constant heat production due to capture gamma absorption.

1-5.2 Moderator

While the heat generation in the reactor structure is primarily from γ-ray absorption, heat generation within the moderator is primarily from neutron thermalization through elastic scattering. For elastic scattering $q'''(x)$, the volumetric heat generation rate at some location x may be approximated by[39]

$$q'''(x) \approx \Sigma_s \phi_f(x) \xi E \quad , \qquad (1\text{-}42)$$

where

Σ_s = macroscopic elastic scattering cross section of the fast neutron flux $\phi_f(x)$ and energy E

ξ = average energy decrement per collision.

1-6 THERMAL DESIGN BASIS

In view of the many variables that affect the power generation within the reactor fuel, it is clear that an accurate computation of the relative power distribution in the reactor is quite complicated. The simple approximations presented in this chapter for uniform, unperturbed cores may be regarded as useful in providing very rough estimates for preliminary design. However, any actual design must be based on realistic power distributions obtained from the nuclear designer. The major results of the nuclear calculations can be relayed to the thermal designer in terms of nuclear hot-channel factors. These factors, together with an estimate of the axial power-distribution shape, can serve as a basis for the initial plant thermal design. The interaction of the initial thermal and nuclear designs are discussed in Sec. 5-2.3.

REFERENCES

1. G. H. FARBMAN, "The Pressurized Water Reactor," Paper No. 65-15, Westinghouse Nuclear Power Seminar (1965).

2. J. K. PICKARD, Ed., *Nuclear Power Reactors*, pp. 70-73, D. Van Nostrand Co., Princeton, New Jersey (1957).

3. H. J. von HOLLEN and C. F. CURREY, "Design Features of San Onofre Nuclear Station," *Westinghouse Engineer*, **25**, 5, 145 (1965).

4. E. U. POWELL and R. M. HARPER, "R. E. Gina Nuclear Power Plant Unit No. 1," *Proc. American Power Conference*, **30**, 298 (1968).

5. STUART McLAINE and J. H. MARTENS, Eds., *Reactor Handbook*, 2nd ed., Vol. IV, pp. 557-560, Interscience Publishers, New York (1964).

6. D. K. DAVIES, "Nuclear Steam Generators," *Proc. American Power Conference*, **27**, 310 (1965).

7. D. KALAFATI, "Thermodynamic Cycles of Nuclear Power Stations," Israel Program for Scientific Translation (1965).

8. F. A. ARTUSA, "Turbines and Cycles for Nuclear Power Plant Application," *Proc. American Power Conference*, **29**, 280 (1967).

9. "Consolidated Nuclear Steam Generator for Merchant Ship Application," BAW-1243, Babcock & Wilcox Co. (August 1962).

10. International Atomic Energy Agency, *Directory of Nuclear Reactors*, Vol. IV, *Power Reactors*, pp. 39-45, Vienna (1962).

11. *Ibid.*, pp. 163-168.

12. *Ibid.*, pp. 169-174.

13. *Ibid.*, pp. 157-162.

14. *Ibid.*, pp. 3-8.

15. W. J. DOWIS, "Basis of Design for Hanford New Production Reactor (NPR)," HW-SA-2981, Hanford Works (April 1963).

16. J. A. WRIGHT, "Supercritical Pressure Reactor Technology," Paper No. 65-8, Westinghouse Nuclear Power Seminar (1965).

17. S. GLASSTONE and M. C. EDLUND, *Elements of Nuclear Reactor Theory*, p. 198, D. Van Nostrand Co., Princeton, New Jersey (1952).

18. *Ibid.*, p. 215.

19. "1000 MW(e) Closed Cycle Water Reactor Study," USAEC Report WCAP-2385, Vol. 1, Westinghouse Atomic Power Division (1963).

20. International Atomic Energy Agency, *op. cit.*, pp. 21-32.

21. J. K. PICKARD, *op. cit.*, pp. 77-80.

22. A. RADKOWSKY and R. T. BAYARD, "Physics of Seed and Blanket Cores," *Proc. 2nd UN Conf. Peaceful Uses of Atomic Energy*, Vol. 13, p. 128 (1958).

23. J. K. PICKARD, *op. cit.*, p. 111.

24. G. N. HAMILTON and J. A. ROLL, "Power Distribution and Reactivity Measurements in Critical Lattices Containing Thimble Control," WCAP-1894, Westinghouse Atomic Power Division (1964).

25. S. GLASSTONE and M. C. EDLUND, *op. cit.*, p. 266.

26. A. AMOUYAL, P. BENOIST, and J. HOROWITZ, "Nouvelle Méthode de Détermination du Facteur d'Utilization Thermique d'une Celle," *J. Nuclear Energy*, **6**, 79 (1957).

27. J. R. LAMARSH, *Introduction to Nuclear Reactor Theory*, pp. 382-389, Addison-Wesley, Reading, Mass. (1966).

28. S. GLASSTONE and M. C. EDLUND, *op. cit.*, p. 243.

29. A. A. BISHOP, P. NELSON, and E. A. McCABE, Jr., "Thermal and Hydraulic Design of the CVTR Fuel Assembly," CVNA-115, Westinghouse Atomic Power Division (June 1962).

30. D. RANDALL and S. St. JOHN, "Xenon Spatial Oscillations," *Nucleonics*, **16**, *3*, 82 (1958).

31. S. GLASSTONE and M. C. EDLUND, *op. cit.*, p. 65.

32. J. F. PERKINS and R. W. KING, "Energy Release from Decay of Fission Products," *Nucl. Sci. Eng.*, **3**, 726 (1958).

33. M. R. SMITH, "The Activity of Fission Products of U-235," AEC Report XDC 60-1-157, General Electric Corp. (1959).

34. D. STROMINGER, J. M. HOLLANDER, and G. T. SEABORG, "Table of Isotopes," *Rev. Mod. Phys.*, **39**, *2*, Part 2, 585 (1958).

35. F. E. OBENSHAIN and A. FODERARO, "Energy from Fission Product Decay," WAPD-P-652, Westinghouse Atomic Power Division (1955).

36. T. ROCKWELL, *Reactor Shielding Design Manual*, pp. 429-433, D. Van Nostrand Co., Princeton, New Jersey (1956).

37. STUART McLAIN and J. H. MARTENS, *op. cit.*, pp. 429-433.

38. T. ROCKWELL, *op. cit.*, pp. 353-358.

39. S. GLASSTONE and A. SESONSKE, *Nuclear Power Engineering*, p. 615, D. Van Nostrand Co., Princeton, New Jersey (1967).

2

Fuel Elements

The thermal design of a reactor may be considered to begin with the design of the heat generating elements. Prediction of fuel element behavior in a reactor requires as its first step a knowledge of fuel temperatures during steady state and transient conditions. Therefore, we first review, for the fuels of interest, the properties necessary for temperature estimation and then examine some of the computational methods involved.

2-1 FUEL ELEMENT CHARACTERISTICS

2-1.1 Fuels and Their Thermal Properties

(a) Uranium and its Alloys. Radiation damage to metallic fuel elements is caused largely by the highly energetic fission fragments. The damage mechanisms fall into four categories:

1. displacement of individual atoms (the primary knock-on atoms) from the normal lattice

2. displacement of additional atoms by the primary knock-on atoms to form displacement spikes

3. the presence of fission products as impurities

4. cavity formation at points of mechanical weakness.

These changes result in both axial growth and radial swelling of the fuel.

Pure uranium metal is not a satisfactory fuel for pressurized water reactors designed for power production alone, because it exhibits very poor dimensional stability under prolonged irradiation and its high corrosion rate would result in a rapid fuel element rupture following any cladding failure. Exposure of the failed fuel to 550°F water for a few hours would completely destroy the fuel element, but on the other hand, when reactor operation is for both plutonium production and power, uranium metal is acceptable because its radiation stability is adequate during the short reactor exposure designed to limit higher isotope production. Coolant temperatures may be significantly reduced so that the consequences of any failures will be less severe.

Much of uranium's irradiation instability is traceable to the anisotropy of its alpha phase, which leads to expansion in the direction of the (010) crystal plane and contraction in the (100) plane during low temperature irradiation. One method for improving uranium properties is to add a sufficient amount of an alloying element so that the gamma phase can be retained at low temperatures. The gamma phase has a cubic structure that does not exhibit anisotropic properties.

Considerable effort was expended in attempts to develop alloys that would be fully suitable for PWR service. The most promising were binary alloys of uranium and molybdenum.[1] These gamma stabilized alloys were found to have significantly better aqueous corrosion resistance than pure uranium, and alloys containing 10 to 13.5% molybdenum would appear to exhibit adequate corrosion resistance for use when covered by cladding. Their dimensional stability is better than that of unalloyed uranium, but swelling, while considerably improved, remained a problem.[2] Interest has also been shown in gamma-phase alloys of uranium, niobium, and zirconium. A uranium-molybdenum alloy fuel was initially considered for the blanket of the first Shippingport core, but the superior performance of uranium dioxide led to the use of the ceramic fuel instead.

More recently, attention has been given to developing very low-alloy uranium fuels for a heavy-water moderated PWR. The greater neutron economy achievable with low-alloy uranium is highly important in such reactor systems, and furthermore, the consequences of a fuel element failure are less severe. Since heavy-water units are pressure tube reactors, refueling is easier and severe fuel element failures will not propagate throughout the reactor as they might in the close-packed lattice of a light-water reactor.

The concept employed has been to form alloys using small amounts of suitable metals that will tend to stabilize the gamma or beta phase. When the transformation to the alpha phase takes place, the resulting material consists of small, randomly oriented crystals. The alloys have better dimensional stability and corrosion resistance than cast alpha-phase uranium. The alloys examined in depth have included U - 2 to 2.5 wt% Zr, U - 0.3 wt% Cr, U - 1.5 wt% Mo, and U - Fe alloys.[3,4] The so-called "adjusted uranium" alloy that contains approximately 500 ppm Fe, 250 ppm Al, 600 ppm C, and 20 ppm N has also been studied.

While it has been possible to reduce fuel swelling substantially through alloy addition, the problem has not been completely eliminated. Below about 640°C, the swelling obtained varies greatly with alloy content, and this effect is consistent with the concept that at these temperatures swelling occurs by mechanical processes. The benefits obtained from alloying additions appear due to the influence of the additions on mechanical properties. A minimum swelling rate is reached in the range of 640 to 700°C. At temperatures above this, the rates again increase but are only slightly different for the various alloys.[5]

The Canadians have investigated the use of U_3Si (U - 3.8 wt% Si) for PWR service. While swelling is considerably lower than that of unalloyed uranium, it is higher than that desired. However, the fuel is sufficiently plastic so the addition of a central void appears to offer a way of accommodating a major portion of the swelling.[6]

The water corrosion resistance of uranium is significantly improved by the addition of small amounts of Mo, Zr, Nb + Zr, or Si. Indeed, U_3Si has a corrosion resistance perhaps 500 times that of unalloyed uranium. However, attack of a fuel element of these alloys with a cladding hole leak would be severe enough to require fairly prompt removal of the element from the reactor.

High-alloy uraniums having more satisfactory properties are available. Such alloys provide a means for dispersing highly enriched uranium in a structure having a sufficiently large surface area to attain the high heat removal rates required. The only high-alloy uraniums known to have been used in pressurized water reactors have been alloys of uranium and zirconium. Zirconium's low neutron absorption cross section, high melting point, corrosion resistance, and uranium's high solubility in zirconium make it a natural alloying material. Zirconium alloys have adequate aqueous corrosion resistance and adequate strength when they contain a small amount of tin. In actual practice, the uranium is alloyed with Zircaloy 2, which contains 1.5% tin plus traces of iron, nickel, and chromium. Dimensional stability under irradiation is good. Alloys containing up to 14 wt% uranium have satisfactorily withstood burnups of up to 3.3 at.%. Maintenance of dimensional stability would appear to require that the fuel not be cycled above the phase transition temperature ($\approx$600°C).[7] An alloy of uranium and Zircaloy was used for the meat of plate type sandwiches in the Shippingport reactor seeds.

The thermal design properties of U-Zr alloys have been investigated by Battelle Memorial Institute. Etherington[8] tabulates the thermal conductivity of the alloy and pure components as a function of alloy composition and temperature. Density of the alloy at room temperature is approximately a linear function of the atomic percentages of the constituents.[9] Specific heats may be similarly estimated from that of the components. Further properties may be obtained from Ref. 10. A summary of the significant properties is given in Table 2.1.

Table 2.1

THERMAL PROPERTIES OF URANIUM ALLOYS

Fuel	Uranium	U - 2 wt% Zr	U_3Si (U - 3.8 wt% Si)	U - 12 wt% Mo	Zr - 14 wt% U
Fuel Density (g/cm³)	19.05 (200°F) 18.87 (400°F) 18.33 (1200°F)	18.3 (room temperature)	15.57 ± 0.02 (room temperature)	16.9 (room temperature)	7.16 (room temperature)
Crystal Structure	α, room temp – 1220°F, orth. β, 1200-1238°F, tet. γ, 1400°F-mp, B.C.C.	Orth.	$U + U_3Si_2 > 1706$°F $\epsilon < 1706$°F tet. (ε formed by holding cast alloy at 1472°F)	B.C.C.	α Zr (hex.) ε Zr (hex.)
Melting Temperature (°F)	2070	2060	1805	2102	3240
Conductivity [Btu/(h ft °F)]	15.8 (200°F) 17.5 (600°F) 20.25 (1000°F) 22.00 (1400°F)	12.7 (95°F) 15.6 (572°F) 21.4 (1112°F) 27.8 (1652°F)	8.66 (77°F) 10.1 (149°F)	7.97 (room temperature)	6.36 (68°F) 6.71 (212°F) 7.12 (392°F) 7.52 (572°F) 10.4 (1292°F)
Thermal Expansion [in./(in. °F)]	20.2×10^{-6} for [100] plane $\quad$ 77°F -5.17×10^{-6} for [010] plane $\quad$ to 19.0×10^{-6} for [001] plane $\quad$ 1202°F Volumetric 34.2×10^{-6}	8.0×10^{-6} (105 - 930°F)	$7.67 \pm 0.28 \times 10^{-6}$ (212 - 752°F)	7.23×10^{-6} (212 - 752°F)	3.78×10^{-6} (221 - 626°F) 3.84×10^{-6} (662 - 1022°F)
Heat Capacity [Btu/(lb °F)]	0.0278 (200°F) 0.0410 (1000°F) 0.0464 (1200°F)	0.0287 (200°F)		0.032 - 0.036 (572 - 752°F)	0.0674 (200°F)

The thermal properties of uranium-molybdenum alloys have also been extensively investigated. Room temperature thermal conductivity varies from 0.148 W/cm°C for 8 wt% Mo to 0.138 W/cm°C for 12 wt% Mo.[10] The thermal conductivity of 8 wt% Mo fuel increases linearly with temperature to 0.39 W/cm°C at 790°C.[11] Thermal expansion is not linear with temperature but shows an inflection at 595°C. A total length change of 1.8% is seen at 790°C.[11] Additional properties may be obtained from Ref. 11.

Properties of the ternary uranium, 7.5 wt% Mo, 2.5 wt% Nb, alloy are reviewed by Weiss.[12] Properties of a number of other alloys of interest are available in Refs. 10 and 13. Thermal properties for the most important alloys are summarized in Table 2.1.

(b) Dispersion Fuels. An alternate way of providing a structural base, with the high surface needed, for highly enriched fuel is to physically disperse the fuel in a metallic matrix. Dispersions of UO_2 in aluminum, zirconium alloys, and stainless steels have been investigated, but only the stainless steel and zirconium alloy dispersions have found use in pressurized water reactors.

Stainless-UO_2 dispersions are normally fabricated by powder-metallurgy techniques. Uranium dioxide and stainless-steel powder are blended, pressed, and sintered. Final dimensions and further densification are achieved by cold or hot working. The physical and mechanical properties of the dispersions are influenced by many variables including UO_2 particle size, type and amount of UO_2, type of stainless steel, geometry of the element with respect to the property being measured, and fabrication techniques. Reference 14 provides a compilation of mechanical properties.

Zircaloy-UO_2 dispersions have been used as a replacement for the U-Zr alloy used in the first seed of the Shippingport reactor. Such dispersions may be expected to have greater resistance to radiation damage than the alloy, since the damage would be confined to the area around the UO_2 particles rather than being dispersed throughout the alloy.

Normally, a dispersion fuel element offers good corrosion resistance regardless of the resistance of the fuel particles. Exposure of small amounts of fuel to the coolant due to cladding failure means only a few particles are exposed. If there is stringering of the fuel particles, corrosion can proceed along the interconnected particles. Since UO_2 has good corrosion resistance in high temperature water, the aqueous corrosion resistance of these dispersions is good even when some stringering occurs; however, the radiation damage resistance of such a fuel would be poor.

Resistance to radiation damage of stainless UO_2 dispersions is good, but as with all fuels, radiation damage places some limits on their performance. In a properly fabricated dispersion fuel, the particles are uniformly dispersed throughout the nonfissile matrix that predominates in volume. The fission products released from the fuel are then confined to narrow regions around the fuel particles, and a continuous web of undamaged matrix remains. Radiation induced swelling arises because of growth of the UO_2 particles due to accumulation of fission products and a partial escape of fission gases from the UO_2.[15] The latter effect is the most significant. A gas filled void is created around the particles, and this pressurizes the matrix shell causing it to expand as a thick walled vessel under pressure. The matrix swelling that can be allowed will thus set the maximum burnup. Swelling limits may be determined on the basis of allowable dimensional changes or a maximum strain determined on the basis of the reduced ductility limit of the neutron embrittled matrix.

The specific heat of a dispersion can be obtained by combining those of its constituants linearly in accordance with the dispersion composition. Densities can be obtained in a similar manner providing an allowance is made for the fact that the UO_2 particles are porous, and therefore, densities of the dispersion range from 92 to 98% of the theoretical. To obtain the thermal conductivity of a dispersion of small particles of conductivity k_p, uniformly dispersed in a continuous substance of conductivity k_s, Jakob[16] recommends an equation originally derived by Maxwell:

$$k_d = k_s \; \frac{1 - (1 - a \, k_p / k_s) \, b}{1 + (a - 1) \, b} \; , \qquad (2\text{-}1)$$

where

k_d = thermal conductivity of dispersion

a = $3 \, k_s / (2k_s + k_p)$

b = $V_p / (V_s + V_p)$

V_s = total volume of continuous substance

V_p = total volume of distributed particles.

Equation (2-1) was derived for small values of b, but it has been said that it holds approximately for $b \leqslant 0.5$. The present authors would suggest that its use above $b \leqslant 0.25$ should be with caution. If there is appreciable stringering of the UO_2, the thermal conductivity will be anisotropic and Eq. (2-1) should not be applied.

(c) Uranium Dioxide. This is by far the most popular fuel material for pressurized water reactors, and uranium dioxide, mixed uranium and plutonium dioxides, and mixed thorium and uranium dioxides are the only ceramic fuels that have received serious attention. Although the carbides may be satisfactory from a radiation damage viewpoint, their reaction with water eliminate them from considera-

tion for PWR service. Uranium dioxide has been found to exhibit excellent dimensional stability to high burnup. It does show appreciable radial cracking,[17] but when properly restrained by fuel element cladding, cracking does not lead to dimensional instability. The generation of the fission products leads to a slight swelling of UO_2, which is roughly linear with burnup. Above a critical burnup, the swelling rate increases markedly, and this critical burnup can be increased by using slightly less dense UO_2 or by providing more cladding restraint. The critical burnup for unrestrained UO_2 at normal PWR operating conditions is shown in Fig. 2.1 as a function of the void within the fuel.

It has now been shown that the critical burnup is also a function of the operating temperature of the fuel. The data indicate that the rate of fuel swelling is a function of temperature. Initially, the fuel

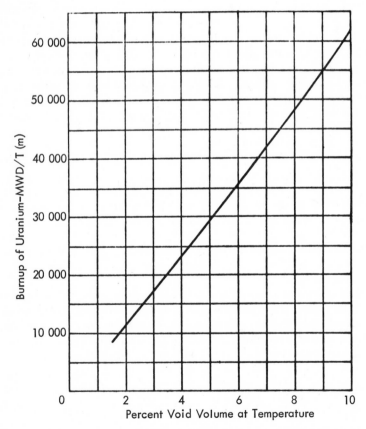

Fig. 2.1 Critical burnup for rapid swelling of unrestrained UO_2. (From *Nucl. Eng. Design*, **6**, 301, 1967.)

swelling fills the pores of the fuel. When that portion of the porosity that is effective in accommodating swelling has been consumed, net dimensional changes occur. Table 2.2 indicates approximate swelling rates and effective porosities for several temperature ranges.[18]

Table 2.2

APPROXIMATE SWELLING RATES AND EFFECTIVE POROSITIES

Temperature Range	Fuel Swelling 10^4 %($\Delta V/V$) per 10 MW day/tonne	Effective Component of Initial Voidage (%)
<1300°C	1.6	30
1300 to 1700°C	1.7	50
>1700°C	0.7	80

At high flux irradiation, appreciable UO_2 sublimation occurs, and this leads to the formation of a central void surrounded by UO_2 of essentially theoretical density. Void migration has been theoretically investigated by De Hales and Horn[20] and Nichols,[21] who derived equations describing the rate of void migration for central temperatures above 2750°F.

At very high power, a molten core is obtained. Although some experimental data indicate such a core is not deleterious,[22] the avoidance of melting is generally accepted as a current design criterion. The volumetric expansion of UO_2 upon melting can lead first to severe swelling of the cladding and subsequently to its destruction over a portion of the fuel rod. Failures of this nature were observed by Eichenberg et al.[23] Successful operation with gross central melting was satisfactorily accomplished by Lyons et al.[24] with hollow pellets, which provided the free volume necessary to accommodate the UO_2 expansion on melting.

An illustration of the effect of cladding restraint is provided by Dayton,[3] who noted for platelet type fuel elements that the increased cladding restraint of $\frac{1}{4}$-in. platelets postponed critical swelling to a burnup over 130% that observed for $\frac{1}{2}$-in. wide platelets. Sophisticated design calculations now recognize that UO_2 at high temperatures has some plasticity, and the deformation of the fuel is affected by elastic, plastic, and creep properties of fuel and cladding materials.[19] Thus, Fig. 2.1 can only be regarded as a crude guide to the behavior of an actual fuel rod.

Current technology provides UO_2 compacts of close to theoretical density by means of pressed and sintered pellets. As the maximum burnups have increased, lower density fuels have been used to reduce swelling. This has lead to renewed interest in vibratory compaction, swaging, or combined compaction and swaging of UO_2 powder as production processes. However, the use of pelletized fuel remains the current (1970) commercial practice.

It has been postulated that, under particular conditions of fuel relocation and cracking, molten fuel could come in contact with the clad, which could be brought to its melting point and burned through. This mechanism may have been one of the factors contributing to the 1966 failure in the Plutonium Recycle Test Reactor (PRTR) rupture test loop, where fuel element failure was followed by burn through of the surrounding pressure tube.

Under the usual PWR operating conditions, UO_2 does not react with the coolant and corrosion resistance is good, so pinhole clad failures do not lead to washout of the fuel element. However, the water-logging of failed elements at low power and the subsequent expulsion of steam at higher power does lead to the escape of some fission products into the coolant. Under some conditions it is possible for the waterlogging effect to be severe enough to cause fuel element failure. Eichenberg et al.[25] have postulated that this waterlogging failure could occur if the defect were blocked by a particle of UO_2 thus restricting the escape of the steam during a start-up. Only a very few such failures have been observed in a large number of in-pile tests[23] with sintered pellets, and no such failure of actual PWR sintered pellet fuel elements in reactor service has yet (1970) been observed, although defective fuel elements have been present. Waterlogging appears to be more of a problem with vibratory compacted or swaged fuel elements than with those using sintered pellets.

Because of the wide use of UO_2 as a reactor fuel, its properties have been the subject of numerous investigations. Specific heat may be computed as

$$C_p = 19.20 + 1.62 \times 10^{-3} \, T - 3.96 \times 10^{-5} \, T^{-2} \quad , \qquad (2\text{-}2)$$

where C_p has the units Btu/lb mole °F and T is °K.[26]

The theoretical density of UO_2 at room temperature is 10.96 g/cm^3, and its thermal expansion is indicated in Fig. 2.2. The density just below and just above the melting point is reported as 9.65 and 8.80 g/cm^3, respectively.[26]

Despite the many investigations of UO_2 thermal conductivity, there remains considerable scatter in the data. The data of a number of recent investigators for unirradiated UO_2 are shown in Fig. 2.3, where all have been corrected to 95% theoretical density using the relationship

$$k_{95\%} = k_{measured} \left(\frac{0.95}{1 - \epsilon} \right) \quad , \qquad (2\text{-}3)$$

where ϵ is the void fraction of the sample. Godfrey et al.[27] and May

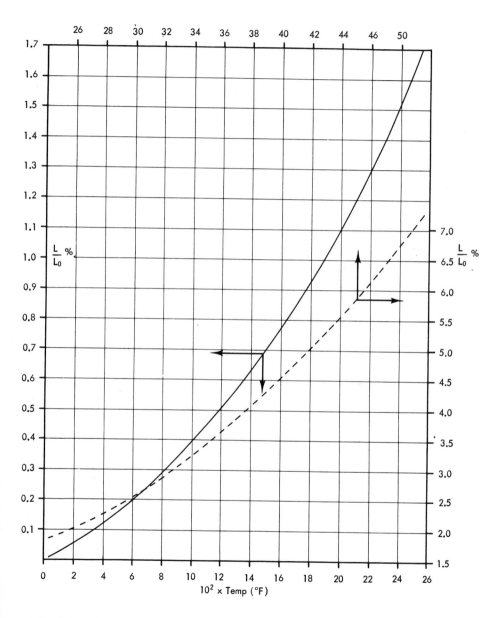

Fig. 2.2   Thermal expansion of UO₂. (From Halden, Wohlers, and Rimbert, "Thermal Expansion of Uranium Dioxide," SRI, USAEC Report TID 5722, 1959.)

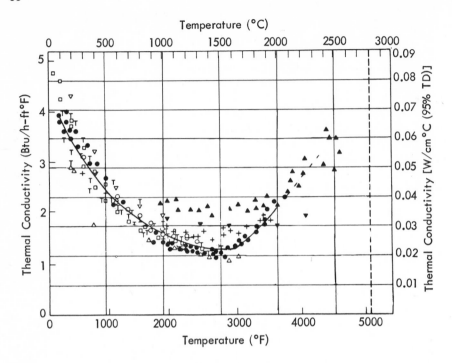

Fig. 2.3   Thermal conductivity of unirradiated UO₂.

Notation O Godfrey et al., Ref. 27, 1964.
          □ Dayton & Tipton, Battelle Memorial Institute Report
            BMI-1448, 1960.
          ∇ Kingery et al., *J. Am. Ceram. Soc.*, **37**, 107, 1954.
          T Howard & Galvin, UKAEA IG Report 51, 1960.
          ⊢ Reiswig, *J. Am. Ceram. Soc.*, **44**, 48, 1961.
          ● Nishijima, Ref. 31, 1965.
          + Bush et al., *Trans. Am. Nucl. Soc.*, **7**, 392, 1964.
          ▼ Feith, Ref. 32, 1963.
          ▲ Feith unpublished data.

et al.[28] have noted that the conductivity of UO_2 increased as the O/U ratio is reduced. This stoichiometric effect may account for some of the data scatter. Belle et al.[29] show that the data scatter is reduced when a revised method is used for correcting the data to a standard porosity. Based on a modified Maxwell-Eucken equation, assuming negligible heat transfer through the pores, they recommend

$$k_p = \frac{1 - \epsilon}{1 + \beta \epsilon} \ (k_{100\%}) \quad , \tag{2-4}$$

where k_p is the conductivity of the porous sample in question, and β is a constant that depends on the material. A reduced data spread may be obtained using $\beta = 0.5$ for fuels of 90% theoretical density and above and $\beta = 0.7$ for fuels of lower density.

The thermal conductivity data below 2500°F generally follows the expected behavior for lattice conduction. In 1961, Bates,[30] on the basis of postirradiation examinations, postulated an increase in conductivity at higher temperatures due to internal thermal radiation, and this seems to be borne out by the more recent data of Godfrey et al.[27] and Nishijima[31] for unirradiated UO_2. However, there is disagreement as to whether this is due to thermal irradiation or electron effects. At present, the best estimate of the conductivity of unirradiated UO_2 would seem to be a curve drawn through the data of Godfrey et al. and Nishijima over the range in which they are available (solid line in Fig. 2.3). Extrapolation of the curve is in fair agreement with the very high temperature data of Feith.[32]

Considerably more uncertainty is attached to the thermal conductivity of UO_2 after irradiation. In 1959, Runnals[33] noted a decrease in conductivity at low temperatures after an irradiation of 9×10^{17} n/cm^2 and no significant change afterward. Other investigations have generally noted qualitatively similar behavior, and Fig. 2.4 compares the suggested curve for unirradiated conductivity with the available data for irradiated UO_2. It seems probable that there is some decrease in conductivity below 1500°F and little change between 2000 and 3000°F. The issue is not clear above 3000°F since the estimates of Bates[30] do not agree with the results of Lyons.[34]

In 1967, Belle et al.[29] surveyed all of the available data and concluded that the conductivity was a function of both burnup and temperature. They proposed the following correlation:

$$k = \left(\frac{1-\epsilon}{1+\beta\epsilon}\right)[A_0 + B_0T + (6.23/T) + (49.82/T) + 0.0139F(1386/T)]^{-1} \quad ,$$

$$(2\text{-}5)$$

where

$\quad k$ = thermal conductivity in Btu/(hr ft °F)

$\quad T$ = °R

$\quad F$ = burnup (fissions/cm^3) $\times 10^{-20}$

$\quad A_0 = 0.116$

$\quad B_0 = 1.88 \times 10^{-4}$

$\quad \epsilon$ = the void fraction.

The empirical constant β has the values indicated for Eq. (2-4).

Stora et al.[35] have argued that the apparent irradiation induced reduction in thermal conductivity is, in reality, due to thermal-stress

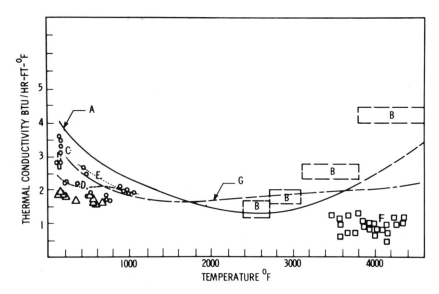

Fig. 2.4 Irradiated UO₂ thermal conductivity and out-of-pile data. (From
Nucl. Eng. Design, **6**, 301, 1967.)

Notation A. Curve based on unirradiated data
         B. Bates, Ref. 30, post-irradiation measurements, 1961.
         C. Bain & Robertson, *J. Nucl. Mater.*, **1**, 109, 1959, post-
             irradiation data.
         D. Dayton & Tipton, Battelle Memorial Institute Report
             BMI-1448 (Rev.), 1960, post-irradiation data,
             (---- heating; .... cooling).
         E. Ibid., 1961 post-irradiation data (△ first cycle heating;
             ○ second-cycle heating; □ third-cycle cooling).
         F. Lyons et al., Ref. 34, 1964 post-irradiation data.
         G. Robertson et al., *J. Nucl. Mater.*, **7**, 225, 1962,
             $\int_0^{2800°C} K dt$ = 97 W/cm.

cracking. They observed that the magnitude of the conductivity reduction increased as the gap between cladding and pellet increased.
When a zero gap existed, essentially no conductivity reduction was
observed. They suggested that when cracking occurs, the pellet
segments move apart to the degree allowed by the available fuel
space; thus, the small gaps introduced into the pellet reduce the
effective conductivity of the fuel. Since the amount of cracking would
gradually increase (up to some maximum) with operation, the effect
could seem to be irradiation related.

The melting point of uranium dioxide is a function of the total
irradiation received by the fuel (Fig. 2.5).[36] After an initial increase,
the melting point, which is affected by chemical composition, gradually drops with burnup. When less than the stoichiometric amount of

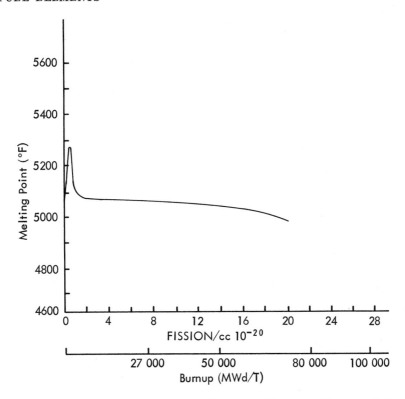

Fig. 2.5   Melting point of UO$_2$ as a function of burnup. (From Ref. 36.)

oxygen is present, the melting point is reduced. It may be observed from the data of Guinet et al,[37] who investigated the entire U-UO$_2$ system, that UO$_{1.8}$ begins to melt at 2690°C in contrast to 2750°C for pure UO$_2$. A brief summary of UO$_2$ properties is provided in Table 2.4, and extensive information is available in Belle.[38]

(d) Thorium Oxide Fuels. Mixed thorium and uranium dioxides were proposed for use as a reactor fuel with the spectral shift control concept, and current interest centers around the use of ThO$_2$ as a blanket in a seed and blanket thermal breeder. The behavior of ThO$_2$ under irradiation is very similar to that of UO$_2$, and thermal conductivity is affected by thermal stress cracking of the fuel pellets in the same manner as the uranium fuel. Belle et al.[29] were therefore able to correlate the conductivity of ThO$_2$ and mixed ThO$_2$ + UO$_2$ by Eq. (2-5) using the constants of Table 2.3.

In-pile thermal conductivities of ThO$_2$-PuO$_2$ mixtures containing 1.1 to 2.7 wt% PuO$_2$ have been measured by Jeffs,[39] who observed conductivities about 25% below those obtained by laboratory measurements of pure ThO_2. Within the scatter of the data, he saw no difference between the compositions tested.

Godfrey et al.[40] have measured the specific heat of ThO_2 over a wide range. These and other thermal properties are summarized in Table 2.4.

(e) Mixed Plutonium and Uranium Oxides. Primary interest in mixed UO_2-PuO_2 fuels stems from their application to fast breeder technology. However, prior to the development of a fast breeder market, there is a program to recycle the plutonium back into the

Table 2.3

CONSTANTS* FOR THERMAL CONDUCTIVITY CORRELATION

Material	A_0	B_0
ThO_2	0	2.21×10^{-4}
ThO_2 + 10 wt% UO_2	0.0225	1.78×10^{-4}

*Belle et al.

Table 2.4

THERMAL PROPERTIES OF CERAMIC FUELS

Fuel	UO_2	UO_2 - 80 at.% PuO_2 - 20 at.%	ThO_2
Fuel Density (g/cm^3)	10.97	11.08	10.01
Melting Temperature (°F)	4980	5036	5970
Thermal Conductivity [Btu/(h ft°F)]	2.54 (930°F) 1.04 (3630°F) (see Fig. 2.3)	2.02 (930°F) 1.04 (3630°F)	7.29 (200°F) 5.34 (400°F) 3.59 (700°F) 2.68 (1000°F) 2.07 (1400°F) 1.68 (2400°F)
Thermal Expansion (in./in.°F)	6.12×10^{-6} (75 - 5070°F)	6.12×10^{-6} (75 - 5035°F)	
Heat Capacity (Btu/lb°F)	0.0567 (90°F) 0.0755 (135°F) 0.090 (3150°F) 0.118 (4050°F)	approximately the same as UO_2	0.0547 (90°F) 0.0696 (1350°F) 0.0775 (3150°F) 0.082 (4050°F)

water cooled reactors where it is being generated. The information available indicates that mixtures of PuO_2 and UO_2 provide a satisfactory water reactor fuel. As would be expected on the basis of the similarity of the two compounds, there is little difference in the behavior of the mixed oxides and UO_2. In view of the small amounts of PuO_2 that would be present in PWR fuel (less than 6%), it is generally satisfactory to use UO_2 properties as an approximation of the mixed oxides. However, it should be observed that the coefficient of thermal expansion of UO_2 - 6 wt% PuO_2 is approximately 10% greater than that of UO_2.

Epstein[41] has measured the melting points of UO_2 - PuO_2 mixtures and has observed melting points of $2840 \pm 20°C$ for UO_2 and $2390 \pm 20°C$ for PuO_2. His data show a typical binary pair without a maximum or minimum in the liquidus or solidus curves, and, for small additions of PuO_2, his results can be closely approximated by assuming a linear decrease in melting point per atom percent of PuO_2 addition. Krankota and Craig[42] observed that the melting point of the mixed oxides decreases slightly with burnup. After 85 000 MWd/tonne burnup, the melting point of $(Pu_{0.25}U_{0.8})O_2$ decreased 50°C.

The thermal conductivity of PuO_2 has been measured by Lagedrost et al.[43] These measurements, corrected to 100% density, show a decrease in conductivity from 0.06 W/cm °C at 300°C to 0.025 W/cm °C at 1200°C. Due to interest in the mixture as a fast reactor fuel, the thermal conductivity of $(U_{0.8}Pu_{0.2})O_2$ has been measured by a number of laboratories.[44,45] Between 1000 and 1900°C, $(U_{0.8}Pu_{0.2})O_2$ of 95% density exhibits thermal conductivities very similar to UO_2 of the same density. Below 1000°C, the thermal conductivity of UO_2 is somewhat higher. As would be expected on the basis of UO_2 behavior, a stoichiometry effect on conductivity is shown by $(U_{0.8}Pu_{0.2})$ mixed oxides. Hetzler[45] found that hypostoichiometric oxides $(P - U)O_{1.98}$ had somewhat lower conductivities than the stoichiometric material. The significant thermal design properties for $(U_{0.8}Pu_{0.2})O_2$ are summarized in Table 2.4. Properties of other mixtures may be estimated by interpolation.

2-1.2 Fuel Element Cladding and Assembly Designs

(a) Cladding Properties. Although the most common PWR fuels have good corrosion resistance, continued exposure of any of these to the coolant would result in coolant activity levels far beyond those consistent with direct maintenance. It is, therefore, the universal practice to clad the various fuels by a thin layer of corrosion resistant metal. Ideally, the cladding should be inert to the coolant, have high strength and ductility that are unaffected by radiation, have a low neutron absorption cross section, and be fabricated easily and economically. Since no such material is known, one must sacrifice some attributes in order to gain those believed most important.

Modern pressurized water reactors use stainless-steel or zir-
conium-alloy clad fuel exclusively. Low neutron cross section, excellent corrosion resistance to low-temperature water, and low cost
made aluminum an early candidate for this use, but unfortunately,
the common aluminum alloys do not have the necessary corrosion
resistance in high temperature water to allow them to be considered.
Argonne National Laboratory has conducted extensive investigations
on various aluminum alloys containing small amounts of nickel (i.e.,
1%) and lesser amounts of iron and other constituents. Although these
alloys have significantly reduced corrosion rates, ANL found the
rates are still excessive at PWR conditions.[46]

• Stainless Steel

With excellent corrosion resistance and high strength, the 300
series stainless steels possess many of the properties of an ideal
cladding. Although their properties are slightly affected by radiation
(yield point increases and ductility decreases appreciably), their
radiation resistance is good, and they are readily fabricated without
special techniques. Their major drawback is a relatively high neutron cross section, which requires an increase in the initial enrichment. These alloys are not suitable for reactors where natural
uranium is the fuel.

Stainless steel is known to be subject to stress assisted corrosion
and stress corrosion cracking in high temperature water when oxygen and halogens are present. Duncan et al.[47] have reported stress
assisted corrosion failures of this nature in the cold worked stainless
cladding of fuel in boiling water reactor fuel. No such cracking has
been reported in pressurized water reactors, perhaps because of the
lower oxygen content of the coolant; however, it presents a severe
problem in superheat systems, where experience has been poor, and
would probably be troublesome in designing a supercritical PWR.

The stainless alloy chosen for a particular case depends on the
fabrication techniques used. All of the 300 series alloys have very
nearly the same thermal design properties, and typical values are
presented in Table 2.5.

• Zirconium Alloys

Hafnium-free zirconium has a very low absorption cross section
(0.18 b compared to 2.43 b for Fe and 4.5 for Ni) and good resistance
to water corrosion at high temperatures. Addition of small amounts
of tin and iron has been found to improve the strength of zirconium
significantly. As a result of extensive investigations at the Bettis
Atomic Power Laboratory, three alloys have been developed that have
the required strength and corrosion resistance—Zircaloy-2, 3, and 4.

Table 2.5

PROPERTIES OF CLADDING MATERIALS

Material	Zircaloy-2	347 Stainless Steel
Composition	1.2 - 1.7% Sn 0.07 - 0.2% Fe 0.05 - 0.15% Cr 0.03 - 0.06% Ni balance Zr	17 - 19% Cr 9 - 12% Ni 0.8% Cb 0.2% max Mn 0.08% max C 1% max Si
Density (g/cm^3)	6.57 (room temperature)	8.03 (room temperature)
Melting Point	3360°F	2550 - 2600°F
Thermal Conductivity [Btu/(h ft^2 °F)]	6.82 (100°F) 6.89 (200°F) 7.11 (400°F) 7.37 (600°F) 7.64 (800°F) 7.77 (900°F)	8.6 (100°F) 9.0 (200°F) 9.8 (400°F) 10.6 (600°F) 11.5 (800°F) 12.4 (1000°F)
Mean Coefficient of Thermal Expansion (in./in. °F)	4.62×10^{-6} (25 - 800°C) (rolling direction) 6.85×10^{-6} (25 - 800°C) (transverse direction)	9.05×10^{-6} (68 - 100°F) 9.25×10^{-6} (68 - 200°F) 9.55×10^{-6} (68 - 400°F) 9.8×10^{-6} (68 - 600°F) 10.0×10^{-6} (68 - 800°F) 10.25×10^{-6} (68 - 1000°F)
Heat Capacity [Btu/(lb °F)]	0.0725 (200°F) 0.0764 (400°F) 0.0789 (600°F) 0.081 (800°F) 0.0831 (1000°F) 0.0853 (1200°F)	0.12 (32 - 212°F)

Although the melting point of zirconium is high (1852°C), a phase change at 862°C affects the mechanical properties. At this temperature, pure zirconium goes from a close packed hexagonal structure (α) to one that is body-centered cubic (β).

Zircaloy tubing or plate is more expensive than stainless steel, and fabrication must be more carefully controlled. Oxygen must be excluded from all welds, and welding must be done in an inert atmosphere in a glove box or similar enclosure. Since zirconium alloys creep at relatively low stresses at PWR temperatures, allowance must be made in the mechanical design of the fuel elements, but the creep can be beneficial since it acts to relieve any high cladding stress. Ibrahim[48] correlated Zircaloy creep by

$$\epsilon = [2.768 \times 10^{-5} \exp(1.5 \times 10^{-2}T + 9.663 \times 10^{-5}\sigma)]$$
$$\times [t^{(1.655 \times 10^{-3}T - 0.297)}] \quad , \tag{2-6}$$

where

ϵ = strain, %

T = temperature, °C

t = time, h

σ = effective stress, psi.

The rate of creep is accelerated by irradiation, and in-pile creep rates may be several times those obtained in out-of-pile tests.

Zirconium and its alloys react significantly with steam at high temperatures $[Zr + 2H_2O(g) \rightarrow ZrO_2 + 2H_2(g)]$, and in a loss-of-coolant accident, the energy release due to this reaction must be considered. A similar reaction occurs with stainless-steel cladding at high temperatures. However, there the reaction rate does not become appreciable until temperatures in excess of 1000°C are reached. If interfacial temperatures rise above 675°C, Zircaloy cladding can react with UO$_2$. Since such temperatures are less than 400°C in normal operation, the reaction need to be considered only for accident situations.

Irradiation of zirconium and its alloys increases their hardness and decreases the ductility, and the decrease in ductility must be considered in the design of reactor components such as pressure tubes. In fuel element design, it often leads to a limitation on the maximum allowable cladding strain.

Thermal and mechanical properties of Zircaloy-2 are presented in Table 2.5.

● *High Nickel Alloys*

The sensitivity of 300 series stainless steels to stress-corrosion cracking under boiling and superheat conditions, as well as the requirement for strength at high temperatures, has led to the consideration of high nickel alloys for supercritical reactors. Various Inconel and Incoloy compositions (up to 72% nickel as contrasted to 8% nickel for 300 series stainless) have been proposed. These alloys are resistant to stress-corrosion cracking and have good high temperature strength. Allio and Thomas[49] have reported that Westinghouse 16-20 alloys (16% chromium and 20% nickel with low carbon and nitrogen) have behaved satisfactorily at high fluxes in an environment of supercritical water. These alloys have a macroscopic neutron absorption cross section of 0.266/cm as compared to 0.300/cm for Incoloy. Reference 50 presents the design properties a number of high nickel alloys.

(b) Fuel Assembly Designs

- *Rods*

Metallic, low enrichment, uranium fuel has almost always been used in the form of clad, solid or annular, cylindrical rods. The tubing for the cladding is commercially available, fabrication is relatively simple, and the necessary surface area is obtained by proper selection of rod size. When aluminum is used as the cladding, a diffusion bond between the clad and the fuel is usually formed by means of a thin layer of aluminum-silicon alloy. Zircaloy clad elements have been formed for the Hanford New Production Reactor (NPR) by coextrusion of a copper-zirconium-uranium billet, with the copper stripped away after extrusion.

Rod elements are also most commonly used for uranium dioxide fuel, and they are generally formed by loading pressed and sintered UO_2 pellets into Zircaloy or stainless-steel tubes to which end plugs are welded. The individual rods are assembled into bundles and end

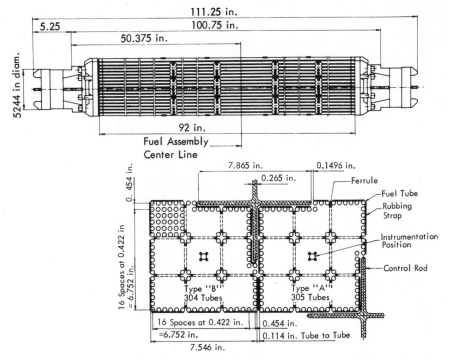

Fig. 2.6 Original Yankee fuel assembly. (From *Directory of Nuclear Reactors*, Vol. IV, p. 34, International Atomic Energy Agency, Vienna, 1962.)

plates, and fittings are affixed. Figure 2.6 shows one of the earlier assemblies for a pressurized water design where brazed ferrules hold the rods together. In some more recent designs (Fig. 1.4), the rods have been positioned by several grids containing spring fingers. This design has the advantages of allowing higher-strength cold-worked cladding to be used, which reduces the amount of absorber in the core, and allowing the fuel rods to expand, which reduces thermal stresses. Assemblies for pressure tube reactors generally contain fewer rods. Ferrules or wire wraps have commonly been used to maintain rod spacing, and metal warts and spacer pads have also been used.

- *Plate Type Elements*

Designs for highly enriched uranium-Zircaloy elements and UO₂-stainless dispersion elements are similar. In both cases, the so called "picture frame" method is used for fabrication, which means that a sheet of the fuel alloy or dispersion is rimmed by a frame of cladding. Upper and lower sheets of cladding are then welded to the frame, and the pack is rolled to final dimensions. A group of fuel plates are then placed in a box-like enclosure made of the cladding material, and this maintains plate spacing and provides an assembly that can be handled. The plate-type elements containing uranium-Zircaloy fuel used in Shippingport Core I are illustrated in Fig. 2.7.

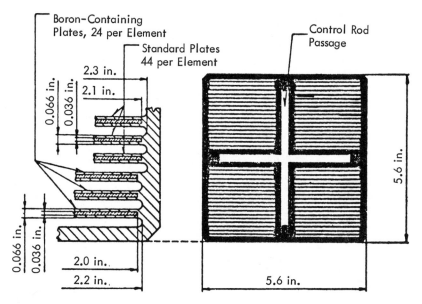

Fig. 2.7 Shippingport Core 1 seed assembly. (From *Directory of Nuclear Reactors*, Vol. IV, p. 21, International Atomic Energy Agency, Vienna, 1962.)

Plate-type elements using a UO_2-stainless dispersion as fuel have been used in the Army Package Power Reactor (APPR).

Plate-type elements for UO_2 fuel have been used in Shippingport Core II. Rectangular platelets of UO_2 fuel are placed in a slotted Zircaloy plate, which is sandwiched between two Zircaloy cover plates. The fairly substantial Zircaloy plates serve to restrain the UO_2 platelets under high burnup. Such plates can be fabricated by the gas-pressure bonding process[3] in which the fuel element can be assembled from plates and strips that are subsequently bonded together at high pressures and temperatures.

- *Tubular Fuel Elements*

Tubular fuel elements can be fabricated from sandwiches of dispersion fuel and cladding. Standard stainless steel forming operations may be used to make the sandwich sheets.[51] Elements of this type are used in the portable reactors (PM series) designed for the US Army nuclear power program.

Annular fuel elements, such as those of the first USSR power station, may be formed from hollow UO_2 pellets. Various vibratory compaction techniques may also be used for annular fuel element fabrication. Multi-pass, concentric ring, annular elements in individual pressure tubes have been proposed for supercritical pressure reactors.[52]

2-1.3 UO$_2$ Fuel Elements

In view of the particular importance of UO_2 fuel elements, their special design properties will be considered.

(a) Gap Conductance. With pressed and sintered pellets there is usually an appreciable resistance to heat transfer between the pellet surface and the cladding. Since bonding agents are not used in PWR design, the interfacial resistance may be that of a gas filled gap or UO_2 in actual contact with the cladding surface. It has often been assumed that the pellet remains nearly centered within the rod and that the gap conductance can be obtained from the conductance of an annular gas gap. If this assumption is correct, then the gap conductance h_g may be estimated from

$$h_g = \frac{k_g}{l + l_0} \quad , \tag{2-7}$$

where

k_g = thermal conductivity of gas in gap (Btu/h °F ft)

l = gap at operating conditions

l_0 = constant specified so as to provide a conductance consistent with that computed at zero contact pressure.

Cohen et al.[53] have investigated the gap conductance for UO_2 stainless-steel clad fuel elements under operating fluxes. The operating gap was obtained by correcting for the thermal expansion of clad and fuel and by assuming the fuel remains centered within the clad. Figure 2.8 shows that the data may be fitted by an equation of the form of (2-7). When determining the gap at operating conditions, an additional correction to the clad diameter should be made to account for elastic deformation of the clad due to the differential between

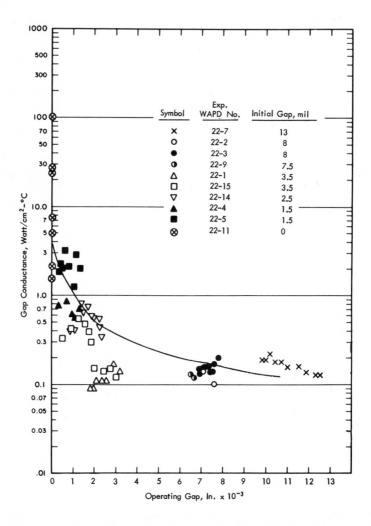

Fig. 2.8   Gap thermal conductance vs. operating gap.   (From Ref. 53.)

external and internal pressure. For an infinitely long cylinder, subject to internal and external pressure, the elastic deformation ΔD_i is given by

$$\Delta D_0 = \frac{D_i}{E(K^2 - 1)} \left\{ P_i[(1 - \mu) + (1 + \mu)K^2] - 2K^2 P_0 \right\} , \quad (2\text{-}8)$$

where

D_i = internal diameter (in.)

D_0 = external diameter (in.)

P_i = internal pressure (lb/in.^{2})

P_0 = external pressure (lb/in.^{2})

E = Young's modulus for the cladding

$K = D_0/D_i$

μ = Poisson's ratio for the cladding.

When low molecular weight gases (He, H$_2$) are present in the small size gaps usually encountered, a correction should be made to account for the temperature discontinuity at the gas-solid interface. Knudsen[54] has postulated that the energy interchange between incident gas molecules and a solid surface may be incomplete. He defined an accommodation coefficient α as the ratio of the temperature differential of the incident and reflected gas molecules to the temperature difference between the solid and the incident molecules. Dean[55] has proposed that Eq. (2-7) be modified to

$$h_g = \frac{k_g}{f(l + l_0)} , \quad (2\text{-}9)$$

where f is the factor by which the bulk thermal conductivity should be divided to obtain an effective conductivity, which allows for the temperature discontinuity. Dean shows f to be given by

$$f = 1 + \left(\frac{\alpha_1 + \alpha_2 - \alpha_1 \alpha_2}{\alpha_1 \alpha_2} \right) \left(\frac{4}{c_p + c_v} \right) \left(\frac{k_g}{\mu} \right) N_{kn} , \quad (2\text{-}10)$$

where

α_1, α_2 = accomodation coefficients for the fuel and clad surfaces

c_p, c_v = specific heats at constant pressure and constant volume, respectively

μ = gas viscosity (lb/ft h)

N_{kn} = Knudsen number (Ω/l)

Ω = mean free path of gas molecules (ft).

The accommodation coefficients may be evaluated from Ref. 56:

$$\alpha = \frac{4m\ m_1}{(m + m_1)^2} \quad , \tag{2-11}$$

where m and m_1 are the respective molecular masses of surface and gas.

When the pellet expands sufficiently to be in direct contact with the cladding, an improved gap conductance results. Several theoretical explanations of the phenomenon of contact conductance have been proposed, and in general, they consider a model in which the solid surfaces are in actual contact only at a few discrete points (Fig. 2.9). Since the thermal conductivity of the solids in contact is in general much greater than the thermal conductivity of the gas filling the interstices, heat flow will tend to channel through the points of contact. When the contact pressure is increased, the peaks in contact will be deformed and the contact points will increase in size and number. The number and size of the contact points will also depend on the surface finishes. At low contact pressures, the primary mode of heat transfer may be by conduction across the gas gaps. The effective distance between the surfaces depends on the size and shape of the surface irregularities.

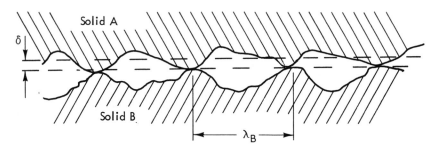

Fig. 2.9   Contact conductance model.

Various analytical approaches have been proposed for computing contact conductance. Cetinkale and Fishenden[57] presented an equation for the contact conductance of two metal surfaces based on calculation of the isotherms at the contact points of the two solids. A somewhat different approach was taken by Fenech and Rohsenow,[58] who found an approximate analytic solution for the heat conduction at a contact point. In general, these approaches have yielded results that are too complicated for practical design problems.

Few experimental measurements of direct use to the fuel rod designer are available. Wheeler[59] measured the contact conductance of seven pairs of materials, including cladding materials and UO_2, and his results for experiments in a vacuum are plotted in Fig. 2.10 as a function of the ratio of contact pressure to yield strength.

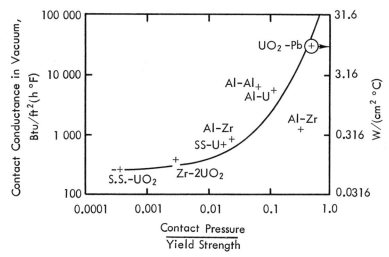

Fig. 2.10 Contact conductance measured by Wheeler. (From *Reactor Handbook*, Vol IV, Interscience Publisher, 1964.)

The previously cited work by Cohen[53] on irradiated specimens included measurements on a number of specimens with clad-fuel contact. The contact resistance obtained for UO_2-SS ranged from 4000 to 250 000 Btu/(h ft^2) on the first start-up. The contact resistance was evaluated by obtaining the total resistance and subtracting the resistances of the fuel and clad. An apparent decrease in thermal conductance after the first start-up may have been due to a decrease in fuel conductivity through irradiation or cracking.

Dean[55] measured the contact resistance of the UO_2-Zircaloy 2 joint as a function surface roughness and contact pressure in an argon atmosphere. In Fig. 2.11, we see that, at the low contact pressure of the experiment, the conductance varied linearly with the contact pressure, and, as expected, it increased with decreased surface roughness. Dean's measurements can be conservatively correlated as

$$h_g = \alpha P + \frac{k_g}{14.4 \times 10^{-6}}, \qquad (2\text{-}12)$$

where

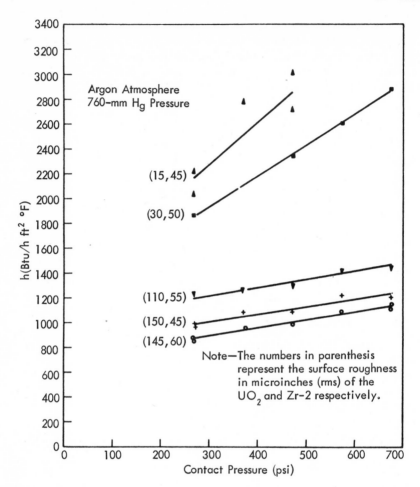

Fig. 2.11 Uranium Dioxide–Zircaloy contact resistance measured by Dean. (From Ref. 55.)

$\alpha = 0.60$ for Zircaloy clad and 0.48 for stainless steel

P = contact pressure (psi)

and other symbols have their previous meanings.

Contact conductances between UO_2 and Zircaloy were also measured by Ross and Stoute.[60] In correlating their results, they took the gap conductance to be the sum of h_s, the conduction through the contact points, and h_f, the gas conductance

$$h_g = h_s + h_f \quad . \tag{2-13}$$

They correlated the conduction through the points of contact by

$$h_s = \frac{k_m P}{a_0 R^{1/2} H} \quad , \tag{2-14}$$

where

k_m = harmonic mean of the thermal conductivities k_1 and k_2 of contacting surfaces $[(2k_1k_2)/(k_1 + k_2)]$ (Btu/h ft°F)

P = contact pressure (psi)

a_0 = empirical constant (0.0905)

R = root mean square of surface projections $[(p_1^2 + p_2^2)/2]^{1/2}$

H = Meyer hardness of softer solid (psi).

The gas conductance was given by

$$h_f = \frac{k_g}{(2.75 - 0.00176P)[(p_1 + p_2) + (g_1 + g_2)]} \tag{2-15}$$

k_g = thermal conductivity of gas in gap

$g_1 + g_2$ = "temperature jump distance."

The "temperature jump distance" is another means of accounting for the temperature discontinuity between the fluid in the gap and the contact surfaces. Ross and Stoute estimated these quantities for helium, argon, and fission gases from their data. The distances are assumed proportional to the mean free path of the gas molecules and, hence, inversely proportional to the temperature.

The best general correlation of the available experimental data would appear to be the semitheoretical one of Shlykov.[61] He assumes, as did the previous investigators, that the total conductance can be expressed as the sum of that of the fluid and of the contact points. Shlykov first defines a maximum relative gap thickness x, where

$$x = \frac{2(p_1 + p_2)}{2l} = \frac{\delta_{max}}{2l} \tag{2-16}$$

and

p_1, p_2 = mean heights of rough projections of surfaces 1 and 2

l = temperature jump distance

δ_{max} = maximum gap thickness.

The temperature jump distance is given by

$$l = \left(\frac{2 - \alpha}{\alpha}\right) \frac{2}{\text{Pr}} \left(\frac{c_p/c_v}{c_p/c_v + 1}\right) \Lambda \quad , \tag{2-17}$$

where

α = accommodation coefficient

Pr = Prandtl number

Λ = mean free path of gas molecules

c_p = specific heat at constant pressure

c_v = specific heat at constant volume.

Shlykov makes use of the work of Shvets and Dyban,[62] who were able to relate X to Y, the ratio of the maximum to effective gas gap, by

$$Y = \frac{10}{3} + \frac{10}{X} + \frac{4}{X^2} - 4\left(\frac{1}{X^3} + \frac{3}{X^2} + \frac{2}{X}\right) \ln(1+X) \quad , \qquad (2\text{-}18)$$

where

$Y = \delta_{\max}/\delta_e$

δ_e = effective (equivalent) gap thickness to be used in calculating the heat transferred across the gas gap.

The Shvets and Dyban correlation is compared to some of the available data in Fig. 2.12. Using these data one can calculate the conductance of the gas gap h_{gas} by

$$h_{gas} = k_g/\delta_e \quad , \qquad (2\text{-}19)$$

where k_g and δ_e have their previous meanings.

To obtain the heat transferred through the contact points, Shlykov assumes the true contact area is a function of the ratio of the surface projections $(p_1 + p_2)$ to the mean radius of a contact spot a and the ratio of contact pressure P to the yield strength of the softer material σ. The total gap conductance then becomes

$$h_g = k_g/\delta_e + f\left(P/\sigma, \frac{a}{p_1+p_2}\right)\frac{\bar{k}}{d} \quad , \qquad (2\text{-}20)$$

where

$\bar{k} = (2k_1 k_2)/(k_1 + k_2)$

k_1, k_2 = conductivity of metal surfaces.

Two dimensionless groups are then defined

$$N_c = h_g \delta_e/k_g \qquad (2\text{-}21)$$

$$N_b = \bar{k}\, \delta_e/a\, k_g \quad . \qquad (2\text{-}22)$$

Equation (2-20) is then rearranged to yield

$$\frac{N_c - 1}{N_b} = f\left(\frac{P}{3}\right)\left(\frac{a}{p_1 + p_2}\right) \quad . \qquad (2\text{-}23)$$

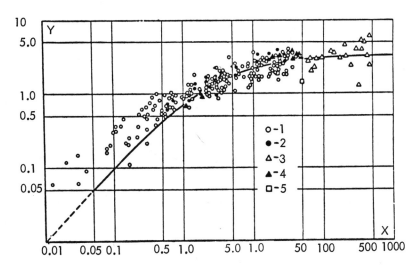

Fig. 2.12 Test data on equivalent gap height in relative coordinates. (From *Thermal Engineering*, **12**, 102, 1966.)

Notation 1 helium, argon, neon
         2 air, helium, hydrogen
         3 air
         4 air
         5 air

By assuming a as 40 and correlating the available data, Shlykov obtains

$$\frac{N_c - 1}{N_b} = 0.32 \left(\frac{P\,K}{3}\right)^{0.86} \quad , \qquad (2\text{-}24)$$

where the constant

$$K = 1 \; , \qquad \text{when } p_1 + p_2 \geqslant 30\mu$$

$$= \left(\frac{30}{p_1 + p_2}\right)^{1/3} \, , \text{ when } 10\mu \leqq p_1 + p_2 \leqq 30\mu \qquad (2\text{-}25)$$

$$= \frac{15}{p_1 + p_2} \; , \qquad \text{when } p_1 + p_2 \leqq 10\mu. \qquad (2\text{-}26)$$

Some of the available data are compared to this correlation in Fig. 2.13.

The contact pressure between the pellet and clad can be estimated by first computing their dimensions while ignoring any elastic deformation of the cladding. The internal pressure required to produce an elastic deformation that would produce a zero gap is given by Eq. (2-8). Since the clad and pellet are in true contact over only a small

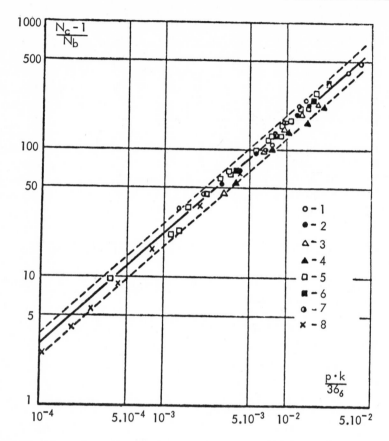

Fig. 2.13 Comparison of experimental data with Shlykov's contact conductance model. (From *Thermal Engineering*, **12**, 102, April 1965.)

Notation 1-4 Steel
          5-6 Steel 30CrMnSiN, different machining methods
          7 Duralumin DT16
          8 Brass

fraction of the total area we may say $P_i = P_{gas} + P_{contact}$. A more so-phisticated treatment of this subject is given by the CYGRO code.[63]

Since UO_2 cracks so extensively at the heat generation levels at which PWR operates, it has been suggested that it is unrealistic to assume an annular gas gap can be retained even if calculations indi-cate there is a significant space between pellet and clad. It is likely that the cracked pellet pieces are lying against the cladding, so the gap conductance would then be computed from one of the contact-con-ductance equations, which assumes a zero contact pressure. How-ever, most computations take the form used by Waldman et al.[64] in the FIGRO computer code, where the gap conductance is assumed to decrease linearly as the gap increases.

(b) Fission Gas Release and Internal Pressure. A significant fraction of the gases produced by fission are released by UO_2. It is generally agreed that below about 600 to 800°C the rate of fission gas release is controlled by recoil and knock out.[65,66] Release rates are low and are not temperature dependent.

In the region between 800 and 1800°C, fission gas release rates are appreciable and markedly temperature dependent. For a number of years, the rate of gas release in this region was believed to be determined by the rate at which the gas diffused out through the solid UO_2 particles. The available data were correlated using a fission gas diffusivity D, which followed an Arrenius rate equation

$$D = D_0 \exp\left(-E/RT\right) \quad , \tag{2-27}$$

where

D_0 = a constant

E = activation energy (cal/g mole)

R = perfect gas low constant (1.986 cal/g mole, °K)

T = absolute temperature (°K).

According to Booth,[67] the activation energy is essentially constant but D_0 varies with the nature of the compact. By using this theory, he developed a method for computing fission gas release based on the diffusion equation for a spherical crystallite of radius a. He expressed his results in terms of F the fraction of the total gas produced which has diffused out of the sphere in time t. From $t = 0$ to $t = 1/(\pi^2 D')$ (at which time $F = 0.57$), the fractional release can be approximated by

$$F = 4\left(\frac{d't}{\pi}\right)^{1/2} - \left(\frac{3D't}{2}\right) \quad . \tag{2-28}$$

For $t > (\pi^2 D't)^{-1} + 1$, Booth shows

$$F = \frac{0.57}{\pi^2 d't} + 1 - \frac{1}{\pi^2 d't} + \frac{6}{\pi^4 D't} \exp(-\pi^2 D't) - \frac{6}{\pi^4 D't} \quad . \tag{2-29}$$

The pseudo diffusion constant $D' = D/a^2$ is experimentally determined at a given temperature T_0. The constant at any other temperature T is given by

$$D'(T, °K) = D'_0 \exp\left[E/R\left(\frac{1}{T_0} - \frac{1}{T}\right)\right] \quad . \tag{2-30}$$

Booth recommended a value of 45 000 cal/g mole for E.

More recent reports indicate that, in the 800 to 1800°C range, fission gas release is controlled by some sort of coupled diffusion-trapping process.[65,67] In such a model, fission gas is assumed to be trapped in lattice defects, and its release is partially controlled by its rate of escape from these traps.

Above 1600 to 1800°C grain growth is rapid and most of the gas produced is released. Soulhier[66] still found that the fractional release rate followed an Arrenius rate law, where the activation energy decreases with increasing density.

A simple empirical approach for calculating fission gas release is presented by Lewis.[68] For given irradiation times, he assigns a maximum percentage of gas release to certain temperature bands. The experimental data are bounded by curves giving the maximum fractional release as a function of time and linear power density.

Once the total fission gas release has been obtained, the internal pressure and deflection may be calculated. Account should be taken of the thermal expansion of fuel and clad and the elastic expansion of the clad. Thus, for cylindrical rods we have

$$V_c(1 + 3\alpha_c\Delta T_c) - V_f(1 + 3\alpha_f\Delta T_f) = \frac{N^*RT}{P_i} - \frac{\pi d^3 L}{4EC}(P_i - P_0) \quad , \quad (2\text{-}31)$$

where

V_c = cold cladding volume

ΔT_c = hot clad, cold clad temperature

V_f = cold fuel volume

α_c, α_f = cladding and fuel linear coefficient of thermal expansion, respectively

ΔT_f = hot fuel, cold fuel temperature

N^* = number of gram moles of gas that has escaped

d = hot inside diameter of clad

R = gas constant (73.8 lb in./g mole °K)

T = temperature of gap (°K)

C = clad thickness

L = clad length

P = external pressure

P_i = internal pressure

E = Young's modulus of elasticity.

The above does not include the effects of irradiation swelling of the fuel or of cladding creep, which must be considered when Zircaloy is used.

In view of the radiation embrittlement of Zircaloy and stainless steel, a limitation is generally placed on cladding strain during normal operation. At higher temperatures, where ductility is greater but strength lower, clad bursting under external depressurization should be evaluated. If data on bursting pressure are not available, the pressure to cause a stress that establishes a 0.2% yield is often taken as the limit. Bursting problems are most serious during a loss-of-coolant accident because of the high cladding temperatures that may ensue.

In fuel plates, unacceptable deformation of the plates is a limit. Lustman,[69] who assumed the plate compartments to deform into trapezoidal prisms, obtained the following expressions for the maximum deformation y and internal pressure P_i

$$y = \frac{0.0138\, a^4}{Ec^3} \left(\frac{N^*RT}{V_0 - 2ya^2/3} - P_0 \right) \qquad (2\text{-}32)$$

$$P_i = (N^*RT)/(V_0 + 2ya^2/3) \quad , \qquad (2\text{-}33)$$

where

V_0 = initial free volume in plate element (cold condition) (in.^{3})

a = edge length of plate compartment square (in.)

and other symbols have their previous meanings. Again creep has been omitted.

2-2 STEADY STATE CONDUCTION

2-2.1 Heat Generation Within a Fuel Plate

(a) Uniform Heat Generation. Let us consider the temperature distribution within the fuel of a thin fuel plate. If we ignore axial conduction, a one dimensional treatment can be used. From a heat balance across a differential element (see Fig. 2.14), we have

$$\left(k + \frac{dk}{dx}\, dx \right)\left(\frac{dT}{dx} + \frac{d^2T}{dx^2}\, dx \right) - k\, \frac{dT}{dx} + q'''\, dx = 0 \quad , \qquad (2\text{-}34)$$

where x is the distance from the fuel element centerline, q''' is the volumetric heat generation rate, and other symbols have their previous meanings. We can simplify this equation to

$$\frac{d}{dx}\left(k\, \frac{dT}{dx} \right) + \frac{d}{dx}\left(k\, \frac{d^2T}{dx^2} \right) + q''' = 0 \quad . \qquad (2\text{-}35)$$

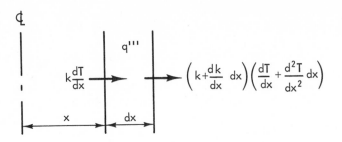

Fig. 2.14 Heat conduction in a fuel plate.

Upon elimination of the third order term, we have

$$\frac{d}{dx}\left(k\,\frac{dT}{dx}\right) + q''' = 0 \quad .$$
(2-36)

By integrating on the assumption that q''' is constant and by imposing the boundary conditions that dT/dx is zero at the centerline, we obtain

$$k\,\frac{dT}{dx} = -x\,q'''$$
(2-37)

and finally

$$\int_{T_c}^{T_x} k\,dT = -\frac{x^2}{2}\,q''' \quad ,$$
(2-38)

where T_c is the center temperature. By substitution of an appropriate expression for thermal conductivity, the temperature at any point may be determined. The assumption of negligible axial conduction can be justified for metallic fuel plates because of their very small thickness. For a UO_2 plate, the very low thermal conductivity of UO_2 provides the justification. The effect of axial conduction has been considered in detail by Fagan and Mengle[70] who provide expressions for the surface heat flux. They indicate that for most power reactor systems the maximum heat flux will be in error by less than 0.5% if axial conduction is neglected.

(b) *Effect of Flux Depression.* In a uniform lattice, diffusion theory indicates the thermal neutron flux ϕ varies across the fuel plate in accordance with

$$\phi = \phi_0 \cosh(\kappa x) \quad ,$$
(2-39)

where ϕ_0 is the flux at the centerline and κ is the reciprocal of the thermal diffusion length. Since q''' is proportional to ϕ in a thermal reactor,

$$q''' = q_0''' \cosh(\kappa x) \quad , \tag{2-40}$$

where q_0''' is the volumetric heat generation rate at the centerline. In actual practice, the flux distribution will probably be computed by the escape probability method (see Sec. 1-2.5). Although a simple, closed form solution is not obtained, the numerical results can generally be fitted quite well by equations of the form of Eq. (2-39) provided κ is appropriately chosen.

If we proceed in the same manner as for a constant rate of heat generation, we obtain analogously to Eq. (2-36)

$$\frac{d}{dx}\left(k \frac{dT}{dx}\right) + q_0''' \cosh(\kappa x) = 0. \tag{2-41}$$

Integration twice with $dT/dx = 0$ at the centerline yields

$$\int_{T_s}^{T_x} k \, dT = \frac{q_0'''}{\kappa^2} \left[\cosh(\kappa a) - \cosh(\kappa x)\right] \quad , \tag{2-42}$$

where a is the half thickness of the plate. We may also express our result in terms of the surface heat flux per unit area q'' by noting that

$$q'' = \frac{q_0'''}{\kappa} \sinh(\kappa a) \quad , \tag{2-43}$$

hence

$$\int_{T_s}^{T_x} kdt = q'' \left[\frac{\cosh(\kappa a) - \cosh(\kappa x)}{\kappa \sinh(\kappa a)}\right] \tag{2-44}$$

and

$$\int_{T_s}^{T_c} kdt = q' \left[\frac{\cosh(\kappa a) - 1}{2a \kappa \sinh(\kappa a)}\right] \quad , \tag{2-45}$$

where T_c is the center temperature.

2-2.2 Heat Generation Within a Fuel Rod

(a) *Constant Heat Generation Across Rod.* From a heat balance across a differential annular ring (Fig. 2.15), we have

$$\theta\left(k + \frac{dk}{dr} dr\right)(r + dr) \frac{dT}{dr}\bigg|_{r+dr} - \theta kr \frac{dT}{dr}\bigg|_r + q'''r\theta \, dr = 0 \quad . \tag{2-46}$$

By rearrangement and omission of higher order terms, we obtain

$$\frac{1}{r} \frac{d}{dr}\left(k r \frac{dT}{dr}\right) + q''' = 0 \quad . \tag{2-47}$$

This may be integrated to yield

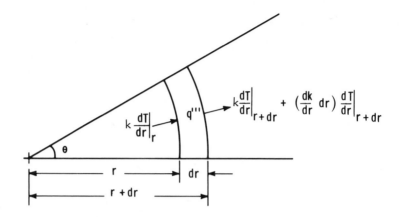

Fig. 2.15 Heat conduction in a fuel rod. (From *Nuc. Eng. Design*, **6**, 301, 1967.)

$$kr \frac{dT}{dr} = - \int_{r_c}^{r} r \, q''' \, dr = - \frac{q'''}{2} (r^2 - r_c^2) \quad . \tag{2-48}$$

$$\int_{T_r}^{T_c} k \, dr = \int_{r}^{r_c} \left[-\frac{q'''}{2} \left(r - \frac{r_c^2}{r} \right) \right] dr = \frac{q'''}{4} [(r^2 - r_c^2) - 2r_c^2 (\ln r/r_c)] \quad , \tag{2-49}$$

where T_c is the center temperature at the central radius r_c and T_r is the temperature at radius r.

When we are dealing with solid cylinders (no central hole), we may simplify our last result to

$$\int_{T_s}^{T_c} k \, dT = \frac{q''' \, r_0^2}{4} \quad , \tag{2-50}$$

where r_0 is the outer radius and T_s is the surface temperature.

We may also express the volumetric heat generation rate in terms of the rate of heat generation per unit length of fuel rod q' as

$$q' = \pi r_0^2 \, q''' \quad , \tag{2-51}$$

then

$$q' = 4\pi \int_{T_s}^{T_c} k \, dT \quad . \tag{2-52}$$

For the approximation of a constant value of k, we obtain

$$(T_c - T_s) = \frac{q'}{4\pi \, k_{av}} \quad . \tag{2-53}$$

From Eqs. (2-52) and (2-53), we have the interesting result that the temperature difference across a fuel pellet is independent of the radius of the fuel pellet. Specifying a given surface temperature and a given rate of power generation per unit length of fuel fixes the central fuel temperature.

(b) Concept of ∫kdT. Equation (2-52) states that q', the rate of heat generation per unit length of cylindrical fuel rod, is directly proportional to the thermal conductivity integral,

$$\int_{T_s}^{T_c} k\,dT \quad .$$

Thus, if values for the integral are available, the power level necessary to produce a given center temperature is readily specified.[71] This is convenient for the designer since it avoids the necessity for performing the integration of the thermal conductivity values with respect to temperature, and it also is a convenient way of reporting experimental data from in-pile irradiations. Under those conditions the power generation, center, and surface temperature may be known.

Hence, the $\int_{T_s}^{T_c} k\,dT$ is known but pointwise values of k are not available. Data are usually given in terms of $\int_0^{T_c} k\,dT$, where

$$\int_{T_s}^{T_c} k\,dT = \int_0^{T_c} k\,dT - \int_0^{T_s} k\,dT \quad . \tag{2-54}$$

Several curves of the integral as a function of its upper limit are shown in Fig. 2.16.

While the concept is of particular value for UO$_2$ fuel rods, it is also useful in the description of UO$_2$ fuel plate behavior. As seen from Eq. (2-38), a knowledge of the integral and plate thickness is sufficient to establish the volumetric power generation required for a given temperature. Indeed, it is possible to relate ∫kdT to the heat output for any geometric shape. Thus, for constant heat generation

$$\int_{T_s}^{T_c} k\,dT = Cq' \quad , \tag{2-55}$$

where C depends on the fuel geometry. Specification of the maximum allowable value of the integral fixes the power capability of the fuel in any given geometry. As previously remarked, the usual design criterion is the avoidance of center melting. Since this is an observable point, a series of tests at varying power levels can be used to determine the ∫kdT at which this first occurs. The observations are not dependent on a precise knowledge of fuel conductivity or temperature distribution within the fuel. Values for the ∫kdT to produce

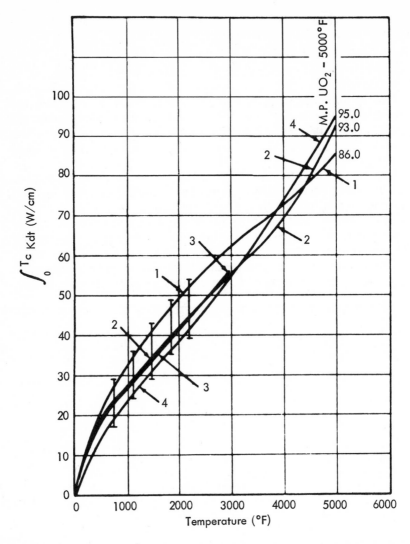

Fig. 2.16 Summary of $\int k\,dT$ for UO_2. (From McNelly, "Liquid Metal Fast Breeder Reactor Design Study," General Electric Co., Report GEAP-4418, 1963.)

Notation   1. Weidenbaum, General Electric Co. Report, GEAP-3771-8, 1963.
2. Duncan, Westinghouse Electric Corp. Report, CVNA-142, 1962.
3. Bates, Ref. 30.
4. Robertson et al., *J. Nucl. Mater.*, **7**, *3*, 225, 1962.

melting that were determined by several investigators are shown in the upper right of Fig. 2.16. More recently, Lyons et al.[72] have re-evaluated this integral in a series of short-time, in-pile tests, and they concluded from metallagraphic examinations that, for 95% dense sintered UO_2 pellets, the average value of the conductivity integral from 0°C to melting was 93.5 W/cm. The statistically determined 95% confidence limits were ±3.5 W/cm. Direct measurement of the integral based on a gas-bulb sensor yielded a value of approximately 90 W/cm. Vibratory compacted fuel was found to have a significantly lower integral even when the density correction was made.

The effect of long time irradiation on the conductivity integral is uncertain. While most earlier observers had concluded that there is significant reduction due to irradiation, some recent data dispute this.[36,73] Stora's previously cited explanation[36] that most of the apparent effects are simply due to thermal cracking and, thus, depend on the available gap may be reasonable.

Soulhier[74] has used the conductivity integral for correlation of fission gas release data. His results are presented as $\int_{400°C}^{T_c} k dT$ (max) vs $F \int_{T_s}^{T_c} k dT$, where F is the fractional gas release, T_c is the center temperature, and T_s is the surface temperature. The integral $\int_{400°C}^{T_c} k dT$ is used as a means of normalizing all experiments performed at a given central fuel temperature to the same surface temperature of 400°C. The product $F \int_{T_s}^{T_c} k dT$ is used to normalize the fission gas released based on the volumetric average heating rate.

(c) Rod with Flux Depression. We have previously shown that diffusion theory indicates the thermal flux distribution across a cylindrical fuel rod in a uniform lattice is given by

$$\phi = A I_0(\kappa r) \quad , \tag{2-56}$$

where

A = a constant

I_0 = a zero order modified Bessel function of the first kind

κ = the reciprocal of the thermal diffusion length in the fuel.

When, as is now more usually done, the escape probability method is used, κ should be regarded as a constant selected to yield a closed form approximation of the results. Since q''' is proportional to ϕ in a thermal reactor

$$q''' = A' I_0(\kappa r) \quad . \tag{2-57}$$

Now let q_0''' be the value of q''' at the center of the pellet, and, since $I_0(0) = 1$, our previous expression becomes

$$q''' = q_0''' \, I_0(\kappa r) \quad . \tag{2-58}$$

The average value of q''' over the entire rod cross section is given by

$$\overline{q}''' = \frac{\int_0^a q'''(2\pi r)\, dr}{\int_0^a 2\pi r \, dr} = \frac{2}{a^2} \int_0^a q''' r \, dr \quad , \tag{2-59}$$

where a is the outer radius of the pellet.

By substitution of our expression for local flux in Eq. (2-59), we obtain

$$\overline{q}''' = \frac{2q_0'''[I_1(\kappa a)]}{(\kappa a)} \quad . \tag{2-60}$$

Substitution of the heat flux expression in our equation for the temperature gradient at any point (Eq. 2-47) and integration yield

$$\frac{q_0''' r [I_1(\kappa r)]}{(\kappa r)} + k \frac{dT}{dr} = 0 \quad . \tag{2-61}$$

On separating variables and integrating from r to a, we obtain

$$\frac{q_0'''}{\kappa^2} \left[I_0(\kappa a) - I_0(\kappa r) \right] = \int_{T_s}^T k \, dT \quad . \tag{2-62}$$

If we rewrite the above in terms of the average heat generation rate, we get

$$\frac{\frac{\overline{q}''' a^2}{4} \left\{ 2[I_0(\kappa a) - I_0(\kappa r)] \right\}}{[(\kappa a)[I_1(\kappa a)]} = \int_{T_s}^T k \, dT \quad . \tag{2-63}$$

At the center of the pellet $r = 0$ and $T = T_c$ and under these conditions Eq. (2-63) becomes

$$\left(\frac{\overline{q}''' a^2}{4} \right) \frac{2[I_0(\kappa a) - 1]}{\kappa a [I_1(\kappa a)]} = \int_{T_s}^{T_c} k \, dT \quad . \tag{2-64}$$

If we let

$$f = \frac{2[I_0(\kappa a) - 1]}{\kappa a [I_1(\kappa a)]} \tag{2-65}$$

and replace $\overline{q}'''$ in terms of q', the rate of heat generation per unit length of rod [Eq. (2-51)], we obtain

$$q'f = 4\pi \int_{T_s}^{T_c} k \, dT \quad . \tag{2-66}$$

The term f is called the "flux depression factor," and its meaning becomes clear when we compare Eqs. (2-66) and (2-52). We see that the thermal power associated with given fuel surface and center temperature is greater for nonuniform than uniform heat generation, the ratio of the two heat ratings being f.

Approximate values of f can be obtained from diffusion theory if values of κ are available. For UO_2 of 95% theoretical density, κ varies from 2 to 3/cm for enrichment values of 2.5 to 6% ^{235}U. Figure 2.17 shows f as a function of enrichment and fuel diameter for pellets of 95% dense UO_2. It will be seen that, for the enrichments used in pressurized water reactors, the value of f is not far from unity. However, this effect should not be ignored since it can mean an increase of several percentages in reactor power output. The fact that f is close to unity can be used to justify the simple approximation that the thermal flux inside the fuel follows a parabolic distribution. If this is done, values of F, the ratio of surface to average flux in the rod, obtained from escape probability theory can be used directly to compute f without the necessity of assigning a value to κ; consequently, for a parabolic flux distribution

$$f = (3 - F)/2 \quad . \tag{2-67}$$

(d) Heat Generation with a Power Tilt. It was indicated in Sec. 1-3.2 that the flux distribution across a cluster of rods in a pressure tube of a D_2O or graphite-moderated reactor is approximated by the function $I_0(r)$. When a single rod is considered (Fig. 2.18) this appears as a flux tilt. A reasonable representation of the distribution has been found to be[75]

$$q'''(r,\theta) = \overline{q}'''(1 + \epsilon r/a \cos \theta), \tag{2-68}$$

where ϵ represents one-half the difference between the minimum and maximum heat generation rate and $\overline{q}'''$ (the average volumetric heat generation rate)

$$\epsilon = (q'''_{max} - q'''_{min})/2\overline{q}''' \quad . \tag{2-69}$$

Since we must now consider both radial and azimuthal variation in temperature, we must use the general form of the steady-state conduction equation

$$k \nabla^2 T + q''' = 0 \quad . \tag{2-70}$$

In cylindrical coordinates with the present heat flux distribution, this becomes

$$\frac{1}{r} \frac{\partial}{\partial r} \left(r \frac{\partial T}{\partial r} \right) + \frac{1}{r^2} \frac{\partial^2 T}{\partial \theta^2} + \frac{\overline{q}'''}{k} \left(1 + \epsilon \frac{r}{a} \cos \theta \right) = 0 \tag{2-71}$$

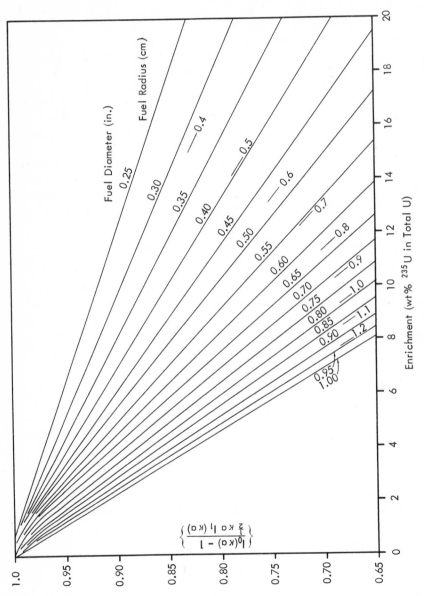

Fig. 2.17 Flux depression factors for UO₂ fuel rods of 95% theoretical density. (From Ref. 71.)

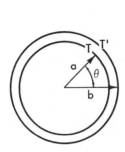
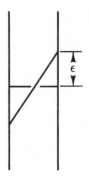

Fig. 2.18 Fuel rod with flux tilt.

in the pellet region, if we assume a constant value for k.* Since in the clad region we have no heat generation, we obtain

$$\frac{1}{r} \frac{\partial}{\partial r} \left(r \frac{\partial T'}{\partial r} \right) + \frac{1}{r^2} \left(\frac{\partial^2 T'}{\partial \theta^2} \right) = 0 , \qquad (2\text{-}72)$$

where T' represents clad temperature.

At the boundary of the pellet and clad there will normally be a gap to which we shall assign a conductance h_g. Since the heat transferred across the pellet, gap, and clad must be equal at $r = a$, we have the boundary conditions at $r = a$

$$h[T(a,\theta) - T'(a,\theta)] = k \left(\frac{\partial T}{\partial r} \right) \Big|_{r=a} \qquad (2\text{-}73)$$

$$k' \frac{\partial T'}{\partial r} \Big|_{r=a} = k \frac{\partial T}{\partial r} \Big|_{r=a} , \qquad (2\text{-}74)$$

where k and k' are the thermal conductivity of the fuel and clad, respectively. If the heat transfer coefficient to the coolant is high, we may say, at $r = b$

$$T'(b,\theta) \approx T_{\text{bulk water}} . \qquad (2\text{-}75)$$

We also note that at $r = 0$, T is not infinite. With these boundary conditions, Eqs. (2-71) and (2-72) may be integrated to yield

$$T = \frac{\overline{q'''}}{4k} (a^2 - r^2) + \frac{1}{2h} a \overline{q'''} + \frac{\overline{q'''} a^2}{2k'} \ln \frac{b}{a} + \psi(r) \cos \theta + T_b \qquad (2\text{-}76)$$

D. G. ANDREWS and M. D. DIXMIER provide a solution for the case of varying k in "Calculation of Temperature Distributions in Fuel Rods With Varying Conductivity and Asymmetric Flux Distribution" *Nucl. Sci. Eng.*, **36**, 259 (1969).

and

$$T' = \frac{\overline{q}'''a^2}{2k} \ln \frac{b}{r} + \psi'(r) \cos \theta + T_b \cdot \qquad (2\text{-}77)$$

We must now evaluate $\psi(r)$ and $\psi'(r)$ by substituting Eq. (2-76) into (2-71) and by solving the resultant differential equation to get

$$\psi(r) = Ar + \frac{\alpha}{8} r^3 \,, \qquad (2\text{-}78)$$

where $\alpha = \epsilon \overline{q}'''/ak$. Similarly, if we substitute Eq. (2-77) into (2-72), we can solve to obtain

$$\psi'(r) = C (1/r - r/b^2). \qquad (2\text{-}79)$$

Using these results in Eqs. (2-73) and (2-74), we may solve for the constants A and C

$$A = \frac{\alpha a^2}{8} \left[\frac{1 + 3 \left(\dfrac{k}{h_g a} + \dfrac{k}{k'} \dfrac{b^2 - a^2}{b^2 + a^2} \right)}{1 + \left(\dfrac{k}{h_g a} + \dfrac{k}{k'} \dfrac{b^2 - a^2}{b^2 + a^2} \right)} \right] \qquad (2\text{-}80)$$

and

$$C = \frac{a^4}{4} \frac{k}{k'} \left[\frac{b^2/(b^2 + a^2)}{1 + \left(\dfrac{k}{h_g a} + \dfrac{k}{k'} \dfrac{b^2 - a^2}{b^2 + a^2} \right)} \right] \cdot \qquad (2\text{-}81)$$

If desired, the maximum fuel temperature at any radius may now be determined, and this occurs at $\theta = 0$

$$T_{\max} = \frac{\overline{q}'''}{4k} (a^2 - r^2) + \frac{1}{2 h_g} a \, \overline{q}''' + \frac{\overline{q}'''a^2}{2k'} \ln \frac{b}{a} + T_b + \frac{\epsilon \, \overline{q}'''}{8 ak}$$

$$\times \left(\frac{1 - 3 \, \xi}{1 + 9 \, \xi} a^2 \, r_{\max} - r_m^3 \right) \,, \qquad (2\text{-}82)$$

where

$$\xi = \frac{k}{h_g a} + \frac{k}{k'} \frac{b^2 - a^2}{b^2 + a^2} \qquad (2\text{-}83)$$

and r_m, the radial location of the maximum fuel temperature, is given by

$$r_m = \frac{2a}{3\epsilon} \left\{ \left[1 + 3/4 \, \epsilon^2 \left(\frac{1 + 3\xi}{1 + \xi} \right) \right]^{1/2} - 1 \right\} \cdot$$

We may also determine the maximum heat flux [Btu/(h ft^2)], which also occurs at $\theta = 0$

$$q''_{\max} = k' \left(\frac{2 T'}{2 r} \right)_{a = b} = \frac{\overline{q}'''a^2}{2 b} + \frac{1}{2} \epsilon \, \overline{q}'''a^3 \, [(1 + \xi)(b^2 + a^2)]^{-1} \,, \qquad (2\text{-}84)$$

hence,

$$\frac{q''_{\max}}{q''_{\text{mean}}} = 1 + \frac{ab\ \epsilon}{(1 + \xi)(b^2 + a^2)} \quad . \tag{2-85}$$

For $b = a + \Delta r'$ where $a \gg \Delta r'$, the last equation simplifies to

$$\frac{q''_{\max}}{q''_{\text{mean}}} = 1 + \frac{\epsilon}{2\left[1 + \dfrac{k}{a}\left(\dfrac{1}{h_g} + \dfrac{\Delta r'}{k'}\right)\right]} \quad . \tag{2-86}$$

An example of what is obtained in a typical case is useful: Assume $\epsilon = 0.2$, $k' = 12$ Btu/h ft °F, $k = 1.6$ Btu/h ft °F, $a = 0.4$ in., $h_g = 1000$, $\Delta r' = 0.013$, then $q_{\max}/q_{\text{mean}}$ is approximately 1.09.

2-2.3 Annular Fuel Elements

For a hollow cylinder of outer radius a and inner radius b, diffusion theory calculations give the flux distribution as

$$\phi = C'\phi_0 \left[I_0(\kappa r) + \frac{I_1(\kappa b)}{K_1(\kappa b)}\ K_0(\kappa r)\right] \quad , \tag{2-87}$$

where

K_0 = zero order, modified Bessel function of second kind

K_1 = first order, modified Bessel function of second kind

C' = constant evaluated so that $\phi = \phi_0$ at $r = a$.

For heat removal at the outer surface only, we write

$$\int_{T_s}^{T_c} k\,dT = \frac{1}{4r}\ q' \left\{\frac{\kappa b[I_1(\kappa b)K_0(\kappa a) + I_0(\kappa a)K_1(\kappa b)] - 1}{\frac{1}{2}\kappa^2 ab[I_1(\kappa a)K_1(\kappa b) - I_1(\kappa b)K_1(\kappa a)]}\right\} \quad . \tag{2-88}$$

When heat is removed at both surfaces, the situation is complicated if different boundary conditions hold at the two surfaces. For the particular case when T_s is the same at both surfaces, one gets

$$\int_{T_s}^{T_r} k\,dT$$

$$= \frac{1}{2}\ q'b \left(\frac{[I_0(\kappa b) - I_0(\kappa r)] + [K_0(\kappa b) - K_0(\kappa r)] + \kappa R \ln \dfrac{r}{b}\ [I_1(\kappa r) - \lambda K_1(\kappa R)]}{\frac{1}{2}\ \kappa b \left\{\dfrac{R}{b}\ [I_1(\kappa R) - \lambda K_1(\kappa R)] - [I_1(\kappa b) - K_1(\kappa b)]\right\}}\right),$$

$$\tag{2-89}$$

where

$\lambda = I_1(\kappa b)/K_1(\kappa b)$

R = radius at which maximum fuel temperature occurs.

One may obtain R from

$$R\ln\left(\frac{a}{b}\right)\left[I_1(\kappa R) - \lambda K_1(\kappa R)\right] = \frac{1}{\kappa}\left[I_0(\kappa a) - I_0(\kappa b)\right] + \frac{\lambda}{\kappa}\left[K_0(\kappa a) - K_0(\kappa b)\right] .$$

(2-90)

2-2.4 Oxide Elements at High Temperatures

In Sec. 2-1.1, it was observed that porous oxide fuel, irradiated at high heat fluxes, shows large columnar grains distributed around a cylindrical central void. In out-of-pile experiments, MacEwan and Lawson[76] showed that columnar grains would be produced at temperatures above 1700°C if a sufficiently high temperature gradient is maintained. The columnar grains resulted from the migration of voids, transversely oriented with respect to the newly formed grains, toward the high temperature regions.

The observed grain growth is attributed to a vaporization-condensation process that results in a net movement of a pore at high temperatures. It is assumed that fuel vaporization occurs at the high temperature end of the pore and condensation at the low temperature end. Nichols[21] has developed a theoretical model for this process. The velocity of an elliptical pore, which Nichols shows to be independent of its size, is given by

$$v = \frac{qP_0\Omega\Delta H_v[N_a(M_1 + M_2)]^{1/2}\exp[-\Delta H_v/(RT)]}{16Pl^2T^{3/2}(2\pi KM_1M_2)^{1/2}}\frac{dT}{dr} , \qquad (2-91)$$

where

P_0 = constant in vapor pressure equation

$$P = P_0\exp[-\Delta H_v/(RT)]$$

(P_0 is 1.64×10^{14} dynes/cm^2 for UO_2)

Ω = atomic volume (3×10^{-23} cm^3 for UO_2)

ΔH_v = heat of vaporization ($\approx 142\,600$ cal/mole for UO_2)

M_1 = gram molecular weight of matrix (g)

M_2 = gram molecular weight of vapor (g)

P = pressure of gas vapor in pore (dynes/cm^2)

N_a = Avogadro's number (6.023×10^{23}/mole)

l = cross-sectional radius for collisions between matrix and vapor molecules (3×10^{-8} cm for UO_2)

K = Boltzman's constant (1.38×10^{-16} erg/°C)

r = pellet radius (cm)

R = Ideal Gas Law constant (cal/g mole°K)

T = temperature (°K).

Nichols takes the region in which all pores have had sufficient time to migrate to the central void as the columnar grain growth region. Using Eq. (2-91), one may compute the radial boundary of the grain growth region r_{cg}. Figure 2.19 presents the results of the Nichols calculations for a typical UO₂ pellet. He assumed that the surface temperature of the pellet was 800°K and that a parabolic temperature gradient existed across the fuel. Helium was assumed to be the primary vapor constituent. It will be observed that r_{cg} may become a

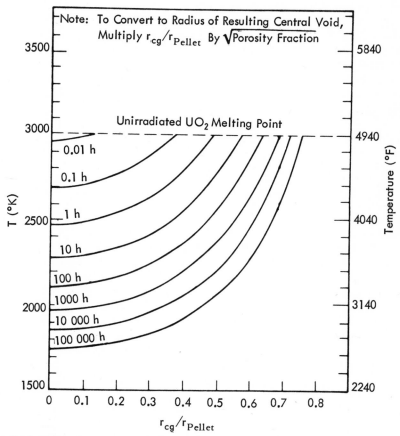

Fig. 2.19 Columnar grain growth radius in UO₂ rods. (From *J. Nucl. Mater.*, **22**, 214, 1967.)

significant fraction of r_0, the total pellet radius, at high temperatures. The radius of the central void r_v is computed by

$$(r_{cg}/r_0)\epsilon = r_v \quad , \tag{2-92}$$

where ϵ is the initial void fraction of the pellet.

Void migration complicates the computation of pellet temperatures. We now have a pellet of varying porosity; the porosity in the grain growth region being essentially zero. The thermal conductivity is now a function of both local porosity and temperature. Simple closed form analytical solutions are not available, and numerical techniques are required. The pellet is first divided into a number of radial rings. If a sufficiently large number of rings are chosen, properties may be assumed constant across each annular ring. In one procedure,[63] it is assumed that the heat flux q_{av}'' and thermal conductivity k_{av} may be evaluated at the center of the annular ring and that the equation for the temperature drop across a slab may be used. Then the temperature drop across an annular ring ΔT_r is given by

$$\Delta T_r = \frac{q_{av}''(\Delta r)}{k_{av}} \quad , \tag{2-93}$$

where r is the thickness of the ring.

When fewer rings are chosen, more accurate results are obtained by modifying Eq. (2-49) to

$$\int_0^{T_{r1}} k\,dT = \int_0^{T_{r2}} k\,dT + \left\{ \frac{q'''}{4} [(r_2^2 - r_1^2) - 2r_1^2(\ln r_2/r_1)] \right\}, \tag{2-94}$$

where T_{r1} and T_{r2} equal temperatures at the inner and outer radius of ring. If the temperature at $r_2(T_{r2})$ is known, the $\int_0^{T_{r2}} k\,dT$ is known for a given porosity. Then $\int_0^{T_{r1}} k\,dT$ can be obtained, and T_{r1} is known.

Both of the above schemes are iterative. A surface temperature of the pellet must be assumed, and the calculation then proceeds inward. The final temperature distribution is then used to compute a revised estimate of fuel dimensions and gap conductance h_g. With a new h_g, a revised pellet surface temperature can be computed.

Since void migration is a function of time, the results obtained would be used to compute r_{cg} and r_v at the end of a given time period. The temperature distribution calculations are then repeated using the revised fuel properties. The radii of the inner fuel rings are appropriately modified to account for any central void.

In doing such time-dependent calculations, one would generally consider also the effects of fuel swelling, cladding creep, and variations in the rate of power production. In many fuel element designs, central temperatures are below 2700°F, so void migration is negligible and the simpler design procedures may be used.

2-3 TRANSIENT CONDUCTION

2-3.1 Rapid Transients in Fuel Rods

(a) Analytical Techniques. Under transient conditions, when heat storage must be considered, the general conduction equation takes the form

$$c_p \rho \frac{\partial T}{\partial t} = \nabla(k\nabla T) + q''', \qquad (2-95)$$

where t represents time, c_p specific heat, ρ density, and other symbols have their previous meanings.

Let us consider a fuel pellet of radius a surrounded by cladding having an outside radius b: If we ignore axial conduction, we may write for pellet region

$$k_1\left(\frac{\partial^2 T_1}{\partial r^2} + \frac{1}{r}\frac{\partial T_1}{\partial r}\right) + q''' = c_{p_1} \rho_1 \frac{\partial T_1}{\partial t}, \quad (0 < r \leqslant a) \qquad (2-96)$$

and for the clad region

$$k_2\left(\frac{\partial^2 T_1}{\partial r^2} + \frac{1}{r}\frac{\partial T_2}{\partial r}\right) = c_{p_2} \rho_2 \frac{\partial T_2}{\partial t}, \quad (a \leqslant r \leqslant b) . \qquad (2-97)$$

We shall consider a step change in heat transfer coefficient at the outer clad at $t = 0$ and a subsequent reduction in heat generation rate. This corresponds to the situation arising during a transient when the fuel element is suddenly blanketed by steam (departure from nucleate boiling occurs, see Sec. 4-3.2) and the film coefficient is drastically reduced. The heat generation rate is reduced upon reactor scram.

Let us define a set of dimensionless groups as follows:

$$B_1 = \frac{h_g b}{k_2} \qquad B_2 = \frac{hb}{k_2}, \qquad (2-98)$$

where h_g is the gap conductance and h the film coefficient at rod surface

$$R = \frac{r}{b}, \qquad R_p = \frac{a}{b}, \qquad \tau = \left(\frac{k_2}{c_p \rho_2}\right)\frac{t}{a^2} \qquad (2-99)$$

$$C_p(R) = \frac{c_p(r)\,\rho(r)}{c_{p_2}\rho_2}, \qquad K(R) = \frac{k(r)}{k_2} \qquad (2-100)$$

$$Q(\tau) = \frac{q'''(t)}{q'''(0)}, \qquad T^+ = \frac{k_2 T}{q'''(0)\,a^2} . \qquad (2-101)$$

Then Eqs. (2-96) and (2-97) can be written as

$$K \left(\frac{\partial^2 T^+_1}{\partial R^2} + \frac{1}{R} \frac{\partial T^+_1}{\partial R} \right) + Q = C_p \frac{\partial T^+_1}{\partial \tau} \quad , \quad (0 \leqslant R \leqslant R_p) \quad (2\text{-}102)$$

$$\frac{\partial^2 T^+_2}{\partial R^2} + \frac{1}{R} \left(\frac{\partial T^+_2}{\partial R} \right) = \frac{\partial T^+_2}{\partial \tau} \quad , \quad (R_p < R \leqslant 1) \quad . \quad (2\text{-}103)$$

The boundary conditions are

$$B_1(T_1^+ - T_2^+) = -K \frac{\partial T^+_1}{\partial R} \quad , \quad (\text{at } R = R_p) \tag{2-104}$$

$$B_1(T_1^+ - T_2^+) = \frac{\partial T^+_2}{\partial R} \quad , \quad (\text{at } R = R_p) \tag{2-105}$$

$$B_2(T_2^+ - T_\infty^+) = -\frac{\partial T^+_2}{\partial R} \quad , \quad (\text{at } R = 1) \quad , \tag{2-106}$$

where T^+ is the dimensionless bulk coolant temperature.

These equations may be solved by a Hankel transform[77] or a Finite Integral transform.[78] In both cases, the exact solutions are in terms of infinite series. By using a finite integral transform technique, Matsch[78] obtained the solution as follows:

$$T^+(R,\tau) = \sum_n C_n(\tau) X_n(r) \quad , \tag{2-107}$$

where the values X_n are obtained by considering an associated equation of the form

$$\nabla K(R) \, \nabla X(R) + (\lambda_n)^2 \, X(R) = 0 \tag{2-108}$$

to which the solutions are a set of eigenfunctions (X_n) true for discrete values of $(\lambda_n)^2$.

Thus, we have for the pellet

$$T_1^+(R,\tau) = \Sigma \, C'_n(\tau) \, X'_n \tag{2-109}$$

and for the clad

$$T_2^+(R,\tau) = \Sigma \, C''_n(\tau) \, X''_n \, . \tag{2-110}$$

Matsch has shown that the eigenfunctions are given by

$$X'_n = J_0 \left(\frac{\lambda_n R}{\sqrt{k^\tau}} \right) \tag{2-111}$$

$$X''_n = C_{1n} J_0(\lambda_n R) + C_{2n} Y_0(\lambda_n R), \tag{2-112}$$

where J_0 is a Bessel function of the first kind, zero order and Y_0 a Bessel function of the second kind, zero order.

The eigenvalues λ_n are obtained from the determinantal equation:

$$\left| \left[J_0\left(\frac{\lambda_n R_p}{\sqrt{K'}}\right) - \frac{\lambda_n\sqrt{K'}}{B_1} J_1\left(\frac{\lambda_n R_p}{\sqrt{K'}}\right) \right] \quad Y_0(\lambda_n R_p) \right. $$

$$\left. \lambda_n\sqrt{K'} \ J_1\left(\frac{\lambda_n R_p}{\sqrt{K'}}\right) \qquad Y_1(\lambda_n R_p) \right| \left[J_0(\lambda_n) - \frac{\lambda_n}{B_2} J_1(\lambda_n) \right]$$

$$+ \left| \begin{matrix} J_0(\lambda_n R_p) & \left[J_0\left(\frac{\lambda_n R_p}{\sqrt{K'}}\right) - \frac{\lambda_n\sqrt{K'}}{B_1} J_1\left(\frac{\lambda_n R_p}{\sqrt{K'}}\right) \right] \\ J_1(\lambda_n R_p) & \lambda_n\sqrt{K'} \ J_1\left(\frac{\lambda_n R_p}{\sqrt{K'}}\right) \end{matrix} \right| \left[Y_0(\lambda_n) - \frac{\lambda_n Y_1(\lambda_n)}{B_2} \right] = 0 ,$$

$$(2\text{-}113)$$

where K' is the value of K in the pellet region (assumed constant) and J_1 a Bessel function of the first kind, first order.

Once the values of λ_n have been ascertained, the constants C_{1n} and C_{2n} may be evaluated from

$$C_{1n} = \frac{\left| \begin{matrix} \left[J_0\left(\frac{\lambda_n R_p}{\sqrt{K'}}\right) - \frac{\lambda_n\sqrt{K'}}{B} J_1\left(\frac{\lambda_n R_p}{\sqrt{K'}}\right) \right] & Y_0(\lambda_n R_p) \\ \lambda_n\sqrt{K'} \ J_1\left(\frac{\lambda_n R_p}{\sqrt{K'}}\right) & Y_1(\lambda_n R_p) \end{matrix} \right|}{\left| \begin{matrix} J_0(\lambda_n R_p) & Y_0(\lambda_n R_p) \\ J_1(\lambda_n R_p) & Y_1(\lambda_n R_p) \end{matrix} \right|} \qquad (2\text{-}114)$$

$$C_{2n} = \frac{\left| \begin{matrix} J_0(\lambda_n R_p) & \left[J_0\left(\frac{\lambda_n R_p}{\sqrt{K'}}\right) - \frac{\lambda_n\sqrt{K'}}{B_1} J_1\left(\frac{\lambda_n R_p}{\sqrt{K'}}\right) \right] \\ J_1(\lambda_n R_p) & \lambda_n\sqrt{K'} \ J_1\left(\frac{\lambda_n R_p}{\sqrt{K'}}\right) \end{matrix} \right|}{\left| \begin{matrix} J_0(\lambda_n R_p) & Y_0(\lambda_n R_p) \\ J_1(\lambda_n R_p) & Y_1(\lambda_n R_p) \end{matrix} \right|} . \qquad (2\text{-}115)$$

Matsch obtains the values of C_n using the Laplace transformation for solution of N simultaneous differential equations. To do so, he defines five additional quantities

$$P_n = 2\pi \int_0^1 (X_n)^2 \ R \ dR \qquad (2\text{-}116)$$

$$H_{n,m} = 2\pi \int_0^1 C_p(R) \ X_n \ X_m \ R \ dR \qquad (2\text{-}117)$$

$$A_n = 2\pi \int_0^{RP} X_n \ R \ dR \qquad (2\text{-}118)$$

$$U_n = 2B_2 \ (X_n)_{R=1} \qquad (2\text{-}119)$$

$$\overline{V}_n = \sum_{n=1}^{n} Q_{m,n} \frac{\int_0^1 T^+_{(R,0)} X_n \ R \ dR}{\int_0^1 (X_n)^2 \ R \ dR} + T^+_\infty \ V_m + A_m \ \overline{Q}(\tau), \qquad (2\text{-}120)$$

where $\overline{Q}(\tau)$ is the Laplace transform of $Q(\tau)$.

The Laplace transform of $C_n(\tau)$ is then obtained by solution of the determinantal equation

$$
\overline{C}_n = \frac{
\begin{vmatrix}
[(H_{1,1})s + (\lambda_1)^2 \, P_1] \dots \overline{V}_1 \dots \dots \dots (H_{1,N})s \\
\dotfill \\
(H_{1,n})s \dots \dots \dots \overline{V}_n \dots \dots \dots (H_{n,N})s \\
\dotfill \\
(H_{1,N})s \dots \dots \dots \overline{V}_N \dots [(H_{N,N})s + (\lambda_N)^2 \, P_N]
\end{vmatrix}
}{
\begin{vmatrix}
[(H_{1,1})s + (\lambda_1)^2 \, P_1] \dots \dots (H_{1,n})s \dots \dots (H_{1,N})s \\
\dotfill \\
(H_{1,n})s \dots \dots [(H_{n,m})s + (\lambda_n)^2 \, P_n] \dots \dots (H_{n,N})s \\
\dotfill \\
(H_{1,N})s \dots \dots (H_{n,N})s \dots \dots [(H_{n,m})s + (\lambda_N)^2 \, P_N]
\end{vmatrix}
} \cdot \qquad (2\text{-}121)
$$

After the solution of these (N) determinants, the values of $\overline{C}_N$ are transformed from functions of (s) to functions of (τ) by using the inverse Laplace transform. The values of $C_n(\tau)$ and X_n are then substituted into Eqs. (2-109) and (2-110) to provide the desired result.

Matsch found that only the first three eigenvalues are needed to obtain the accuracy required by most calculations.

(b) Finite Difference Procedure. In the case of very severe transients, the foregoing analytical techniques may not provide the desired accuracy due to large changes in fuel temperature and coolant conditions. This fact, coupled with the obvious complexity of the analytical procedures and the availability of digital computers, has led to an increased use of numerical techniques. Discrete time and space intervals are considered and the general conduction Eq. (2-95) is rewritten in finite difference form. If axial conduction is ignored, we may write, for an annular region at a given elevation,

$$
V_j \, C_p[T_{j,i-1}] \times \left(\frac{T_{j,i} - T_{j,i-1}}{\Delta\theta_i} \right)
$$

$$
= q_j' + \frac{T_{j-1,i-1} - T_{j,i-1}}{R_{j-1,j}} - \frac{T_{j,i-1} - T_{j+1,i-1}}{R_{j,j+1}} , \qquad (2\text{-}122)
$$

where

$$V_j = \text{volume of region } j, \text{ per unit of length}$$

$$C_p[T_{j,i-1}] = \text{volumetric heat capacity of pellet at the temperature of region } j \text{ at the end of time step } i-1$$

$$T_{j,i} = \text{temperature of region } j \text{ at the end of time step } i-1$$

$$\Delta\theta_i = \text{time increment}$$

q'_j = heat generation per unit of time and of length in region j

$R_{j-1,j}$ = resistance between region j - 1 and j computed as

$$\frac{1}{R_{j-1,j}} = \frac{k_p[T_{(j\,=1,j)i\,-1]}[A_{j-1,j}]}{r_j - r_{j-1}} \tag{2-123}$$

with

$k_p[T_{(j\,-1,j),,i-1}]$ = conductivity of UO_2 at a temperature, which is the average temperatures of regions j - 1 and j at the end of time step i - 1

$A_{j-1,j}$ = heat transfer area between regions j - 1 and j

r_{j-1} and r_j = average radii of these regions.

For the last region in contact with the clad, we write

$$\frac{1}{R_{j,c}} = h_g \times A_{j,c} \quad , \tag{2-124}$$

with h_g = contact conductance.

The basic equation may be solved as

$$T_{j,i} = \frac{q'_j\,\Delta\theta_i}{V_j\,C_p[T_{j,i-1}]} + m_{j-1,j}T_{j-1,i-1} + m_{j,j+1}\,T_{j+1,i-1}$$

$$+ (1 - m_{j-1,j} - m_{j,j+1})\,T_{j,i-1} \quad , \tag{2-125}$$

where

$$m_{j-1,j} = \frac{\Delta\theta_i}{V_j\,C_p[T_{j,i-1}]R_{j-1,j}} \tag{2-126}$$

$$m_{j,j+1} = \frac{\Delta\theta_i}{V_j\,C_p[T_{j,i-1}]R_{j,j+1}} \quad . \tag{2-127}$$

The foregoing formulation is called an "explicit" solution since the temperatures at the new time i may be calculated directly (explicitly) given the conditions at time i - 1. Equations of this nature are subject to numerical instability if the time step chosen is too large. Thus, Eq. (2-125) will yield a negative (unstable) value for $T_{j,i}$ if

$$(m_{j-1,j} + m_{j,j+1} - 1)T_{j,i-1} \tag{2-128}$$

$$\geqslant \frac{q'_j\,\Delta\theta_i}{V_j\,C_p[T_{j,i-1}]} + m_{j-1,j}T_{j-1,i-1} + m_{j,j+1}\,T_{j+1,i-1} \quad .$$

Since the right-hand side of Eq. (2-128) is always positive, we can avoid this condition by assuring ourselves that

$$m_{j-1} + m_{j,j+1} - 1 \leq 0 \quad . \tag{2-129}$$

Thus, the maximum value of $\Delta\theta_i$ may be determined as

$$\Delta\theta_i \leq \frac{VC_p[T_{j,i-1}](R_{j-1,j})(R_{j,j+1})}{R_{j-1,j} + R_{j,j+1}} \quad . \tag{2-130}$$

The minimum of the $\Delta\theta_i$ values determined for the several segments is used.

There are two disadvantages to this procedure: First, we are computing the net heat flow into a given annular segment based on the temperatures at the previous time; and second, the restriction on the size of the time increment may require an excessive amount of computation for problems extending over long time periods. These difficulties can be obviated by using the "implicit" form of the difference equation. Here we determine heat flows from the temperature differences at the advanced position in time. Thus, Eq. (2-122) becomes

$$V_j C_p \left[\frac{T_{j,i} + T_{j,i-1}}{2} \right] \times \frac{(T_{j,i} - T_{j,i-1})}{\Delta\theta_i}$$
$$= q_j' + \frac{(T_{j-1,i} - T_{j,i})}{R_{j-1,j}} - \frac{(T_{j,i} - T_{j+1,i})}{R_{j,j+1}} \quad . \tag{2-131}$$

Initially, the average specific heat may be assumed to be equal to its value at the previous time. We then have a set of linear equations that may be solved simultaneously for the $T_{j,i}$. If the specific heat changes significantly with temperature, an iteration may be required using updated values of C .

While the implicit method removes the tight restrictions on the value of $\Delta\theta_i$ chosen, use of a large value of $\Delta\theta_i$ increases the error due to discretization. The discretization error is of $O[\Delta\theta_i + (\Delta r)^2]$.

2-3.2 Slow Transients in Fuel Rods

Since large scale computers are not universally available, one needs a less tedious analytical technique available than that described in Sec. 2-3.1. Fortunately, many of the significant transients to which fuel rods are subjected are relatively slow. Consider a loss-of-flow accident where the maximum clad temperature is of greatest concern: For a UO_2 fuel rod, the maximum occurs several seconds after initiation of the accident. This may be considered a slow thermal transient and a lumped parameter technique is adequate for its calculation.

• Lumped Parameter Technique

In the lumped parameter technique suggested by Tong,[79] the thermal resistances and capacitance of the pellet and clad are evaluated at their average condition in time and space. Each quantity is lumped at the middle of the physical geometry and axial conduction is neglected. We again shall consider the situation where there is a step reduction in the coolant heat transfer coefficient and a subsequent reduction in heat generation rate due to a reactor scram.

The rate equations for the heat transfer from the UO$_2$ fuel rod can be written as

$$q_n' = C_1 \frac{dT_1}{dt} + \frac{T_1 - T_2}{R_1} \qquad (2\text{-}132)$$

and

$$\frac{T_1 - T_2}{R_1} = C_2 \frac{dT_2}{dt} + \frac{T_2 - T_c}{R_2}, \qquad (2\text{-}133)$$

where

q_n' = nuclear heating (Btu/sec ft of fuel rod)

C_1 = thermal capacitance of pellet (Btu/°F ft, $C_1 = \pi r_1^2 c_{p1} \rho_1$)

C_2 = thermal capacitance of clad [Btu/°F ft, $C_2 = 2\pi r_2 (\Delta r) c_{p2} \rho_2$, for thin clad]

R_1 = resistance of UO$_2$ and gap (sec ft °F/Btu)

  = $[1/(4\pi k_1)] + [1/(2\pi r_1 h_g)]$, where k_1 is UO$_2$ thermal conductivity and h_g is the gap conductance

R_2 = resistance of coolant film = $1/(2\pi r_2 h)$ [(sec ft °F)/Btu]

T_1 = average pellet temperature (°F)

T_2 = average clad temperature (°F)

T_c = bulk coolant temperature (°F).

After a pipe rupture, the system pressure drops with time and so does the saturation temperature of the coolant; hence, $T_c = T_c(t)$. The time t is counted from the instant of rupture. From the Laplace transformation of Eqs. (2-132) and (2-133), we get

$$T_2(s) = \frac{R_2 q_n'(s) + (C_1 R_1 s + 1)T_c(s) + R_2 C_1 T_1(0) + R_2 C_2 (R_1 C_1 s + 1)T_2(0)}{R_1 R_2 C_1 C_2 s^2 + (R_1 C_1 + R_2 C_2 + R_2 C_1)s + 1}$$

$$(2\text{-}134)$$

$T_1(s)$

$$= \frac{\left(R_2 C_2 s + 1 + \dfrac{R_2}{R_1}\right) R_1 q_n'(s) + T_c(s) + \left(R_2 C_2 s + 1 + \dfrac{R_2}{R_1}\right) R_1 C_1 T_1(0) + R_2 C_2 T_2(0)}{R_1 R_2 C_1 C_2 s^2 + (R_1 C_1 + R_2 C_2 + R_2 C_1)\, s + 1}.$$

$$(2\text{-}135)$$

By knowing coolant temperature and fuel rod power as a function of time, the histories of pellet and clad temperatures may be computed from the inverse transformation of Eqs. (2-134) and (2-135). We may do so by letting

$$\Delta(s) = R_1 R_2 C_1 C_2 s^2 + (R_1 C_1 + R_2 C_2 + R_2 C_1)s + 1$$

$$= (\tau_a s + 1)(\tau_b s + 1) \qquad\qquad (2\text{-}136)$$

then

$$\mathcal{L}^{-1}\, \frac{1}{\Delta(s)} = \frac{1}{\tau_a - \tau_b}\, [\exp(-t/\tau_a) - \exp(t/\tau_b)] \qquad (2\text{-}137)$$

and

$$\mathcal{L}^{-1}\, \frac{K}{\Delta(s)} = K \mathcal{L}^{-1}\left(\frac{1}{\Delta s}\right). \qquad\qquad (2\text{-}138)$$

Hence, where K is any constant term, the time invarient terms may be evaluated. We also note that

$$\mathcal{L}^{-1}\, \frac{s}{\Delta s} = \frac{d}{dt}\, \mathcal{L}^{-1}\left(\frac{1}{\Delta s}\right) \qquad\qquad (2\text{-}139)$$

so those terms having a linear function of s in the numerator can be evaluated.

The nuclear heating terms can generally be represented by the sum of a group of exponential terms. Therefore,

$$\mathcal{L}^{-1}\, \frac{q_n'(s)}{\Delta(s)} = \mathcal{L}^{-1}\, \frac{q_o'}{\Delta s}\, [a_1 \exp(-b_1 t) + a_2 \exp(-b_2 t) + \ldots]$$

$$= \frac{q_o'}{\tau_a - \tau_b}\, [a_1 \exp(-b_1 t) + a_2 \exp(-b_2 t) + \ldots]$$

$$\times\, [\exp(-t/\tau_a) - \exp(-t/\tau_b)]. \qquad (2\text{-}140)$$

If we represent the coolant temperature as a function of s, then, by means of a partial fraction expansion, we obtain

$$\mathcal{L}^{-1}\, \frac{T_c(s)}{\Delta(s)} = \mathcal{L}^{-1}\left[\frac{A}{(\tau_a s + 1)} + \frac{B}{(\tau_b s + 1)} + \ldots + \frac{N}{(\tau_n s + 1)}\right]. \qquad (2\text{-}141)$$

In the analysis of a loss-of-flow transient, two simplifications can be made: First, when the pumps lose power, the system pressure does not change significantly and the coolant temperature T_c remains approximately constant; and second, the maximum clad temperature usually occurs within 10 sec of the instant of the loss of power to the pump. Hence, the decay heat can be assumed constant during this short time period, and our boundary conditions now become

for $t \leqslant 0$: $q_n' = q_n'(0)$, $R_2 = R_{2,0}$

for $0 < t \leqslant t_1$: $q_n' = q_n'(0)$, $R_2 = R_{2,\text{film boiling}}$

for $t \geqslant t_1$: $q_n' = \beta q_n'(0)$, $R_2 = R_{2,\text{film boiling}}$.   (2-142)

By taking advantage of the constancy of T_c, we may solve Eqs. (2-132) and (2-133) for T_1 and then differentiate with respect to t to obtain dT_1/dt. We then may rewrite Eq. (2-132) as

$$q_n' = C_1 C_2 R_1 \frac{d^2\theta}{dt^2} + \left(C_1 + C_2 + \frac{C_1 R_1}{R_2}\right) \frac{d\theta}{dt} + \frac{\theta}{R_2} , \qquad (2\text{-}143)$$

where $\theta = T_2 - T_c$.

When the Laplace transform is taken, we obtain

$$\frac{1}{s}\left[1 - \beta \exp(t_1 s)\right] = C_1 C_2 R_1 \left[\overline{\theta} s^2 - \theta\,(0)s - \frac{d\theta\,(0)}{dt}\right] + \left[C_1 + C_2 + \frac{C_1 C_2}{R_2}\right]$$

$$\times \left[\overline{\theta}s - \theta\,(0)\right] + \frac{\overline{\theta}}{R_2} , \qquad (2\text{-}144)$$

where $\overline{\theta}$ represents the Laplace transform of θ .

The value of $\theta\,(0)$ is given by

$$\theta\,(0) = q_n'(0) R_{2,0} \qquad (2\text{-}145)$$

and $\dfrac{d\theta\,(0)}{dt}$ from the relationship

$$T_1(0) = q_n'(0)(R_1 + R_{2,0}) \qquad (2\text{-}146)$$

and Eq. (2-133).

Substitution of these numerical values, followed by the inverse transformation, yields θ as a function of time.

When the heat transfer coefficient undergoes a step reduction at $t = 0$ and the heat generation is reduced to 15% of the steady-state value at $t = t_1$, Matsch obtains

$\theta = 1.19 - 0.683 \exp(-0.466t) - 0.488 \exp(-4.79t)$ $(t < t_1)$

$\theta = 0.177 - \exp(-0.466t)[0.683 - 1.121 \exp(0.466t_1)]$ (2-147)

     $- \exp(-4.794t_1)[0.488 + 0.1108 \exp(4.79t_1)]$ $(t > t_1)$.

Figure 2.20 shows the comparison of this solution with the integral transform solution of the same problem.

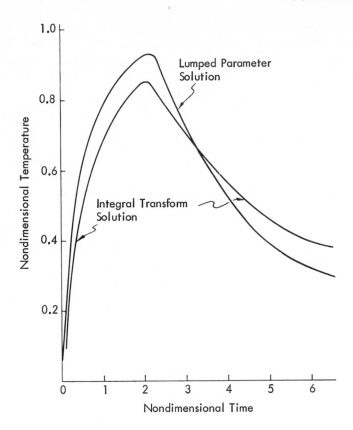

Fig. 2.20 Comparison of solutions for fuel element transient by lumped-parameter and finite integral transform technique. (From *Nucl. Sci. Eng.*, **11**, 340, 1961.)

The lumped parameter technique is basically equivalent to the use of an electrical analog. The conditions at the nodal points of the electrical network represent the average conditions of a particular region. To use such an analog, we note the correspondence between voltage and temperature, between current and flow, and between the product of electrical resistance and capacity of the electrical system and thermal diffusity. Thus, Fourier's law of $q = \Delta T / R_t$ is represented by Ohm's law for current flow $i = \Delta E / R$. The change in system thermal energy is given by

$$\frac{dQ}{dt} = c_p \, \rho \, V \, \frac{dT}{dt} \quad , \tag{2-148}$$

where

Q = heat content (Btu)

c_p = specific heat

V = volume

ρ = density.

The change in electrical energy is represented by

$$\frac{dQ_e}{dt} = C \frac{dE}{dt} , \qquad (2\text{-}149)$$

where Q_e is the electric charge on the condenser and C is the condenser capacitance.

As a simple illustration, let us consider the behavior of a fuel pellet in which heat generation has ceased, which is being cooled at its outer radius by a coolant at some constant temperature T_c, and which has a very high heat transfer coefficient. Since we are considering only the average temperature of the pellet, we may write

$$C_1 \frac{dT}{dt} = - \frac{(T - T_c)}{R_1} , \qquad (2\text{-}150)$$

where

C_1 = thermal capacitance of the pellet (Btu/°F ft, $C_1 = \pi r_1^2 c_p \rho_1$)

R_1 = thermal resistance of pellet (sec ft °F/Btu).

The solution of this equation may be put in the form

$$q' = \frac{T_o - T_c}{R_1} \exp[-t/(R_1 C_1)]. \qquad (2\text{-}151)$$

The equivalent electrical circuit is shown in Fig. 2.21(a), and we obtain analogously to Eq. (2-137)

$$i = \frac{E_o}{R_i} \exp[-t/(R_1 C_1)] . \qquad (2\text{-}152)$$

In equations of this form that describe circuit transients, the denominator of the exponential (in this case $R_1 C_1$) is called the time constant of the element, and its dimensions are in seconds.

Now let us take our previous problem where the heat generation rate is a function of time, and both fuel rod and coolant thermal resistance must be considered. The equivalent electrical circuit is shown in Fig. 2.21(b). Note the direct correspondence between the circuit elements and the thermal capacitances and resistances of Eqs. (2-132) and (2-133). Greater accuracy can be obtained by using additional nodal points.

The electrical analog technique is widely used for control and accident analyses and is a powerful tool in allowing a ready combination of both reactivity and thermal effects.

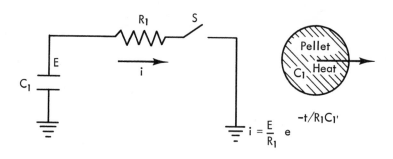

(a)

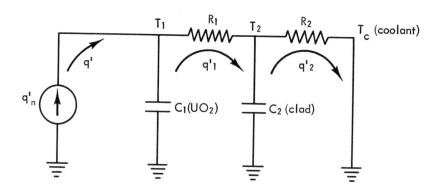

(b)

Fig. 2.21 Equivalent electrical circuits for fuel rod transients.

REFERENCES

1. C. R. TIPTON, Ed., *Reactor Handbook*, Vol. I, *Materials*, 2nd ed., p. 193, Interscience Publishers, New York (1960).

2. C. R. TIPTON, *ibid.*, pp. 195-196.

3. R. W. DAYTON, "Objectives of U.S. Research in Nuclear Fuels for Civilian Power Reactors," Third International American Symposium on Peaceful Application of Nuclear Energy, Pan American Union, Washington, D.C. (1961).

4. C. COLLET, J. P. LANQUE, and M. COLUMBIE, "Study of Mechanical and Thermal Properties of Uranium Alloys with Small Additions," *Mem. Sci. Rev. Met.*, **64**, 393 (April 1967).

5. F. W. ALBOUGH, S. H. BUSH, J. J. CADWELL, D. R. de HALAS, and D. C. WOSTER, Communication from Battelle Northwest Laboratory appearing in *Reactor Materials*, **10**, *3*, 136 (1967).

6. M. A. FERADAY, G. H. CHALDER, and K. D. COTMAN, "Irradiation of U_3Si—Interim Results after 7360 MWd/Tonne Irradiation," AECL-2648, Atomic Energy of Canada Ltd. (1967).

7. C. R. TIPTON, *op. cit.*, p. 201.

8. H. ETHERINGTON, *Nuclear Engineering Handbook*, pp. 10-32, McGraw-Hill Book Co., New York (1958).

9. F. A. ROUGH, "An Evaluation of Data on Zr-U Alloys," BMI-1030, Battelle Memorial Institute, Columbia, Ohio (1955).

10. C. R. TIPTON, *op. cit.*, pp. 175-204.

11. S. CERNI, "SNAP-23A Phase I Quarterly Progress Report, Sept. 1-Nov. 30, 1967," USAEC Report WANL-3800-9, Westinghouse Astronuclear Laboratory (1967).

12. H. D. WEISS, "Properties of Mulberry," USAEC Report UCID-15170, University of California, Lawrence Radiation Laboratory (1967).

13. S. McLAIN and J. H. MARTENS, Eds., *Reactor Handbook*, Vol. IV, *Engineering*, 2nd ed., p. 177, Interscience Publishers, New York (1964).

14. C. R. TIPTON, *op. cit.*, pp. 315-321.

15. C. E. WEBER and H. HIRSCH, "Dispersion Type Fuel Elements," *Proc. Intern. Conf. Peaceful Uses At. Energy*, **9**, 196 (1956).

16. MAX JAKOB, *Heat Transfer*, Vol. I, p. 85, John Wiley & Sons, New York, (1949).

17. C. R. TIPTON, *op. cit.*, p. 295.

18. P. HUEBOTTER, "Fast Reactor Fuel Element Design," Paper presented to 7th Annual AMU-ANL Faculty Student Conference (1968).

19. C. M. FRIEDRICH and W. H. GUILINGER, "CYGRO—2A, FORTRAN IV Computer Program for Stress Analysis of the Growth of Cylindrical Fuel Elements with Fission Gas Bubbles," USAEC Report WAPD-TM-547, Bettis Atomic Power Laboratory (1966).

20. D. R. De HALES and G. R. HORN, "Evolution of Uranium Dioxide Structure During Irradiation of Fuel Rods," *J. Nucl. Mater.*, **8**, 20 (1963).

21. F. H. NICHOLS, "Theory of Columnar Grain Growth and Central Void Formation in Oxide Fuel Rods," *J. Nucl. Mater.*, **22**, 214 (1967).

22. J. L. BATES and W. E. ROAKE, "Irradiation of Fuel Elements Containing Uranium Dioxide Powder," Reprint V-90 1959, Fifth Nucl. Energy Conf., Eng. Joint Council, New York (April 1959).

23. J. D. EICHENBERG, P. W. FRANK, T. J. KISIEL, B. LUSTMAN, and K. H. VOGEL, "Effects of Irradiation on Bulk Uranium Dioxide," WAPD-183, Bettis Atomic Power Laboratory (1957).

24. M. F. LYONS, R. C. NELSON, T. J. PASHOS, and B. WEIDENBAUM, "Uranium Dioxide Fuel Rod Operation with Gross Central Melting," *Trans. Am. Nucl. Soc.*, **6**, 155 (1963).

25. J. D. EICHENBERG, P. W. FRANK, T. J. KISIEL, B. LUSTMAN, and K. H. VOGEL, "Effects of Irradiation on Bulk Uranium Dioxide," USAEC Report TID-7546, Fuel Elements Conf., Paris (1958).

26. A. W. LEMMON, "Analysis of Efficiency of Cooling and Extent of Reaction in the PWR," EADL-1, Report by Battelle to Bettis Atomic Power Laboratory.

27. T. G. GODFREY, W. FULKERSON, T. G. KOLLIE, J. P. MOORE, and D. L. McELROY, "Thermal Conductivity of Uranium Dioxide and Armco Iron by an Improved Radial Flow Technique," ORNL-3556, Oak Ridge National Laboratory (1964).

28. J. F. MAY, M. J. F. NOTLEY, R. L. STOUTE, and J. A. L. ROBERTSON, "Observation on Thermal Conductivity of Uranium Dioxide," AECL-1641, Atomic Energy of Canada, Ltd. (November 1962).

29. J. BELLE, R. M. BERMAN, W. F. BOURGEOIS, J. COHEN, and R. C. DANIEL, "Thermal Conductivity of Bulk Oxide Fuels," WAPD-TM-586, Bettis Atomic Power Laboratory (February 1967).

30. J. L. BATES, "Thermal Conductivity of Uranium Dioxide Improves at High Temperatures," *Nucleonics*, **19**, 6, 83 (June 1961).

31. T. J. NISHIJIMA, "Thermal Conductivity of Sintered Uranium Dioxide and Al_2O_3 at High Temperatures," *J. Am. Ceramic Soc.*, **48**, 31 (1965).

32. A. D. FEITH, "Thermal Conductivity of Uranium Dioxide by Radial Heat Flow Method," USAEC Report TM-63-9-5, General Electric Co., Cincinnati, Ohio (1963).

33. O. J. C. RUNNALS, "Uranium Dioxide Fuel Elements," CRL-55, National Research Council of Canada, Chalk River (1959).

34. M. F. LYONS, D. H. COPLIN, T. J. PASHOS, and B. WEIDENBAUM, "UO_2 Pellet Thermal Conductivity from Irradiations with Central Melting," *Trans. Am. Nucl. Soc.*, **7**, 1, 106 (1964).

35. J. P. STORA, D. B. deDESIGORGER, R. DEIMAS, P. DASCHAMPS, B. TRAVARD, and C. RIONIGOT, "Conductibilité Thermique de l'Oxyde d'Uranium Fritté dans les Conditions d'Utilisation en Pile," French Report CEA-R-2586 (1964).

36. J. A. CHRISTENSEN, "Irradiation Effects on Uranium Dioxide Melting," HW-69234, Hanford Works, Richland, Wash. (March 1962).

37. P. GUINET, H. VAUGOYEAU, and P. BLUM, "The UO_2 — U System at High Temperatures," French Report CEA-R-3060 (1966).

38. J. BELLE, Ed., *Uranium Dioxide Properties and Nuclear Applications*, U. S. Atomic Energy Commission, Washington, D. C. (1961).

39. A. T. JEFFS, "Thermal Conductivity of ThO_2 — PuO_2 During Irradiation," *Trans. Am. Nucl. Soc.*, **11**, 497 (1968).

40. T. G. GODFREY, J. A. WOOLLEY, and J. M. LEITMAKER, "Thermodynamic Function of Nuclear Materials," USAEC Report, ORNL-TM-1596, Oak Ridge National Laboratory (1966).

41. L. F. EPSTEIN, "Ideal Solution Behavior and Heats of Fusion from the UO_2 —PuO_2 Phase Diagram," *J. Nucl. Mater.*, **23**, 340 (1967).

42. J. L. KRANKOTA and C. N. CRAIG, "Melting Point of High Burnup PuO_1— UO_1," *Trans. Am. Nucl. Soc.*, **11**, 132 (1968).

43. J. F. LAGEDROST, D. F. ASKEY, V. W. STORKOK, and J. E. GATES, "Thermal Conductivity of PuO_2 as Determined from Thermal Diffusivity Measurements," *Nucl. Appl.*, **4**, 54 (1968).

44. F. W. ALBAUGH, Battelle Northwest Laboratory Communication to *Reactor Materials*, **20**, 207 (1968).

45. F. J. HETZLER, T. E. LANNIN, K. J. PERRY, and E. L. ZEBROSKI, "Thermal Conductivity of Uranium and Uranium Plutonium Oxides," USAEC Report GEAP-4879, General Electric Co. (1967).

46. C. R. TIPTON, *op. cit.*, p. 497.

47. R. N. DUNCAN, W. H. ARTL, and J. S. ATKINSON, "Toward Low-Cost High Performance BWR Fuel," *Nucleonics*, **23**, 4, 50 (1965).

48. E. F. IBRAHIM, "An Equation for Creep of Cold Worked Zircaloy Pressure Tube Material," AECL-2928, Atomic Energy of Canada Ltd. (1965).

49. R. J. ALLIO and K. C. THOMAS, "Improved Iron-Base Cladding for Water Reactors," *Nucleonics*, **23**, 6, 72 (1965).

50. C. R. TIPTON, *op. cit.*, pp. 636-664.

51. C. R. TIPTON, *op. cit.*, p. 312.

52. J. H. WRIGHT, "Supercritical Pressure Reactor Technology," Westinghouse Nuclear Power Seminar Paper 65-8 (1965).

53. I. COHEN, B. LUSTMAN, and J. D. EICHENBERG, "Measurement of Thermal Conductivity of Metal Clad Uranium Dioxide Rods During Irradiation," WAPD-228, Bettis Atomic Power Laboratory (1960).

54. M. KNUDSEN, *Kinetic Theory of Gases*, John Wiley & Sons, New York (1950).

55. R. A. DEAN, "Thermal Contact Conductance," MS Thesis, University of Pittsburgh (1963).

56. J. H. JEANS, *Kinetic Theory of Gases*, Cambridge University Press, Cambridge, England (1940).

57. J. N. CETINKALE and M. FISHENDEN, "Thermal Conductance of Metal Surfaces in Contact," p. 271, *Proceedings of General Discussion on Heat Transfer*, Institution of Mech. Engrs., London (September 1951).

58. H. FENECH and W. M. ROHSENOW, "A Prediction of Thermal Conduction of Metallic Surfaces in Contact," *J. Heat Transfer, Trans. ASME Series C*, **85**, 15 (1963).

59. R. G. WHEELER, "Thermal Contact Conductance of Fuel Element Materials," HW-60343, Hanford Works, Richland, Wash. (1959).

60. A. M. ROSS and R. L. STOUTE, "Heat Transfer Coefficient Between Uranium Dioxide and Zircaloy-2," CFRD-1075, Atomic Energy of Canada Ltd. (1962).

61. Y. L. SHLYKOV, *Teploenergetika*, **12,** *10*, 79–83 (1965). Also available in English translation: "Thermal Contact Resistance," *Thermal Engineering*, **12,** 102 (April 1966).

62. I. L. SHVETS and E. P. DYBAN, *Inzh. fiz. zh.*, **3,** (1964).

63. C. M. FRIEDRICH and H. W. GUILINGER, "CYGRO-2, a FORTRAN IV Computer Program for Stress Analysis and the Growth of Cylindrical Fuel Elements with Fission Gas Bubbles," WAPD-TM-547, Bettis Atomic Power Laboratory (1966).

64. L. A. WALDMAN, L. L. LYNN, and I. GOLDBERG, "FIGRO—a CDC 6600 Computer Program for Analysis of Swelling and Calculation of Temperature in Bulk-Oxide Cylindrical Fuel Elements," WAPD-TM-618 Addendum 1, Bettis Atomic Power Laboratory (1967).

65. R. M. CARROLL and O. SISSMAN, "Fission Gas Release During Fissioning of Uranium Dioxide," *Nucl. Appl.*, **2,** 142 (1966).

66. R. SOULHIER, "Fission Gas Release from Uranium Dioxide During Irradiation up to 2000°C," *Nucl. Appl.*, **2,** 138 (1966).

67. A. H. BOOTH, "A Method of Calculating Fission Gas Diffusion from UO_2 Fuel and Its Application to X-2 Loop Test," CRDC-721, National Research Council of Canada, Chalk River (1957).

68. W. B. LEWIS, "Engineering for the Fission Gas in Uranium Dioxide Fuel," *Nucl. Appl.*, **2,** 171 (1966).

69. B. LUSTMAN, "Fission Gas Pressure Within PWR Core Fuel Rods and Proposed PWR Core 2 Fuel Elements," WAPD-PWR–PMM-1034, Bettis Atomic Power Laboratory (January 1957).

70. J. R. FAGAN and J. O. MINGLE, "Effect of Axial Heat Conduction in Fuel Plates on Maximum Heat Flow Rates and Temperatures," *Nucl. Sci. Eng.*, **18,** 443 (1964).

71. J. A. L. ROBERTSON, "$\int kdt$ in Fuel Irradiations," CRFD-835, Atomic Energy of Canada Ltd. (1959).

72. M. F. LYONS, D. H. COPLIN, H. HAUSNER, B. WEIDENBAUM, and T. J. PASHOS, "Uranium Dioxide Powder and Pellet Thermal Conductivity During Irradiation," USAEC Report GEAP-5100-1, General Electric Co. (1966).

73. D. J. CLOUGH and J. B. SAYERS, "Measurement of Thermal Conductivity of Uranium Dioxide under Irradiation in the Temperature Range 150-1000°C," Report AERE-R-4690, Harwell, England (1964).

74. R. SOULHIER, "Comportment des Gas de Fission Dans les Elements Combustibles à Oxide d'Uranium—Tentative de Synthese des Resultats Experimentaux," French Report DM/1629 (1967).

75. J. RANDLES, "Heat Diffusion in Cylindrical Fuel Elements of Water Cooled Reactors," AEEW-R96, Atomic Energy Establishment, Winfrith, United Kingdom (1961).

76. J. R. MacEWAN and V. B. LAWSON, "Grain Growth in Sintered Uranium Dioxide," *J. Am. Ceram. Soc.*, **45,** 42 (1962).

77. F. E. TIPPETS, "An Analysis of the Transient Conduction of Heat in a Long Cylindrical Fuel Element for Nuclear Reactors," HW-41896, Hanford Works, Richland, Wash. (1956).

78. L. A. MATSCH, "Transient One Dimensional Temperature Distribution in a Two Region Infinite Circular Cylinder," MS Thesis, University of Pittsburgh (1960).

79. L. S. TONG, "Simplified Calculation of Thermal Transient of a Uranium Dioxide Fuel Rod," *Nucl. Sci. Eng.*, **11,** 340 (1961).

3

Hydrodynamics

The rate of heat removal from a reactor core and the dynamic forces on the core and internals depend strongly on the flow behavior of the system. In this chapter, the basic flow characteristics of friction, turbulence, void distribution, and depressurization are described. Specific applications such as hydrodynamic problems in the reactor vessel and flow instability in a core are then discussed.

3-1 BASIC FLOW CHARACTERISTICS

3-1.1 Single Phase Flow Friction

Single phase flow pressure drop is generally calculated in accordance with

$$\Delta P_{\text{friction}} = \left(\frac{fL}{D_e}\right) \frac{\rho V^2}{2g_c} + \sum_i \left(K_i \frac{\rho V_i^2}{2g_c}\right) , \qquad (3-1)$$

where

f = skin friction factor due to the wall shear in a straight flow channel. Empirical values for f can be obtained from the Moody curve[1] in Fig. 3.1.

K_i = form friction factor due to the i th change in the cross section or restriction in the flow channel. The value of K for a sudden expansion K_e and for a sudden contraction K_c are given by Kays and London,[2] and their values at high Reynolds numbers are reproduced in Fig. 3.2.

V = fluid velocity through the bare rod bundle

V_i = fluid velocity in the smaller channel at area change i

D_e = equivalent diameter of the straight flow channel and is (4 × cross-sectional area/perimeter).

Analytical expressions have been developed to describe the friction characteristics of various flow regimes. For circular channels, the laminar friction factor can be calculated

$$f = 64/\text{Re} , \qquad (3-2)$$

116

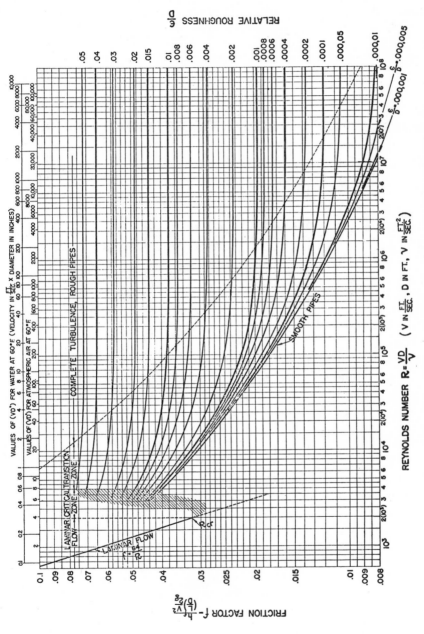

Fig. 3.1 Moody friction factor chart. (From *Trans. ASME*, 66, 671, 1944.)

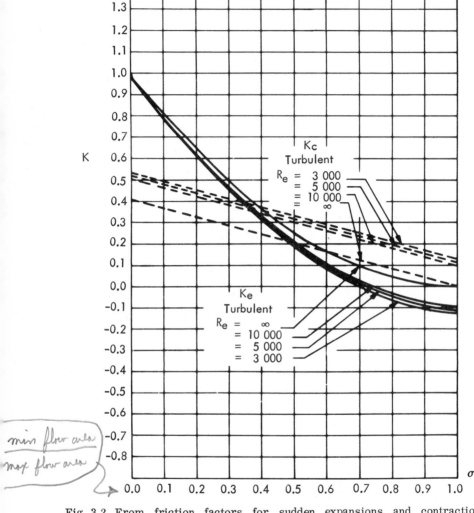

Fig. 3.2 From friction factors for sudden expansions and contractions.
(From W. M. KAYS and A. L. LONDON, *Compact Heat Exchangers*, The
National Press, Palo Alto, California, 1955.)

where Re is the Reynolds number. The turbulent friction factor in a
smooth channel can be calculated from the approximate relationship

$$f = C\,Re^{-0.2} \quad , \tag{3-3}$$

where $C = 0.184$ for isothermal flow in commercially available smooth tubes. The effect of surface roughness is indicated in Fig. 3.1 in terms of the ratio of the height of the surface projections ϵ to the pipe diameter D. The reader is referred to Refs. 3 and 4 for the pressure-loss coefficients for bends, valves, and fittings.

Effect of Heating. In a channel where one wall is heated or cooled, the friction factor is changed due to the change of viscosity near the wall. For turbulent flow, Seider and Tate[5] suggested

$$f/f_{ISO} = \left(\frac{\mu_{wall}}{\mu_{bulk}}\right)^{0.14} , \qquad (3-4)$$

where f_{ISO} is the friction factor measured under isothermal conditions, and μ is the fluid viscosity. For water flowing at 2000 psia, the effect has been correlated by Esselman et al.,[6] LeTourneau et al.,[7] and Mendler et al.[8] as

$$f/f_{ISO} = 1 - 0.0019 \, \Delta T_f , \qquad (3-5)$$

where

$\Delta T_f = q''/h$

$h = 0.023 \, (k_b/De)(Re_b)^{0.8}(Pr_b)^{0.4}$

k_b = thermal conductivity of fluid at the bulk temperature

Pr_b, Re_b = Prandtl and Reynolds numbers, respectively, at bulk temperature.

A limiting value of 0.85 has been given for Eq. (3-5) by its authors.

Rohsenow and Clark[9] examined the Seider and Tate[5] relationship using water flowing at pressures of 1500 to 2000 psi. They found the exponent for Eq. (3-4) was 0.60 for the frictional pressure loss alone but 0.14 for the pressure loss due to both momentum and frictional losses. They noted that many of the data points gave values for f/f_{ISO} below 0.85. The relationship

$$\frac{f_{friction}}{f_{ISO-friction}} = \left(\frac{\mu_{wall}}{\mu_{bulk}}\right)^{0.6} \qquad (3-6)$$

is recommended.

Core Pressure Drop. The reactor cores of almost all pressurized water reactors consist of an array of rod bundles. Hence, the flow characteristics within the core are those of the bundles of which it is composed. The core pressure drop may be considered to be composed of three components:

1. Pressure loss along the bundle of bare rods

2. Pressure loss across the spacer grids or wires

3. Pressure loss at core entrance and exit.

The entrance and exit losses may be evaluated as those due to sudden expansions and contractions as previously described.

The pressure loss along bare rods is usually predicted by assuming it is similar to that for flow inside a tube and by using the equivalent diameter concept. The validity of using the D_e concept in predicting the pressure drop in a rod bundle was investigated by Deissler and Taylor.[10] By an iterative procedure, they plotted the velocity profile in square and triangular lattices as shown in Figs. 3.3 and 3.4, respectively. These velocity profiles were calculated from a generalized velocity profile[11] based on the data of Deissler[12] and Laufer.[13] From these velocity profiles, friction factors and Reynolds numbers can be calculated by integrating the profiles to obtain bulk (or average) velocities, since both friction factors and

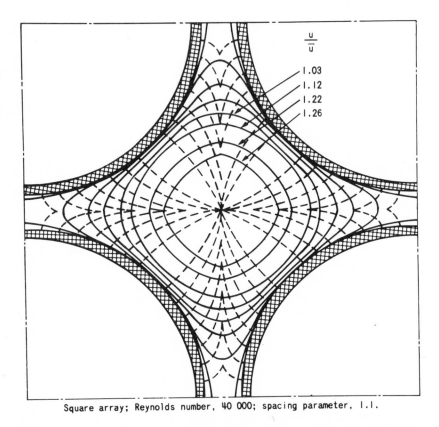

Square array; Reynolds number, 40 000; spacing parameter, 1.1.

Fig. 3.3   Predicted velocity distribution between tubes. (From Ref. 10.)

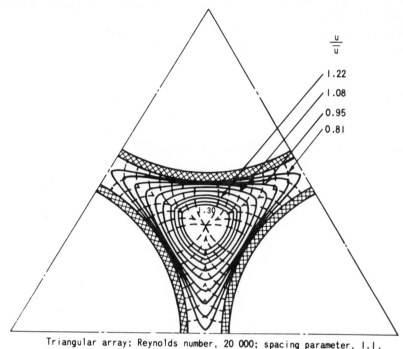

Triangular array; Reynolds number, 20 000; spacing parameter, 1.1.

Fig. 3.4   Predicted velocity distribution between tubes. (From Ref. 10.)

Reynolds numbers are based on bulk velocities. The predicted friction factors for triangular and square arrays are shown in Figs. 3.5
and 3.6. Deissler's predictions are in the vicinity of the line based
on circular tube data. However, there is an effect of pitch/diameter
which would not be observed if the D_e concept held strictly. The
experimental data shown have too much scatter to indicate any trend.

A number of other investigators have considered the effect of the
pitch-to-diameter ratio:

Miller et al.[14] tested a 37-rod bundle of 3-ft heated length with
0.625-in. o.d. rods in triangular lattice of 1.46 pitch-to-diameter ratio
(p/d), and found the friction factor to be represented by

$$f = 0.296 \, Re^{-0.2} \quad ,$$

(3-7)

which is 60% higher than would be obtained by fitting the Moody curve.

LeTourneau et al.[7] tested rod bundles of square lattice with p/d
ratios of 1.12 and 1.20 and of triangular lattice with p/d ratio of 1.12.
These data fall within a band between the Moody curve for smooth

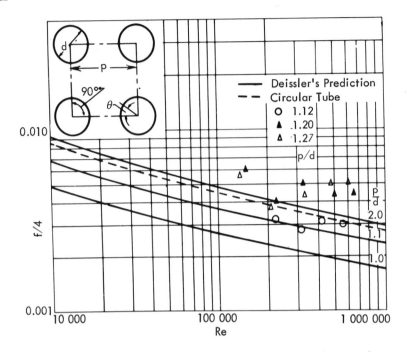

Fig. 3.5   Comparison of predicted and measured friction factors for square lattices. (From Ref. 10.)

tubes and a curve 10% below that in a Reynolds number range of 3×10^3 to 10^5.

Wantland[15] tested a 100-rod bundle of square lattice of $\frac{3}{16}$-in. rod o.d. and 6-ft length with p/d of 1.106 and a 102-rod bundle of tri-angular lattice of $\frac{3}{16}$-in. rod o.d. and 6-ft length with p/d ratio of 1.190. For Prandtl numbers between 3 and 6, he obtained:

1. For square lattices at Re = 10^3 - 10^4 and Pr = 3 - 6,

$$f = 1.76 \, Re^{-0.39} \quad , \tag{3-8}$$

which is about 30% higher than Eq. (3-3).

2. For triangular lattices at Re = 2×10^3 - 1×10^4,

$$f = 90.0 \, Re^{-1} + 0.0082 \quad , \tag{3-9}$$

which is about 25% higher than Eq. (3-3).

Dingee et al.[16] tested 9-rod bundles in water of both square and triangular lattices of 0.5-in. rod o.d. and 24-in. long, p/d of 1.12, 1.20, and 1.27. The square lattice data are 5 to 20% higher than

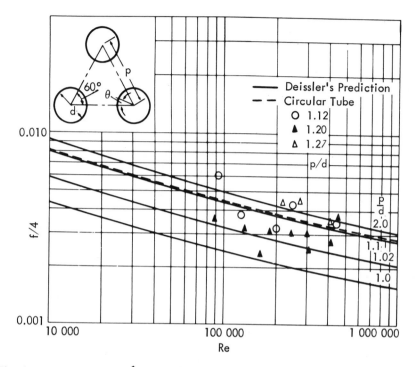

Fig. 3.6 Comparison of predicted and measured friction factors for tri-angular lattices. (From Ref. 10.)

Deissler's theoretical prediction,[17] and the triangular lattice data agree with the same prediction but with a scatter of about ±15%.

In summary, for water flow in both square and triangular lattices, the friction factors are lower than the Moody curve by 0 to 10% for p/d less than 1.20 and higher than the Moody curve by 0 to 20% for p/d = 1.27 and by 60% for p/d = 1.46.

The pressure losses across spacer grids or wires are from drag-type pressure losses. These are generally calculated using the pressure-loss coefficients for sudden contractions and expansions. Berringer and Bishop[18] tested the Yankee fuel rod bundle with both cylindrical ferrule spacers and egg-crate strap grids. The test sec-tion bundle was composed of 36 rods of 0.335-in. o.d. in a square lattice with p/d of 1.27. The ferrule is 0.5-in. long having 0.265-in. o.d. with a 20-mil wall thickness. The strap is $1\frac{1}{8}$-in. high and $\frac{1}{32}$-in. thick.

Comparison of the ferrule- and strap-pressure drops indicates that the pressure drop across a level of straps was more than four times that across a full ferruled section. Prediction of the pressure drop across the ferrule or strap using the loss coefficients for sudden contraction and expansion agrees with the data within 17%. The friction factors for the bare rod section are about 15% higher than the Moody curve in a pipe in the Reynolds number range of 10 000 to 30 000.

The pressure drop across a crossed-wire grid of a square lattice rod bundle was reported by de Stordeur.[19] The pressure drop measured from a crossed circular wire grid was about 10% lower than that of strap grid.

Bishop et al.[20] tested the CVTR rod bundle with helically wrapped wire as the spacer in water flow. The rod bundle was composed of 19 rods of 0.498-in. o.d. in a triangular lattice with p/d of 1.20. The axial pitch of the wrapping wire varies from 4 to 15 in. An unwrapped rod bundle was also tested, and the test results were reported as follows:

1. The slope of the friction factor vs Reynolds number curve is approximately the same as that for smooth pipe for Reynolds numbers less than 10^5.

2. Increasing the axial pitch of the wire wrap decreases the friction factor.

3. The unwrapped rod bundle gives a friction factor of 10% below that of a smooth pipe.

4. The rod bundle with axial pitch of 15 in. had approximately the same friction factor as a smooth pipe. The rod bundle with an axial pitch of 12 in. had a 10% higher friction factor, the one with axial pitch of 8 in. had a 25% higher friction factor, and the unit with an axial pitch of 4 in. had a 60% higher friction factor than that of a smooth pipe.

The total pressure drop across a core or a reactor vessel is often expressed as

$$\Delta P_{core} = K_{core} \frac{\rho V^2}{2g_c} \tag{3-10}$$

$$\Delta P_{vessel} = K_{vessel} \frac{\rho V^2}{2g_c} , \tag{3-11}$$

where ρ is the average density in the core and V is the average flow velocity inside the core. For example, the K values for the Yankee reactor are

$$K_{core} = 15, \qquad K_{vessel} = 34 ,$$

and the K values for the SELNI reactor are

$$K_{core} = 18, \qquad K_{vessel} = 52$$

3-1.2 Two-Phase Flow Void Fraction and Pressure Drop

Although there is no net void in the outlet of a pressurized water reactor under normal operating conditions, there is substantial sub-cooled boiling within the cores of modern plants. Bulk boiling is allowed in the hottest channels; further, during most accident situations, boiling occurs throughout most of the core. Neither steady state nor transient behavior can be understood without a knowledge of two-phase flow fundamentals. Since the details of two-phase flow behavior have been discussed in Ref. 21, only a summary will be presented here.

Void Fraction. Because of the relatively low density of steam compared to liquid water, the steam vapor phase is called void. The void fraction α is defined as the ratio of local vapor volume to the total local flow volume, that is,

$$\alpha = \frac{A_v}{A_v + A_l} \quad , \tag{3-12}$$

where A_l is the cross sectional area occupied by the liquid and A_v is the cross sectional area occupied by the vapor. The average density, $\bar{\rho}$, of a two-phase mixture then becomes

$$\bar{\rho} = \alpha \rho_v + (1 - \alpha)\rho_l \quad , \tag{3-13}$$

where ρ_v and ρ_l are the vapor and liquid densities, respectively. The slip ratio S is defined as the ratio of vapor velocity to liquid velocity

$$S = \frac{V_v}{V_l} = \frac{\chi}{1 - \chi} \frac{1 - \alpha}{\alpha} \frac{\rho_l}{\rho_v} \quad , \tag{3-14}$$

where χ = flow quality = mass flow rate of vapor/mass flow rate of mixture.

The void fraction in a heated channel may be described with the aid of Fig. 3.7. Initially, the entire fluid is highly subcooled, and no void is present. When the liquid adjacent to the wall becomes superheated, bubbles form. In region I, where the bulk of the liquid is still highly subcooled, the voids are a thin layer attached to the wall. In region II, where the subcooling is low, the void fraction increases, and bubbles are detached from the wall and recondense very slowly. In region III, the bulk liquid has reached saturation, and bulk boiling occurs.

Maurer[22] has correlated the void fraction in region I in terms of δ, the effective thickness of the vapor film on the wall. Thus,

$$\alpha = \frac{4\delta}{D_e} \tag{3-15}$$

and δ is the maximum of 0.00033 ft or

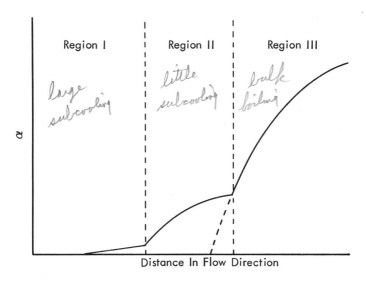

Fig. 3.7   Void fraction in boiling region.   (From Ref. 23.)

$$\delta = \frac{q_b'' \, k_l \, \Pr_l}{1.07 \, h^2 (T_{sat} - T_{bulk})} \quad , \tag{3-16}$$

where

q_b'' = heat transfer rate due to boiling = $q_{total}'' - h(T_{sat} - T_b)$

h = forced convection heat transfer coefficient

k_l = thermal conductivity of the liquid

$\Pr_l$ = Prandtl number of the liquid.

Bowring[23] has proposed that the detached region begins at some critical superheat, and he has also suggested an empirical method for predicting α in region II.   He assumed a slip ratio of unity and no appreciable condensation of the vapor, but this latter assumption may not always be valid.

Thom et al.[24] have correlated void fractions in subcooled boiling for the 750- to 1000-psi range.   Their correlation, which is in terms of the apparent density $\bar{\rho}$, appears to be somewhat simpler and more accurate.   Tong[25] has extended their correlation to 2000 psi, and the modified correlation is

$$\bar{\rho} = \rho_l - \frac{\gamma X'(\rho_l - \rho_v)}{1 + X'(\gamma - 1)} \quad , \tag{3-17}$$

where

ρ_l, ρ_v = liquid and vapor densities, respectively

$$X' = \left(H_{in} - \frac{4Lq''}{D_e G} - \beta H_l\right) \Big/ (H_v - \beta H_l)$$

$$\gamma = \rho_l/(\rho_v S) = \exp\{4.216[(y - 8.353)^2/(8.353)^2 - 1]^{1/2}\}$$

$y = \ln (p/3206);$ p = pressure in psia

β = ratio of enthalpy at inception of detached region to the saturation enthalpy = $1 - 0.15 q''/G$

H_{in} = inlet enthalpy to channel, Btu/lb

H_v, H_l = saturation enthalpies of vapor and liquid respectively, Btu/lb

G = mass velocity, lbs/(h ft^2)

L = heated length, ft .

The above equation was developed from uniform heat flux data; although it has been applied to channels with nonuniform heat flux and mixing by replacing $(4Lq''/D_e G)$ by the enthalpy rise to the point in question, experimental verification is lacking.

When bulk boiling begins, the enthalpy of the fluid H is expressed as

$$H = \alpha\rho_v H_v + (1 - \alpha)\rho_l H_l \quad . \tag{3-18}$$

The void fraction and slip ratio during bulk boiling vary with the flow pattern. At the pressures and flows encountered in a PWR, the pattern existing at the onset of boiling will be small vapor bubbles dispersed through a liquid core (bubbly flow). At higher void fractions, the small bubbles coalesce into large elongated bubbles, and slugs of liquid and vapor follow each other (slug flow). If the enthalpy is increased beyond the range normally observed in a PWR, the vapor slugs form a continuous core with an annulus of liquid adjacent to the wall (annular flow).

The simplest treatment of bubbly flow is due to Bankoff.[26] If β is defined as the ratio of vapor volumetric flow Q_v to total volumetric flow $Q_v + Q_l$, we have

$$\beta = \frac{Q_v}{Q_v + Q_l} \quad , \tag{3-19}$$

and may define a flow factor C such that

$$C = \alpha/\beta = \alpha + (1 - \alpha)/S \quad . \tag{3-20}$$

Bankoff[26] proposed

$$C = 0.71 + 0.0001 p \quad , \tag{3-21}$$

where p is in psia. Revised values for C have been proposed by Kholodovski[27] and Hughmark.[28]

More recently, Zuber and Findlay[29] have proposed a more sophisticated model applicable to the bubbly and slug flow regimes. They
define local superficial velocities $u = (Q_v + Q_l)/A$, $u_v = (Q_v/A)$, and
$u_l = (Q_l/A)$ based on the total flow area A. Velocity and void distributions were assumed to follow

$$\frac{u}{u_c} = 1 - \left(\frac{r}{R}\right)^n \quad , \tag{3-22}$$

$$\frac{\alpha - \alpha_w}{\alpha_c - \alpha_w} = 1 - \left(\frac{r}{R}\right)^n \quad , \tag{3-23}$$

where r is the radial distance, R the tube radius, and the subscripts
c and w refer to centerline and wall conditions, respectively. For
adiabatic flow, α_w is taken as zero, and then C, the flow factor, is
given by

$$C = \frac{\alpha}{\beta} = \frac{\overline{u}_v}{\alpha(\overline{u})} = \frac{n + 1}{n + 2} \quad , \tag{3-24}$$

where n is a constant and $\overline{u}_v$ and $\overline{u}$ are the mean values of u_v and u,
respectively. To estimate the bubble slip velocity, Zuber and
Findlay use the terminal bubble velocities estimated by Griffith and
Wallis[30] and Harmathy.[31] For the slug flow regime, they obtain $\overline{V}_v$,
the weighted mean velocity of the vapor as

$$\overline{V}_v = \left(\frac{\overline{u}_v}{\alpha}\right) = \frac{(\overline{u})}{C} + 0.35 \left[\frac{g\Delta\rho D}{\rho_l}\right]^{1/2} \quad , \tag{3-25}$$

and for the bubbly flow regime

$$\overline{V}_v = \left(\frac{\overline{u}_v}{\alpha}\right) = \frac{(\overline{u})}{C} + 1.53 \left[\frac{\sigma g\, g_c\, \Delta\rho}{\rho_l^2}\right]^{1/4} \quad , \tag{3-26}$$

where $\Delta\rho = \rho_l - \rho_v$ and σ = surface tension.

For small terminal bubble rise velocities, where

$$C = \overline{u}/\overline{V}_v \quad , \tag{3-27}$$

the value of C is less than unity when $\alpha_c > \alpha_w$ and greater than unity
when $\alpha < \alpha_w$. For the former case, C is close to 0.8.

Other descriptions of the bubbly and slug flow regimes have been
suggested by Marcheterre and Hoglund[32] and Petrick.[33]

The most widely used void fraction correlation in the annular flow
regime is that of Martinelli and Nelson,[34] who presented the data as a
plot of α vs quality for a series of different pressures. Thom[35] has
modified these on the basis of improved data and has proposed a correlation of the form

$$\alpha = \frac{\gamma X}{1 + X(\gamma - 1)} \quad , \tag{3-28}$$

where X is the flow quality and γ is an empirical constant equal to
$P/(\rho_l S)$. Thom proposed the values of γ shown in Table 3.1.

Table 3.1

VALUES OF γ							
Pressure (psia)	14.7	250	600	1250	2100	3000	3206
γ	246	40.0	20.0	9.80	4.95	2.15	1.0

Pressure Drop. During boiling, the increase in the fluid volume increases the velocity of the steam and, therefore, its momentum; consequently, a two-phase pressure drop consists of three components—frictional loss, momentum change, and elevation pressure drop

$$\Delta p_{total} = \Delta p_{friction} + \Delta p_{acceleration} + \Delta p_{elev} \quad . \quad (3\text{-}29)$$

At low void fractions ($\alpha < 0.30$), two-phase pressure drop may be evaluated by the homogeneous model proposed by Owens.[36] The elevation pressure drop is given by

$$\Delta p_{elev} = \int_0^L \rho dL \approx \bar{\rho} \Delta L \quad . \quad (3\text{-}30)$$

For a local boiling flow, $\bar{\rho}$ can be obtained from Eq. (3-17). The friction pressure drop is obtained from

$$\Delta p_{friction} = \frac{f \Delta L}{D_e} \frac{\bar{v} G^2}{2 g_c} \quad , \quad (3\text{-}31)$$

and the acceleration pressure drop term from

$$\Delta p_{acc} = \frac{G^2}{g_c} \frac{d\bar{v}}{dL} \Delta L \quad , \quad (3\text{-}32)$$

where G is the mass velocity (lbs/h ft^2) and $\bar{v}$ is the average specific volume of the mixture at the location considered. For calculations of the two-phase flow pressure drop at restrictions, the homogeneous model is recommended for both low and high qualities.

The pressure drop obtained during high-void-fraction flow again depends on the flow pattern; however, a general empirical correlation for calculating the two-phase frictional pressure drop has been developed by Baroczy.[37] His work may be considered an extension of that of Lockhart and Martinelli[38] and Martinelli and Nelson,[34] all of whom defined the two-phase pressure drop in terms of the single-phase pressure drop

$$\phi_{lo}^2 = \left(\frac{\Delta P}{\Delta L}\right)_{TP} \Bigg/ \left(\frac{\Delta P}{\Delta L}\right)_l \quad , \quad (3\text{-}33)$$

where

$$\phi_{lo}^2 = \text{two-phase frictional pressure drop multiplier}$$

$(\Delta P/\Delta L)_{TP}$ = two-phase pressure drop per unit length

$(\Delta P/\Delta L)_l$ = single-phase pressure drop obtained at same mass velocity when fluid is entirely liquid .

By defining a property index $[(\mu_l/\mu_v)^{0.2}(\rho_l/\rho_v)]$, Baroczy[37] was able to obtain a correlation for ϕ_{lo}^2, which was independent of pressure, and he also observed that his correlation could be used with the gas-phase pressure drop $(\Delta P/\Delta L)_g$ by observing that

$$\frac{(\Delta P/\Delta L)_l}{(\Delta P/\Delta L)_g} = \frac{(\mu_l/\mu_v)^{0.2}}{(\rho_l/\rho_v)} \quad . \tag{3-34}$$

His correlation is given in two sets of curves:

1. A plot of the two-phase multiplier ϕ_{lo}^2 as a function of the property index $(\mu_l/\mu_v)^{0.2}/(\rho_l/\rho_v)$, as shown in Fig. 3.8.

2. Plots of a two-phase multiplier ratio as a function of the property index, quality, and mass velocity as shown in Fig. 3.9.

This ratio multiplies ϕ_{lo}^2 whenever G deviates from 1×10^6 lb/(h ft^2).

At high void fractions, the use of the homogeneous model for computation of the acceleration pressure drop is not desirable since the effect of slip may be significant. It is convenient to write the acceleration pressure drop as

$$\Delta P_{acc} = r\, \frac{G^2}{g_c \rho_l} \quad , \tag{3-35}$$

where r is a dimensionless acceleration multiplier. When the inlet fluid contains no voids, r is given by

$$r = \frac{(1 - X_e)^2}{(1 - \alpha_e)} + \frac{X_e^2}{\alpha_e} \left(\frac{\rho_l}{\rho_v}\right)_{sat} - 1 \quad , \tag{3-36}$$

where

X_e = flow quality at channel exit

α_e = void fraction at channel exit.

By proper evaluation of α, the effect of slip is included. The value of r is independent of the manner of heat addition (sinusoidal, uniform, etc.) along the channel.

3-1.3 Flow Mixing and Redistribution

In a rod bundle, the flow channels formed by four adjacent fuel rods are open to each other through the gap between two neighboring fuel rods, and the flow in one channel mixes with that of the others. There is also cross flow between channels because of the pressure differential between the channels. The local fluid mixing, caused

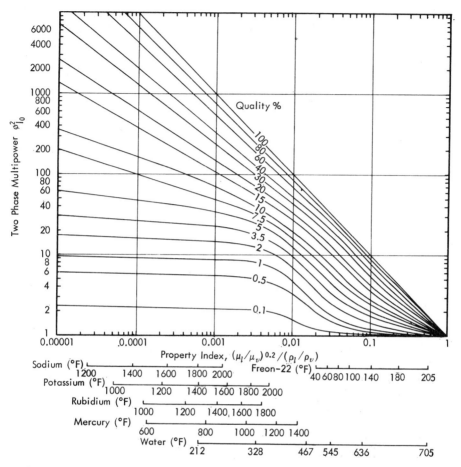

Fig. 3.8 Two-phase fraction pressure drop correlation for $G = 1 \times 10^6$ lb/(h ft^2). (From Ref. 37.)

by turbulence, reduces the enthalpy rise of hot channel. On the other hand, flow leaving the hot channel increases its enthalpy rise. The calculation of the net result is quite complicated although the equation describing the enthalpy exchange between two open channels m and n can easily be written. The energy balance across an axial increment ΔZ due to cross flow and mixing is

$$W_m \frac{\Delta H_m}{\Delta Z} = W_{n-m}(H_n - H_m) + \rho \epsilon (H_n - H_m) + q'' p_m \quad , \quad (3\text{-}37)$$

where

$$p_m = \text{heated perimeter of channel } m \text{ (ft)}.$$

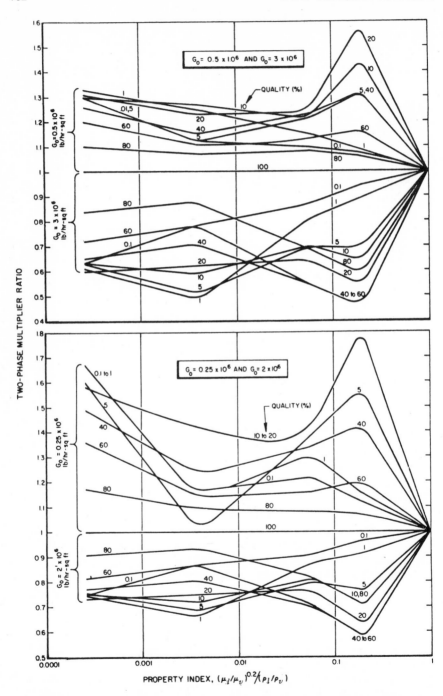

Fig. 3.9   Mass-velocity correction vs. property index.   (From Ref. 37.)

W_m = axial flow rate in channel m (lb/sec).

W_{n-m} = lateral cross-flow rate per unit length (lb/sec ft).

H_m, H_n = local enthalpy of channels m and n, respectively

ΔH_m = enthalpy rise in channel m through ΔZ (Btu/lb).

ϵ = mixing coefficient (a function of axial velocity and the gap between rods)

$\rho\epsilon$ = flow exchange rate per unit length (lb/sec ft), approximately 0.06 lb/sec ft for a typical PWR fuel assembly.

When the geometry changes to three parallel open channels, the above equation becomes much more complicated. Selection of flows that yield a uniform pressure at the exit of all three channels is even more difficult. To calculate the local enthalpy, density, and mass velocity of a reactor core consisting of semi-open multi-channels, a self-correcting calculation method has been developed.[39] A selected region of the core is divided into a number of contiguous vertical channels that extend the height of the core. The term channel as used here refers to a portion of the core where the fluid, density, velocity, pressure, etc., are considered constant at any elevation. Adjacent channels are considered to be semi-open, i.e., exchange of mass, energy, and momentum is permitted, but some appreciable resistance to cross flow between channels is encountered.

The region height is divided into a number of steps of equal length. Static pressure and coolant density distributions are assigned at the region inlet along with a guess as to the inlet velocity distribution. The change in density, velocity, and static pressure per length step are determined successively for each channel using difference equations that describe the exchange of mass, energy, and momentum with the adjacent channels. The resulting density, velocity, and static pressure at the top of each length step are used as input items for the next length step. This procedure is continued stepwise up to the top of the region.

If the total pressure distribution at the top of the core region is considered as a function of the inlet pressure, density, and velocity distributions, the functional dependence may be expressed as

$$P_j^o = P_j^o(P_1^i, P_2^i, \ldots, P_n^i, \rho_1^i, \rho_2^i, \ldots, \rho_n^i, V_1^i, V_2^i, V_n^i)(j = 1, 2, \ldots, n),$$

$$(3-38)$$

where the superscripts i and o represent inlet and outlet values, respectively, and j is the number of the channel.

Since the flow leaving the core enters a large plenum across which significant pressure differentials do not exist, the basic criteria to be satisfied are that the outlet total pressure be uniform and the total mass flow rate must be constant, i.e.,

$$P_1^o = P_2^o = P_3^o = \ldots = P_n^o \quad , \tag{3-39}$$

and

$$\sum_{j=1}^{n} A_j \, \rho_j^i \, V_j^i = \text{a constant} \quad . \tag{3-40}$$

As the flow enters the core from a large plenum with only small pressure differences across it, these basic criteria can be achieved only by adjusting the inlet velocity distribution, V_j^i.

Let us consider a two-channel core, for example: If the inlet pressures and densities are fixed,

$$P_1^o = \phi(V_1, \, V_2)$$
$$P_2^o = \psi(V_1, \, V_2) \quad , \tag{3-41}$$

then

$$dP_1^o = \phi_1 \, dV_1 + \phi_2 \, dV_2$$
$$dP_2^o = \psi_1 \, dV_1 + \psi_2 \, dV_2 \quad , \tag{3-42}$$

where

$$\phi_1 = \frac{\partial \phi}{\partial V_1} \quad , \qquad \phi_2 = \frac{\partial \phi}{\partial V_2}$$
$$\psi_1 = \frac{\partial \psi}{\partial V_1} \quad , \qquad \psi_2 = \frac{\partial \psi}{\partial V_2} \quad , \tag{3-43}$$

and

$$[dP^o] = \begin{bmatrix} \phi_1 & \phi_2 \\ \psi_1 & \psi_2 \end{bmatrix} [dV^i] \quad . \tag{3-44}$$

Let

$$[T] = \begin{bmatrix} \phi_1 & \phi_2 \\ \psi_1 & \psi_2 \end{bmatrix} \tag{3-45}$$

and

$$[T^{-1}] = \begin{bmatrix} \dfrac{\psi_2}{\phi_1\psi_2 - \phi_2\psi_1} & \dfrac{-\phi_2}{\phi_1\psi_2 - \phi_2\psi_1} \\[4mm] \dfrac{-\psi_1}{\phi_1\psi_2 - \phi_2\psi_1} & \dfrac{\phi_1}{\phi_1\psi_2 - \phi_2\psi_1} \end{bmatrix} \quad . \tag{3-46}$$

Thus, for a given inlet pressure distribution and inlet density distribution, the following applies:

$$[dP^o] = [T] \, [dV^i] \quad , \tag{3-47}$$

where

$[dP^o]$ = a column matrix with elements dP_j^o

$[T]$ = an n by n matrix with elements $\partial P_j^o / \partial V_k^i$

$[dV^i]$ = a column matrix with elements dV_k^i.

Since, for square matrices, $[T][T^{-1}] = I$, an identity matrix, premultiplication of Eq. (3-47) by $[T^{-1}]$ gives

$$[dV^i] = [T^{-1}][dP^o] \qquad (3\text{-}48)$$

provided $[T]$ is not singular.

Consider the pressure residues at the region outlet to be given by the relation

$$\Delta P_j^o = \overline{P}^o - P_j^o \quad , \qquad (3\text{-}49)$$

where $\overline{P}^o$ is the average outlet total pressure, and let the changes in velocities ΔV_k^i associated with the pressure residues ΔP_j^o be given by a relation analogous to Eq. (3-48)

$$[\Delta V^i] = [T^{-1}]\{[\Delta P^o] - \lambda[1]\} \quad , \qquad (3\text{-}50)$$

where

$[\Delta V^i]$ = a column matrix with elements ΔV_k^i

$[\Delta P^o]$ = a column matrix with elements ΔP_j^o

$[1]$ = a unit column matrix

λ = a scalar quantity to be determined.

Equation (3-40) allows us to determine λ. If the initial choice of velocities satisfies Eq. (3-40), and all subsequent choices satisfy this constraint, then

$$[A][\rho][\Delta V^i] = 0 \quad , \qquad (3\text{-}51)$$

where $[A]$ is a row matrix with elements A_j, $[\rho]$ is a square matrix with leading diagonal ρ_j^i, and all other elements are zero. Combining Eqs. (3-50) and (3-51) and solving for λ gives

$$\lambda = [A][\rho][T^{-1}][\Delta P^o]/\{[A][\rho][T^{-1}][1]\} \quad . \qquad (3\text{-}52)$$

Thus, if the $[T]$ matrix is known and is nonsingular, λ may be calculated from Eq. (3-52) and substituted in Eq. (3-50) to give the changes in inlet velocities associated with the outlet pressure distribution P_j^o.

To obtain $[T]$, the inlet velocity to one channel is changed by a preassigned small fraction ϵ and the resulting changes in outlet pressures for all the channels are determined by the step-wise procedure described above. The elements of the first column of the $[T]$ matrix are determined from this calculation. The original velocity distribution is restored, and the procedure repeated for each channel. Thus,

the inlet velocity to each channel is changed by the same small fraction ϵ, and in turn, the elements of each column of the $[T]$ matrix are
determined. The inverse of the $[T]$ matrix is then determined, and λ
is calculated using Eq. (3-52). Substituting in Eq. (3-50) gives the
matrix $[\Delta V^i]$, which is then used to determine a new inlet velocity
distribution using the relation

$$[V'^i] = [V^i] + [\Delta V^i] \quad , \tag{3-53}$$

where $[V^i]$ and $[V'^i]$ are the column matrices for the original and new
inlet velocities, respectively.

This entire procedure is repeated until the error in the outlet
pressure distribution is less than a preassigned value. If the core
pressure drop is small, and the difference in heat input between the
adjacent channels is large, natural circulation within the core may be
developed. The procedure just described does not account for this.

The degree of mixing and redistribution calculated depends on the
expressions used for evaluating ϵ and the lateral cross flow W_{n-m}.
On the basis of analytical studies of small size bundles, Rowe[40] concluded that the cross-flow resistance was low. In the analysis of the
behavior of a 25-rod bundle, Weisman et al.[41] assumed that the cross-
flow resistance was so low that no lateral pressure existed across
the bundle at any elevation. They correlated their data by defining a
thermal diffusion coefficient α, such that

$$\alpha = \epsilon / V \, b \quad , \tag{3-54}$$

where V is the superficial velocity (ft/sec) and b is the gap between
two rods. For their bundle (0.422-in. diam rods on a 0.535-in.^{2} pitch),
they found $\alpha \approx 0.076$ and essentially independent of mass velocity (G up
to 2.75×10^6) and quality. Since their spacer grids contained small
mixing vanes, it is expected that α for bundles without these vanes
would be lower.

Most investigators have preferred to correlate their data on the
basis of a modified Peclet number Pe, where

$$\text{Pe} = V \, D_e / \epsilon \tag{3-55}$$

and D_e = equivalent diameter. It will be observed that the Peclet
number equals $(D_e / \alpha b)$. For bundles of bare rods, Bell and LeTourneau[42] reported

$$1/\text{Pe} = \epsilon / (V \, D_e) = 0.003 \quad ; \quad 10^4 < \text{Re} < 5 \times 10^4 \quad . \tag{3-56}$$

They believed the data indicated that the correlation would be valid up
to Re = 2×10^5. For rectangular channels, Slember[43] reports

$$\epsilon / (V \, D_e) = 0.0015 \quad ; \quad \text{Re} > 10^5 \quad . \tag{3-57}$$

Waters[44] reported on the mixing obtained in wire wrapped bundles.

He found that α increased from about 0.1 to 1 as the wrap pitch was changed from 0.7 to 3 wraps/ft.

The effect of various assumed values of the Peclet number on the enthalpy rise variation across a closed channel containing an array of fuel rods was evaluated by Lowe,[45] who concluded that the reduction in the enthalpy rise hot-channel factor depended on both Pe and a dimensionless geometric factor p/b, where p is the channel pitch and b is the rod gap.

The assumption of a negligible pressure gradient across a small enclosed bundle appears to be reasonable. However, extension of this assumption to a full-size open core, where significant pressure gradients may exist, is highly questionable. Essentially no published information is available on the evaluation of lateral flow resistances.

3-1.4 Sonic Velocity and Critical Flow

A sudden change in fluid velocity causes a large pressure change that is seen as a pressure wave, across which there is discontinuity in pressure and velocity. The pressure wave, which may be either a compression wave (high pressure behind a wave front) or a rarefaction wave (low pressure behind a wave front), propagates at sonic velocity relative to the flow. It can be set up by the sudden closing of a valve in a flow line, by the rupture of a high pressure piping system (e.g., a loss-of-coolant accident), or by a steam burst in a reactor power excursion. The steam burst imparts kinetic energy, which is converted into a pressure pulse when the flow is interrupted. Pressure waves of this general nature are often called steam hammer or water hammer.

The pressure and velocity changes across an acoustic wave in one dimensional flow can be derived from the momentum equation

$$\frac{\partial u}{\partial t} + u \frac{\partial u}{\partial x} = - \frac{1}{\rho} \frac{\partial P}{\partial x} \quad , \tag{3-58}$$

where u is the fluid velocity, P the pressure, and x the distance. Since the velocity change with respect to distance is relatively small in a straight pipe, the $\partial u/\partial x$ term is negligible, and Eq. (3-58) becomes

$$\frac{\partial u}{\partial t} = - \frac{1}{\rho} \frac{\partial P}{\partial x} \quad . \tag{3-59}$$

The pressure wave travels at the velocity of sound a, and therefore, it will travel a distance (at) in time t. Let

$$\theta = x \pm at \quad , \tag{3-60}$$

where the negative sign is required for a wave moving in the direction opposite to u. Substituting Eq. (3-60) into Eq. (3-59), one obtains

$$\pm a \, \frac{du}{d\theta} = - \frac{1}{\rho} \frac{dP}{d\theta} \quad , \tag{3-61}$$

which yields by integration

$$\frac{P_2 - P_1}{u_2 - u_1} = \pm \rho \, a \quad . \tag{3-62}$$

Equation (3-62) shows that, in subcooled water with a density of 62 lb/ft^3 and a sonic velocity of 5000 ft/sec, a 3-ft/sec change in fluid velocity across the wave front causes a pressure pulse of 200 psi.

When a one-dimensional acoustic wave travels in a fluid of equal and opposite velocity, the wave becomes stationary with respect to the earth. We then have critical flow at this point (fluid at sonic velocity), and the downstream pressure signals can no longer be transmitted to the upstream fluid. Thus, the critical flow rate is limited by the upstream and critical point conditions but not by the downstream conditions. In the case of a rupture of a PWR piping system, the critical flow rate at the break determines the severity of the accident.

In single phase flow, the sonic velocity a and critical mass flow rate are directly and simply related:

$$a^2 = g_c v^2 / (dv/dP)_s \quad , \tag{3-63}$$

where v is the specific volume and the subscript s indicates the derivative is evaluated at constant entropy. The critical mass flow rate G_c is then given by

$$G_c^2 = a^2 \rho^2 = g_c / (dv/dP)_s \quad . \tag{3-64}$$

Two-phase critical flow is, however, more complex: The sonic velocity in a two-phase mixture varies with the amount of void present and velocity is usually measured at the wave front, where no phase change can take place instantaneously. The critical flow rate, on the other hand, is determined by the sonic velocity *behind* the wave front, where the phase change does take place, and this change depends on the wave shape and the bubble delay time which, in turn, depends on the saturation pressure of the fluid. It is therefore necessary to consider sonic velocity and critical flows of two-phase mixtures separately.

Sonic Velocity. There are two limits for the response of a mixture of liquid and vapor to a pressure pulse: (1) mass transfer between the phases maintaining thermal equilibrium, and (2) no mass transfer (frozen state) with liquid and vapor being independently isentropic. If no mass transfer is assumed, the computed velocity is often called the "frozen sonic velocity." If thermodynamic equilibrium is assumed, the computed velocity is substantially below the "frozen" sonic velocity and the velocity actually observed at low and moderate pressures.

If the vapor and liquid may be considered a homogeneous mixture, the sonic velocity may be derived quite simply from Eq. (3-63) by using the mean density $\bar{\rho}$, where

$$\bar{\rho} = \alpha\,\rho_v + (1 - \alpha)\rho_l \qquad (3-65)$$

and α = void fraction; ρ_v, ρ_l = vapor and liquid densities, respectively. The "frozen" two-phase sonic velocity a_{TP} may then be written as[46]:

$$a_{TP}^2 = \left[\frac{\alpha\,\bar{\rho}}{\rho_v a_v^2} + \frac{(1 - \alpha)\bar{\rho}}{\rho_l a_l^2}\right]^{-1}, \qquad (3-66)$$

where a_v, a_l = sonic velocity in vapor and liquid, respectively. At low pressures, where $a_l \gg a_v$, Eq. (3-66) becomes

$$\frac{a_{TP}^2}{a_v^2} = \left[\alpha^2 + \frac{\alpha(1 - \alpha)\rho_l}{\rho_v}\right]^{-1}. \qquad (3-67)$$

Dvornichenko[47] derived a slightly different expression for the frozen sonic velocity

$$\frac{a_{TP}}{a_v} = \left[\sqrt{\chi} + \frac{(1 - \chi)\rho_v}{\sqrt{\chi}\,\rho_l}\right], \qquad (3-68)$$

where χ = quality. Grolmes and Fauske[46] found that Eq. (3-66) fitted their low-void fraction data very well. It therefore may be used to predict the velocity of the sonic wave front in a low-void bubbly flow. At high void fractions, the assumption of a homogeneous mixture is no longer valid, and increasing deviations from Eq. (3-66) are observed.

Henry et al.[48] studied the situation at higher void fractions where slip must be considered. They used $\bar{\rho} = 1/[\chi v_v + (1 - \chi)v_l]$ in Eq. (3-63) and expressed a^2 in terms of the liquid density ρ_l, the gas density ρ_v, and the velocity slip ratio S. Equation (3-66) becomes

$$a_{TP}^2 = [(1 - \chi)\rho_v + \chi\rho_l]^2 \;\Big/\; \left[\chi\rho_l^2\left(\frac{\partial\rho_v}{\partial P}\right)_{sat} + (1 - \chi)\,\rho_v^2\left(\frac{\partial\rho_l}{\partial P}\right)_{sat}\right.$$

$$\left. - (\rho_l - \rho_v)\rho_l\rho_v\left(\frac{\partial\chi}{\partial P}\right)_s + \chi(1 - \chi)(\rho_l - \rho_v)\rho_l\rho_v\left(\frac{\partial S}{\partial P}\right)_s\right], \qquad (3-69)$$

where the subscript s indicates the derivative is evaluated at constant entropy. When it is assumed that no phase change occurs, Eq. (3-69) becomes

$$a_{TP}^2 = \frac{[(1 - \chi)\rho_v + \chi\rho_l]^2}{\left[\chi\rho_l^2\left(\frac{\partial\rho_v}{\partial P}\right)_s + (1 - \chi)\,\rho_v^2\left(\frac{\partial\rho_l}{\partial P}\right)_s + \chi(1 - \chi)(\rho_l - \rho_v)\rho_l\rho_v\left(\frac{\partial S}{\partial P}\right)_s\right]}\,.$$

$$(3-70)$$

Equation (3-68) can be simplified for frozen annular flow (or stratified flow) as follows: For a stationary wave, Henry et al.[48] suggested

$$\frac{\partial S}{\partial P} = \frac{1}{a_{TP}}\left(\frac{\partial V_v}{\partial P} - \frac{\partial V_l}{\partial P}\right) \qquad (3-71)$$

for the vapor phase

$$\frac{\partial P}{\partial z} + \rho_v a_{TP}\frac{\partial V_v}{\partial z} = 0$$

and for the liquid phase

$$\frac{\partial P}{\partial z} + \rho_l a_{TP}\frac{\partial V_l}{\partial z} = 0 \quad,$$

therefore

$$\frac{\partial S}{\partial P} = \frac{-1}{a_{TP}^2}\left(\frac{1}{\rho_v} - \frac{1}{\rho_l}\right) \quad, \qquad (3-72)$$

and, substituting Eq. (3-72) into Eq. (3-70) ,

$$a_{TP}^2 = \frac{\{[(1 - \chi)\rho_v + \chi\rho_l]^2 + \chi(1 - \chi)(\rho_l - \rho_v)^2\}}{\dfrac{\chi\rho_l^2}{a_v^2} + \dfrac{(1 - \chi)\rho_v^2}{a_l^2}} \quad. \qquad (3-73)$$

For incompressible flow at low pressures $(a_l \gg a_v)$, the sonic velocity may be approximated as

$$\left(\frac{a_{TP}}{a_v}\right)^2 = 1 + \frac{1 - \chi}{\chi}\left(\frac{\rho_v}{\rho_l}\right)^2 \qquad (3-74)$$

or, in case of no slip,

$$\left(\frac{a_{TP}}{a_v}\right)^2 = 1 + \frac{1 - \alpha}{\alpha}\left(\frac{\rho_v}{\rho_l}\right) \quad. \qquad (3-75)$$

In high-quality or high-void fraction flow, both Eqs. (3-74) and (3-75) indicate that $a_{TP} \to a_v$:

Henry et al.[48] compared their air-water mixture data with Eqs. (3-66) and (3-73): For the bubbly-flow region, they found the sonic velocity to agree with Eq. (3-66); for stratified flow (non-flowing system), Eq. (3-73) was applicable.

The stratified model of Eq. (3-72), which gives essentially the sonic velocity of vapor, is applicable for a high void steam-water (annular) flow. This is verified by the steam-water data obtained by Collingham and Firey,[49] England et al.,[50] Deich et al.,[51] and Dejong and Firey.[52]

In the latter part of 1968, Edwards[53] reported his analytical study of a transient critical flow with flashing that was controlled by heat conduction. He suggested that the maximum time delay before a bubble forms decreases when the system pressure increases as shown in Fig. 3-10. This figure leads him to conclude that, at a pressure greater than 300 psia and for a pipe length over 1 ft, the critical flow rate can be approximated as that of a homogeneous thermodynamic equilibrium flow. His conclusion is verified by several sets of high pressure blowdown data. On the basis of the Edwards information, one would expect the previously cited low-pressure sonic velocity data of Grolmes and Fauske,[46] which inherently have a long bubble delay time, would agree with the "frozen" model. Data at high pressures, where the bubble delay time is short, are unavailable.

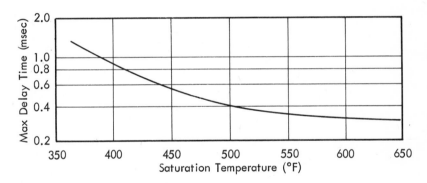

Fig. 3.10 Recommended bubble formation delay time. (From Ref. 53.)

The effect of phase change slows down the pressure wave behind the front and makes it flatter than would be obtained in a fully "frozen" system (e.g., air-water). This effect was also observed by Grolmes and Fauske[46] while studying the characteristics of both compression and rarefaction waves. Behind the wave front, the effects of heat and mass transfer become important and appear to prevent compression waves from steepening into shock waves and significantly lengthen the shape of the rarefaction waves.

Critical Flow in Long Pipes. From the previous discussion, it is clear that, behind the wave front, there is an approach to thermodynamic equilibrium. Since critical flow is determined by the conditions behind the front, some phase change must be considered. In a long pipe line, where there is adequate time for bubble nucleation and growth, thermodynamic equilibrium may be assumed.

Fauske[54] developed a "phases in equilibrium but separated" flow model for a long pipe on the basis of the following assumptions:

1. Average velocities of different magnitude exist for each phase (i.e., slip flow is considered).

2. The vapor and liquid are in phase equilibrium throughout the flow path.

3. Critical flow is attained when the flow rate is no longer increased with decreasing downstream static pressure (i.e., $[\partial G/\partial P]_{H_0} = 0$).

4. The pressure gradient attains a maximum value for a given flow rate and quality (i.e., the exit momentum flux is maximized).

In the absence of friction, the momentum equation for an isentropic annular flow can be written as

$$\frac{G^2}{g_c}\frac{dv}{dz} + \frac{dP}{dz} = 0 \quad , \tag{3-76}$$

or

$$\frac{G^2}{g_c} = -\left(\frac{dP}{dv}\right)_S \quad , \tag{3-77}$$

where the mean specific volume v is given as

$$v = \frac{\chi^2 v_v}{\alpha} + \frac{(1-\chi)^2 v_l}{1-\alpha} \quad , \tag{3-78}$$

and v_v and v_l are the specific volumes of the vapor and liquid, respectively. Introducing the slip ratio S, defined as

$$S = \frac{V_v}{V_l} = \frac{\chi}{1-\chi}\frac{1-\alpha}{\alpha}\frac{v_l}{v_v} \quad , \tag{3-79}$$

Eq. (3-78) becomes

$$v = \frac{[(1-\chi)v_l S + \chi v_v][1 + \chi(S-1)]}{S} \quad . \tag{3-80}$$

The maximization of the pressure gradient is achieved from assumption 4 above by varying the slip ratio; all other quantities are kept constant:

$$\frac{\partial v}{\partial S} = (\chi - \chi^2)\left(v_l - \frac{v_v}{S^2}\right) = 0 \quad . \tag{3-81}$$

Hence, at critical flow, the slip ratio becomes

$$S = (v_v/v_t)^{1/2} = (\rho_l/\rho_v)^{1/2} \; . \qquad (3\text{-}82)$$

The mass flow rate is obtained by substituting Eq. (3-80) into Eq. (3-77)

$$G^2 = \frac{-g_c}{\dfrac{d}{dP}\{[(1 - X)v_t S + Xv_v][1 + X(S - 1)]/S\}} \qquad (3\text{-}83)$$

or, by neglecting the insignificant term dv_l/dp,

$$G^2 = \frac{-g_c}{[(1 - X + SX)X]\dfrac{dv_v}{dP} + [v_v(1 + 2SX - 2X) + v_l(2XS - 2S - 2XS^2 + S^2)]\dfrac{dX}{dP}} \; .$$

$$(3\text{-}84)$$

Zivi[55] has recognized that the work of accelerating the two phases to their ultimate velocities is a significant part of the total flow work. By *assuming a thermal equilibrium* in an annular flow and by *neglecting the wall friction,* he obtained the maximum exit flow rate by maximizing the exit kinetic energy E of the flow

$$\frac{\partial E}{\partial \alpha} = \frac{G}{2}\left[2V_v \frac{\partial V_v}{\partial \alpha} X + 2V_l \frac{\partial V_l}{\partial \alpha}(1 - X)\right] = 0 \quad , \qquad (3\text{-}85)$$

which gives the slip ratio as

$$S = \frac{V_v}{V_l} = \left(\frac{\rho_l}{\rho_v}\right)^{1/3} \quad . \qquad (3\text{-}86)$$

Equation (3-86) agrees with that of Cruver and Moulton,[56] who used a criterion of maximum entropy of the system.

Later, Moody[57] used the energy equation to get

$$G = \left(2g_c J \frac{H_o - H}{v^2}\right)^{1/2} \quad , \qquad (3\text{-}87)$$

where H_o = upstream reservoir enthalpy and H = local enthalpy. He then assumed $(\partial G/\partial s)_P = 0$, where s is entropy, when the flow is a maximum, and obtained Eq. (3-86). Moody[58] extended this model to a real two-phase flow (frictional, separate, or homogeneous) and provided graphs for predicting the maximum steam/water flow rate in terms of pipe $\bar{f} L/D$ and upstream stagnation properties.

The data at low qualities disagree with a slip ratio of either $(\rho_l/\rho_v)^{1/2}$ or $(\rho_l/\rho_v)^{1/3}$. This disagreement is due to the metastability of the liquid phase. The correct value of slip ratio is not a constant but a function of quality and pressure. Fauske[59] achieved better agreement with low-pressure experimental data using Armand's slip ratio,[60] obtaining

$$\alpha = \frac{(0.833 + 0.167\chi)\chi v_v}{(1 - \chi)v_l + \chi\, v_v} \quad . \tag{3-88}$$

This correlation is recommended for calculation of α during low-pressure critical flow from pipes.

For subcooled and low-quality blowdown at low pressures, Henry[48] suggests an empirical correction factor N be used for correcting the homogeneous model as

$$G_c^2 = \frac{-g_c}{N\left[\chi\,\dfrac{\partial v_v}{\partial P}\bigg|_s + v_v\,\dfrac{\partial \chi}{\partial P}\bigg|_s\right]} \quad , \tag{3-89}$$

where $N = 20\chi$, for $P < 350$ psia and $\chi \leqslant 0.02$.

Recently, Edwards[53] suggested for pressures higher than 300 psia and for pipes longer than one foot that the critical flow rate is close to that for a homogeneous equilibrium flow. This suggestion appears to be supported by recent high-pressure blowdown data.[61]

Critical Flow in Short Pipes, Nozzles, and Orifices. Two types of choking mechanisms in a short pipe (or a square-edge orifice) were observed visually by Zaloudek,[62] who saw that an upstream choke can form at a *vena contracta* and a downstream choke can form as the back pressure is built up at the exit edge by flashing.

In 1947, Burnell[63] recognized the existence of a metastable state in the flow of flashing water through nozzles and hypothesized that the water surface tension retarded the formation of vapor bubbles thus causing the water to be superheated. He developed a semi-empirical method for predicting the flow of flashing water through square-edge

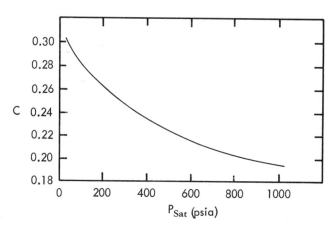

Fig. 3.11 Pressure coefficient for Burnell critical-flow equation. (From *Engineering,* **164,** 572, 1947).

orifices and correlated the discharge mass flow rate as

$$G_{crit} = \sqrt{2g_c\rho_l\left[P_{upstream} - (1 - C)P_{sat}\right]} \quad , \qquad (3\text{-}90)$$

where C is directly related to the bubble delay time which is a function of P_{sat}. The value of C, recommended for design use, is given in Fig. 3.11. The value of C determines the pressure undershoot at the exit due to superheating of the liquid. This pressure undershoot is limited by the maximum tension sustainable by the liquid under a superheated state. Briggs[64] has given these limiting tensions of water as a function of temperature, but the experimental data do not demonstrate clearly how long the liquid can remain in tension. The effect of pipe length and diameter on the critical flow rate is summarized in Fig. 3.12. For very short pipe lengths, the effect of entrance shape

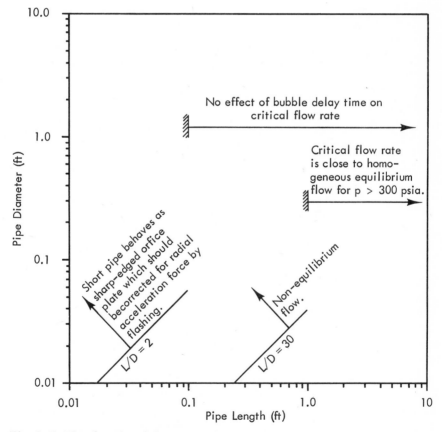

Fig. 3.12 Pipe-length and diameter effects on critical flow models. (Based on analysis by Edwards, Ref. 53.)

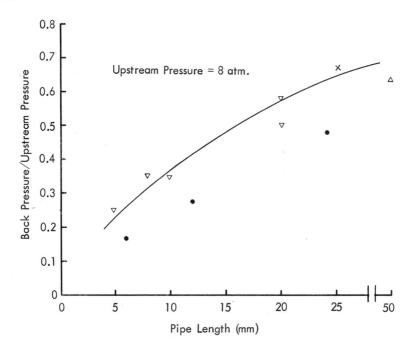

Fig. 3.13 Pipe-length effect on back pressure.
       Notation ▽ Uchida & Nairai, *Proc. 3rd Intern. Heat Trans. Conf.*,
             5, 1, 1966. (i.d. = 5 to 20 mm)
           × Zaloudek, Hanford Report, No. HW-77594, 1963.
             (i.d. = 12.2 mm)
           ● Fauske, *Chem. Eng. Prog. Symp. Series*, 61, No. 59,
             1965. (i.d. = 6.1 mm)
           △ Isbin & Chen, *Energia Nucleare*, **13**, 7, 1966.
             (i.d. = 12.2 mm, length = 50 mm)

should also be considered.[53] Tong has plotted the back pressures vs
pipe lengths from various sets of data as shown in Fig. 3.13, and this
indicates qualitatively that the back pressure is smaller in a shorter
pipe because of a shorter transition time for the liquid to flash. For
a sharp-edge orifice, the curve gives a back pressure of one atmosphere, which also agrees with many experimental observations.

Decay of Pressure Waves. When a pressure wave reaches a rigid
dead end, it is reflected as a wave of equal magnitude and sign; that
is, a rarefaction wave is reflected as a rarefaction wave and a compression wave as a compression wave. When a wave reaches an open
end or large reservoir, it is reflected as a wave of equal magnitude

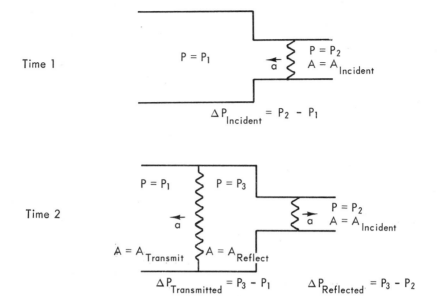

Fig. 3.14 Transmission and reflection of acoustic wave at area change.

but of opposite sign. When a wave encounters a change in area, a portion of the wave is transmitted in the original direction of travel, and a portion is reflected back. It may be shown[65] that the amplitude of the transmitted wave is given by

$$\frac{\Delta P_{\text{transmitted}}}{\Delta P_{\text{incident}}} = \frac{2A_{\text{incident}}}{A_{\text{incident}} + A_{\text{transmission}}} , \qquad (3\text{-}91)$$

and the ratio of reflected ΔP to the incident ΔP is

$$\frac{\Delta P_{\text{reflected}}}{\Delta P_{\text{incident}}} = \frac{A_{\text{incident}} - A_{\text{reflection}}}{A_{\text{incident}} + A_{\text{reflection}}} . \qquad (3\text{-}92)$$

This behavior is illustrated in Fig. 3.14.

In a frictionless system, the combination of forward and reflected waves would be undamped and would set up a standing wave. In any real system, the friction at the walls gradually reduces the amplitude of the waves. In a straight pipe, Lieberman and Brown[65] give the decay with time t as

$$\Delta P = (\Delta P_0) \exp(-f u \, t/D) , \qquad (3\text{-}93)$$

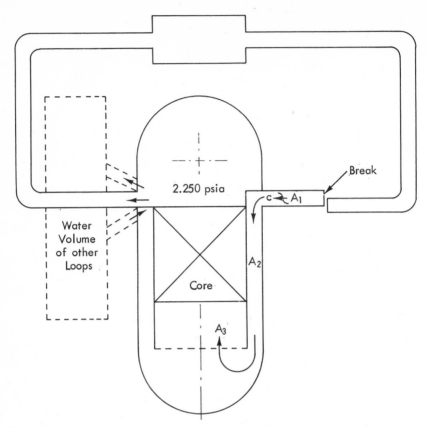

Fig. 3.15 Passage of rarefaction wave after break.
Notation A_1—Flow area of inlet pipe, 4.12 ft^2.
A_2—Annular area beside thermal shield, 26.4 ft^2.
A_3—Frontal area of reactor core, 92.0 ft^2.

where

D = diameter of the pipe

f = Fanning Friction Factor

u = fluid velocity

ΔP_0 = ΔP at zero time.

For a pipe diameter of 1 ft, Fanning Friction Factor of 0.005, and water velocity of 20 ft/sec, the time constant D/fu is 10 sec; thus, the frictional effect is relatively small.

When a pressure wave is reflected by a body that can deflect significantly, the amplitude of the reflected wave is appreciably reduced. The reader is referred to Streeter and Wylie[66] for discussion of this case. In a reactor system, the piping and major components deflect very little and can usually be considered as rigid; however, the deflection of any thin wall internal structure should be considered.

The major attenuation of the acoustic waves proceeding through a reactor system arises because of the area changes involved. Consider the simplified reactor system shown in Fig. 3.15 where a break in the inlet pipe is occurring: Pressure at the break may be assumed to change in a series of small discrete jumps. If, in the first jump, the exit pressure has dropped so that the amplitude of the wave in the pipe is ΔP_1, then from Eq. (3-91), the wave front in thermal shield passage is equal to

$$\Delta P_2 = \Delta P_1 \left(\frac{4.12 \times 2}{26.4 + 4.1} \right) = 0.27(\Delta P_1) \quad . \tag{3-94}$$

For the reactor core, the wave front amplitude will be given by

$$\Delta P_3 = \left(\frac{26.4 \times 2}{26.4 + 92} \right) \Delta P_2 = 0.120(\Delta P_1) \quad . \tag{3-95}$$

3-2 REACTOR VESSEL HYDRODYNAMICS

3-2.1 Flow in Plenums

The flow streams or vortices in the lower plenum may affect the flow distribution at the core inlet. The downward jet formed by the flow coming down between the thermal shield and the vessel wall causes a low pressure region at the edge of the core inlet, which will reduce the flow in the outer assemblies. The pressure at the center of a vortex with a horizontal plane of rotation is usually lower than the surrounding pressure; thus, the flow rate to any fuel assembly located above a vortex is reduced.

The most effective way to even off the inlet flow is to increase the flow resistance at the bottom of the core. According to Prandtl's equation for velocity distribution improvement,[67]

$$\frac{\Delta V_{\text{after screen}}}{V_{\text{avg}}} = \frac{1}{K+1} \frac{\Delta V_{\text{before screen}}}{V_{\text{avg}}} \quad , \tag{3-96}$$

where

$$K = \frac{\Delta P_{\text{screen}}}{\rho \, V_{\text{avg}}^2 / 2g_c} \quad . \tag{3-97}$$

A similar relationship can be applied to the core inlet. For example, consider the situation where the Euler number at the core inlet is

$$\text{Eu} = \frac{\Delta P_{\text{core inlet}}}{\rho V_{\text{jet}}^2 / 2 g_c} \leqslant 10 \quad . \tag{3-98}$$

Under the most adverse conditions, K is then equal to 10. To obtain the pressure drop at the inlet of the hot channel, we add the stagnation pressure of the jet to the average inlet pressure drop. This leads to (ΔP of maximum flow channel/ΔP of average channel) = 11/10. Since ΔP is proportional to V^2, the ratio of the maximum inlet flow rate to the average inlet flow rate is $(11/10)^{1/2}$.

3-2.2 Flow Induced Vibrations

Hydraulic Vibration of Core Structure. Vibration of a core structure may be caused by the periodic suction of a venturi flow, by the wake of a vortex, or by the impulse of an impinging jet.

When a high-speed flow passes through a gradually narrowing passage, the pressure head of the stream is converted into a velocity head, which creates a suction force on the wall. If the wall is movable or flexible, the passage will be reduced automatically to zero and the flow will be stopped. As soon as the flow becomes stagnant, the stream pressure increases to its maximum value, pushing the wall back, thus providing a wide passage again. These suction and pushing forces can act periodically and thus vibrate the core structure. This mechanism appears to govern the vibration of parallel fuel plates.

Parallel fuel plate vibration has been analyzed by Miller,[68] Scavuzzo,[69] and Remick.[70] Miller applied a method of "neutral equilibrium" where the pressure and plate restoring forces were balanced. He was then able to determine a critical velocity V above which significant vibration will occur, and he expresses this vibration inducing velocity for fuel plates assemblies with long edges attached to side plates as

$$V_c = [15 \, g_c \, E \, t^3 \, d / \rho b^4 \, (1 - \gamma^2)]^{1/2} \quad , \tag{3-99}$$

where

t = plate thickness

b = plate width

d = flow channel depth

E = Young's modulus of elasticity

γ = Poisson's ratio.

Miller's results are frequently applied, and Wambsganss,[71] who recently extended the work to include second order terms, concluded that the critical flow velocity could be from 0.63 to 0.85 times those derived by Miller.

Miller and Kennison[72] have analyzed the flow-induced vibration of a blade suspended in a flow channel, which widens at a point downstream of the leading edge—a condition similar to that observed by a control-rod blade. They concluded that there are three possible motions: (1) decaying vibrations, (2) divergent vibrations, and (3) static deflection against the channel wall. The motion observed is dependent on the insertion length and flow rate. For short insertion lengths, there is a critical velocity above which divergent oscillations are obtained. They also conclude that a critical insertion length exists above which no oscillations can be sustained but where deflection against the channel wall is possible. Wambsganss[73] concludes that the analysis explains experimental observations qualitatively but not quantitatively.

When a structural member receives the thrust of an impinging jet, it usually vibrates as the strength of jet varies. The worst vibration occurs when the natural frequency of the structural member equals that of the oscillating jet. Such jets may be caused by pumping pulses or vortex formation. According to Roshko[74] and Rouse,[75] a vortex at high Reynolds numbers (5×10^5 to 3.5×10^6) begins with laminar boundary layer separation and ends where the separated boundary layer becomes turbulent and the wake broadens further and becomes periodic. The vortices are shed at a frequency that is a function of the geometry of the body, spacing between adjacent bodies, and the flow velocity. The shedding frequency is represented by St, the Strouhal number,

$$St = f_v\, L/V \quad , \tag{3-100}$$

where

f_v = vortex shedding frequency

L = a characteristic dimension

V = the stream velocity.

When the Reynolds number is in the range of 3.6×10^6 to 1×10^7 the vortex is in the transcritical range, and the drag and Strouhal number remain constant at approximately 1.2 as the velocity is changed.

If the source of the vortices or pressure pulses can be identified, the frequency of the oscillations can be estimated. If the natural frequency of the structure is substantially above the frequency of the expected oscillation, vibration problems will not be significant. The response of complicated structures to an arbitrary dynamic excitation is difficult to predict. Bohm[76] has developed an analytical model that approximates the internals as an interconnected beam-type structure and uses a transfer-matrix approach for determination of natural frequencies.

The complexity of most reactor coolant systems makes it difficult to predict the frequency and magnitude of hydraulic forcing functions; therefore, scale models of system components are often tested under simulated operating conditions.

Hydraulic Vibration of Fuel Rods. The hydraulic vibration of cylindrical fuel rods, with their axes parallel to the flow, has been studied by Burgreen et al.,[77] Quinn,[78] Sogreah,[79] Pavlica and Marshall,[80] Paidoussis,[81] and Morris.[82] The earliest correlation is that due to Burgreen, who found that single rods vibrate at their natural frequency (reduced slightly by the viscous damping in water) and that the amplitudes of the vibrations are given by

$$\frac{\delta}{d} = (0.83 \times 10^{-10})^3 \, C^3 \left(\frac{\rho V^2}{\mu \, \omega}\right)^{0.77} \left(\frac{\rho_1 V^2 L^4}{EI}\right)^{0.42} , \qquad (3\text{-}101)$$

where

δ = maximum rod deflection

d = rod diameter

C = 5 for pin ended rod; 1 for rigidly held rod; and 2.08 for one end rigidly held, the other pin ended

ω = the natural frequency of vibration

ρ_1 = rod density

E = Young's modulus of elasticity

I = moment of inertia

V = axial velocity

L = rod length.

Paidoussis[81,83] has extended the work of Burgreen et al.,[77] and his most recent correlation for deflection amplutudes is

$$\frac{\delta}{d} = \alpha_1^{-4} \left[\frac{u^{1.8}\left(\frac{L}{\alpha}\right)^{1.8} Re^{0.25}}{1 + u^2}\right] \left(\frac{D_e}{d}\right)^{0.4} \left[\frac{B^{2/3}}{1 + 4B}\right] [5 \times 10^{-4} \times K] , \qquad (3\text{-}102)$$

where

α_1 = first-mode beam eigenvalue

$B = M + m/M$, M = rod mass, m = fluid mass

$u = (M/EI)^{1/2}(VL)$

V = axial velocity

D_e = hydraulic diameter of the flow channel

K = constant that is 1 for quiet flow and 5 for realistic disturbance levels.

This correlation shows much less dependence on fluid viscosity than Paidoussis's original proposal. It brings it in close agreement with the data of Quinn[78] and Pavlica and Marshall,[80] which show almost no fluid temperature effect.

Paidoussis[83] has also examined the vibration of 19 element wire wrapped bundles and found vibration amplitudes much higher than those of Eq. (3-101) and that they did not increase significantly with flow. Pavlica and Marshall[80] examined the vibration of rod bundles with spring clip spacers, and in correlating the data, they used the stiffness (EI) of the bundle rather than that of the individual rods. Since the intermediate rod-to-rod connectors are not rigid, they used experimental values of (EI) rather than an estimate using single element parameters. With this change, they found their room temperature data agreed with the original Paidoussis correlation. The discrepancy between their 150°F data and the correlation appears to be remedied by the reduced viscosity effect in the revised correlation.

Although no current reactor design uses cross flow, it has been proposed, and such an arrangement does occur in the baffled portion of once-through steam generators. Here, vortices are shed alternately from each side of the tube inducing a periodic force perpendicular to the flow. As before, vortex shedding frequency is represented by the Strouhal number, with the rod diameter being the characteristic dimension. Chen[84] has shown that the Strouhal number in tube banks depends on the tube spacing used.

3-2.3 Hydraulic Design of Control Rods

To obtain a simplified method of analysis for estimating the drop time of a control rod, the basic assumption is made that all the hydraulic forces are proportional to the square of the rod velocity. The equation of motion of the control rod is then

$$\frac{M + m}{g_c} \frac{dV}{dt} = \Sigma F \quad , \tag{3-103}$$

where M is the mass of control rod and m is the virtual mass of the body due to fluid acceleration, i.e.,

$$m = M \, \rho_l / \rho_M \quad . \tag{3-104}$$

The equation of motion can be simplified to

$$\frac{dV}{dt} = C_2 - C_3 \, V^2 \quad . \tag{3-105}$$

The solution of the above equation is

$$t = \frac{1}{2(C_2 \, C_3)^{1/2}} \ln \frac{1 + [1 - \exp(-2 C_3 x)]^{1/2}}{1 - [1 - \exp(-2 C_3 x)]^{1/2}} \quad , \quad (3\text{-}106)$$

where x represents distance traveled.

Asymptotically, as $x \to \infty$ (or $x \geqq 2/ C_3$),

$$t = \frac{C_3 X + \ln 2}{(C_2 \, C_3)^{1/2}} \quad . \quad\quad\quad (3\text{-}107)$$

At the end of the rod's travel, it enters a dashpot that has a small clearance between it and the rod. This clearance produces a high *frictional* force, which rapidly decelerates the rod. The resisting force in the dashpot is linearly proportional to the distance of insertion Z, and the equation of motion when the rod enters the dashpot is

$$\frac{dV}{dt} = C_2 - (C_3 + C_4 \, Z) \, V^2 \quad . \quad\quad (3\text{-}108)$$

The solution to this equation is

$$V^2 = V_0^2 \exp(-2 C_3 Z - C_4 Z^2) + 2 \exp(-2 C_3 Z - C_4 Z^2)$$
$$\times \; C_2 \int_0^Z \exp(2 C_3 Z + C_4 \, Z^2) \, dz \quad , \quad\quad (3\text{-}109)$$

where V_0 is the entering velocity. This may be rearranged to

$$V^2 = V_0^2 \exp(C_3^2/C_4) \exp(-u^2) + (2 C_2/\sqrt{C_4}) \exp(-u^2) \int_{C_3/\sqrt{C_4}}^{u} \exp(u^2) \, du \; , $$
$$(3\text{-}110)$$

where

$$u = C_3/\sqrt{C_4} + \sqrt{C_4} \; Z \quad .$$

Hence the rod velocity in the dashpot can be evaluated at each Z.

3-3 FLOW INSTABILITY

The term "flow instability" refers to flow oscillations of constant or variable amplitude that are analogous to vibrations in a mechanical system. The mass flow rate, pressure drop, and voids may be considered equivalent to the mass, exciting force, and spring of the mechanical system. In this connection, the relationship between flow rate and pressure drop plays an important role. Flow oscillations may be aggravated when there is thermohydrodynamic coupling between heat transfer, void, flow pattern, and flow rate; however, oscillations can occur even when the heat source is held constant. Both *hydrodynamic* and *thermohydrodynamic* instabilities will be discussed, but the more elaborate nuclear-thermohydrodynamic instabilities of boiling channels in water-cooled reactors are beyond the scope of this book.

Flow oscillations are undesirable in boiling, condensing, and other two-phase flow devices for several reasons: First, sustained flow oscillations may cause undesirable forced mechanical vibration of components; second, flow oscillations may cause system control problems, which are of particular importance in liquid-cooled nuclear reactors where the coolant (such as water) also acts as a moderator; third, flow oscillations affect the local heat transfer characteristics and the boiling crisis. The critical heat flux was thus found by Ruddick[85] to be reduced 40% when the flow was oscillating. This adverse effect was also found by Lowdermilk.[86] Recently, Mayinger et al.[87] found a similar reduction of critical heat flux in an oscillating water flow at 2000 psia.

3-3.1 Nature of Various Flow Instabilities

Flow Pattern Instability. This occurs when the flow conditions are close to the point of transition between bubbly flow and annular flow. A temporary increase in bubble population in bubbly-slug flow (arising from a temporary reduction in flow rate) may change the flow pattern to annular flow with its characteristically lower pressure drop. When the driving pressure drop over the channel remains constant, the flow rate will attain a greater value. As the flow rate increases, however, the vapor generated (even for unchanged heat transfer characteristics) may become insufficient to maintain the annular flow. The flow pattern then reverts to that of bubbly-slug flow, and the cycle is repeated. The low-pressure drop characteristics of annular flow have been demonstrated experimentally by Wallis.[88] The cyclic behavior is partly due to the delay incurred in acceleration and deceleration of the flow.

Ledinegg Instability. Consider the operation of a boiler tube to which there is a constant heat input. At low flow, the boiler exit quality and velocity are high since the fluid is entirely, or almost entirely, vapor. This high vapor velocity accounts for much of the pressure drop. When the flow is increased, slightly more vapor is generated, and the pressure drop increases. However, as the flow increases further, the exit quality begins to decrease, and the velocity at the tube exit decreases. The pressure drop decreases and continues to decrease until the tube contents are all water. The pressure drop then increases as the water velocity increases. Experimental observations of this phenomenon are shown in Fig. 3.16.[89]

The effect of this phenomenon on stability can be understood by reference to Fig. 3.17, where we consider the operation of a boiling channel with a constant exit pressure. A portion of the pressure vs flow curve, which occurs at very low flow rates, is shown at the left, and the corresponding curve for the boiler feed system is also shown.

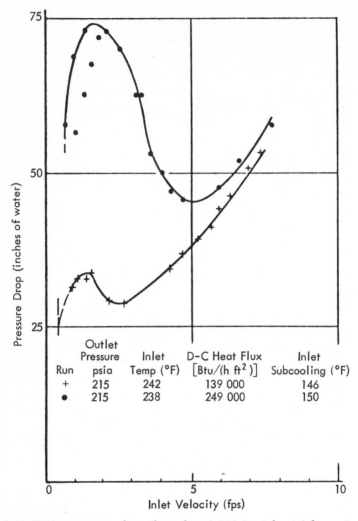

Fig. 3.16 Static pressure drop through a 0.174-in. i.d. stainless-steel AISI-type 347 heated single tube. (From Ref. 89.)

The system will operate where the two curves intersect. If the flow to the boiler increases by a small amount, ΔW, the boiler pressure will become greater than the supply pressure. This will decelerate the flow and the system will then return to the original operating point. If, on the other hand, $\partial(\Delta P)/\partial G$ is negative, as shown in the central portion of Fig. 3.17, an increase in flow will decrease the inlet pressure so that the supply flow will increase and continue to increase. This flow excursion may be predicted by the Ledinegg

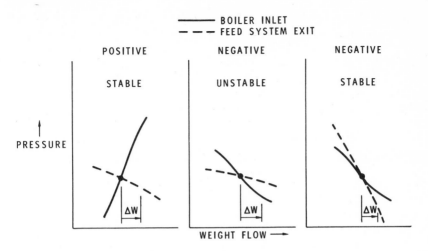

Fig. 3.17 Boiler resistance. (From Ref. 93.)

criterion,[90] which states that a necessary condition for the excursion is $\partial(\Delta P)/\partial G < 0$, where the steady-state characteristic of the channel $G(\Delta P)$ is not single-valued with identical inlet enthalpy and heat addition.

The flow can be stabilized in this region by providing a pump-supply curve whose slope is even more negative than that of the boiler (right hand, Fig. 3.17). If the boiler flow increases, the feed system cannot supply the high pressure needed and the flow will return to the operating point. The system is then statically stable even though $\partial(\Delta P)/\partial G$ is negative. Therefore, the criterion for Ledinegg, or static, stability can be written as

$$\frac{\partial(\Delta P)_{\text{feed}}}{\partial G} - \frac{\partial(\Delta P)_{\text{loop}}}{\partial G} < 0 \ , \qquad (3\text{-}111)$$

where the $(\Delta P)_{\text{feed}}$ is the driving head supplied by the feed pump and $(\Delta P)_{\text{loop}}$ is the flow friction head demanded by the loop.

This type of flow oscillation is also called "pressure drop oscillation" by Stenning and Veziroglu.[91] It can generally be avoided by increasing the pressure drop at channel inlet or by using a pump having a large head reduction at high flow rates.

Density Wave or Dynamic Instability. A temporary reduction in the inlet flow to a boiling channel will increase the rate of evaporation, thereby raising the average void fraction. This disturbance affects the elevation, acceleration, and frictional pressure drop as well as the heat transfer behavior. For certain conditions of channel geometry, thermal properties of the heated wall, flow rate, inlet enthalpy, and heat flux, resonance with sustained oscillations may occur. Stenning and Veziroglu[91] have found that the frequency of a density wave oscillation is higher than that of a pressure drop oscillation (Fig. 3.18). Neal et al.[92] recognized that this oscillation is caused by flow-void feedback when a phase shift of 180° exists between a flow disturbance and its void volume response, and such can occur even when the boiler is operating in a region where $\partial(\Delta P)/\partial G$ is positive. Let us consider a single, closed-loop containing pump, boiler tube with constant heat input, and a condenser and assume that some sinusoidal flow oscillation at a specified frequency is introduced. If the pressure drop across the boiler is examined, pressure oscillations will be observed that are not necessarily in phase with the flow oscillation; they may lag the flow oscillations.

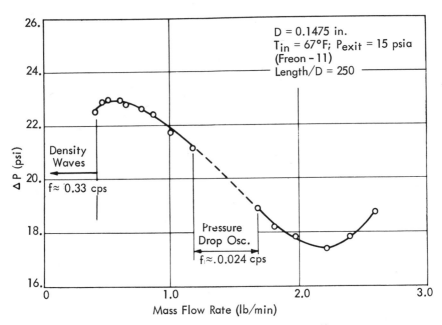

Fig. 3.18 Density and pressure wave oscillation regions.[91] (From *Proc. 1965 Heat Transfer and Fluid Mechanics Inst.*, Stanford Univ. Press, 1965.)

Let us assume that we repeat this process for a number of different imposed frequencies. At each frequency, the lag (phase angle) between the velocity and pressure oscillations is determined as well as the ratio of the amplitude of the flow oscillation A_F to the amplitude of the pressure oscillation A_P. A polar coordinate plot, usually called a Bode diagram, of a typical set of results is shown in Fig. 3.19.[93] At steady state (zero frequency), pressure and flow are in

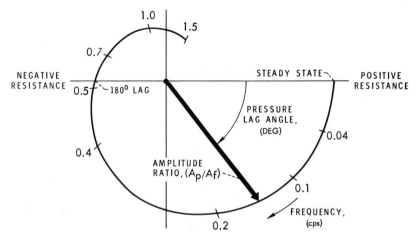

Fig. 3.19 Boiler-inlet impedance in polar coordinates. (From Ref. 93.)

phase, and the boiler has a completely positive resistance. At the location where the curve crosses the horizontal axis again, the pressure and velocity are out of phase by 180°, and the boiler has a completely negative resistance.

To determine whether instability will occur in our system, we must perform a similar experiment with our feed system, and would expect to get results such as shown in Fig. 3.20.[93] The feed system shown will have a positive resistance at all frequencies. For the frequency range where the boiler has a negative resistance - R_B, the feed system has a positive resistance R_F. So long as $R_F > R_B$, the system will be stable. If this is not the case, dynamic instability will result.

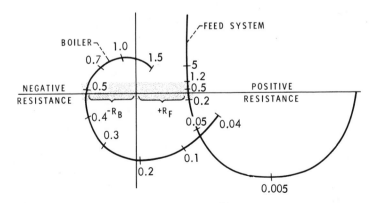

Fig. 3.20 Boiler-inlet and feed-system impedances. (From Ref. 93.)

Thermal Oscillation. This oscillation occurs in a film boiling region or during rapid heating of a cryogenic system. It is a thermal
response of the vapor film to flow disturbances. Disturbances that
can be reinforced by a mechanism such as acoustic resonance become
dominant in the system, and these oscillations are often called
acoustic instabilities. It will be recalled that the velocity of sound is
greatly reduced by the presence of small quantities of void, which
can produce "organ-pipe" resonances in short pipe lengths.

Observed frequencies have been related to the harmonics of a pipe
open at both ends and to Helmholtz resonance. This phenomenon has
been reported by Edeskutz and Thursten,[94] and the inception of oscillations can be predicted by

$$q''/GH_{fg} = 0.005 \ (v_l/v_v) \ , \qquad (3\text{-}112)$$

where H_{fg} = enthalpy change on vaporization and the range of (v_v/v_l)
is 9 to 25.

Cornelius and Parker[95] have detected acoustic instability (5 to 30
cps) of refrigerant Freon 114 in a natural circulation loop at a bulk
temperature below critical temperature but at critical pressure.
Walker and Harden[96] have suggested that the region of pressure and
flow fluctuations associated with a natural circulation loop operating
at supercritical pressures occurs near the maximum in the plot of
the density enthalpy product vs the fluid temperature. Bergles et al.[97]
examined thermal oscillation in boiling-water flow at 1000 psia. They
found the oscillations characterized by a frequency greater than 35
cps and most pronounced in the subcooled region and pressure-drop
amplitudes very large compared to the steady-state values. The
oscillations are considered to be acoustic in nature and induced by
the collapse of subcooled voids.

3-3.2 Effects of Various Parameters on Flow Instability

The effects of various flow-instability parameters, which have
been observed in the studies mentioned in preceding paragraphs, are:

1. High heat input aggravates flow instability because of the resulting high rate of vaporization.

2. Increased inlet subcooling, within a critical value, reduces
stability. Beyond that value, a further increase in subcooling may
reverse the trend and stabilize the flow.

3. Increased resistance at the exit strongly decreases the stability
because it increases the exit pressure drop when a large void is
generated in the channel.

4. Increased resistance at the inlet strongly increases the stability. When the flow is slowed by a disturbance, a large pressure head

will be retained at the inlet and will be available for forcing the fluid through the channel, thereby stabilizing the flow.

5. Increased system pressure increases the stability in proportion to the increase in the reduced pressure, primarily because the difference in specific volumes of vapor and liquid then becomes smaller.

6. Increased static head in a long vertical channel increases the stability of upward boiling flow and decreases the stability of downward boiling flow. This occurs because the buoyancy of the vapor aids upward flow and opposes downward flow. With the latter, there is a tendency for the vapor to agglomerate and remain in the channel.

3-3.3 Theoretical Analysis

Acoustic or thermal oscillations are primarily associated with start-up and transient situations[93] and are usually not the major concern of the designer. Flow-pattern instabilities are imperfectly understood. Experimental observations are recommended. At present, the designer directs his major consideration to Ledinegg and dynamic instability. Analysis for both problems may be carried on simultaneously since Ledinegg instability can be considered a special dynamic case occurring at zero frequency. These problems are fairly well understood, and a theoretical analysis may be made.

Basic Thermohydrodynamic Equations. Tong[21] has reviewed this area extensively, and we shall follow his discussion. We shall first write the conservation equations for one-dimensional flow, with slip, in a vertical channel. For the continuity balance, we have

$$\frac{\partial}{\partial t}\left[\rho_l(1-\alpha)+\rho_v\alpha\right]+\frac{\partial}{\partial z}\left[\rho_l(1-\alpha)u_l+\rho_v\alpha u_v\right]=0 \quad . \quad (3\text{-}113)$$

where z indicates axial distance and u_l and u_v are the liquid and vapor velocities, respectively. For the energy balance, we have

$$\frac{\partial}{\partial t}\left[\rho_l(1-\alpha)H_l+\rho_v\alpha H_v\right]+\frac{\partial}{\partial z}\left[\rho_l(1-\alpha)u_lH_l+\rho_v\alpha u\ H_v\right]=q''', \quad (3\text{-}114)$$

where energy dissipation is neglected, q''' is the heat input per unit volume of fluid and H_l and H_v are the liquid and vapor enthalpies, respectively. The momentum balance may be written as

$$\frac{1}{g_c}\frac{\partial}{\partial t}\left[\rho_l(1-\alpha)u_l+\rho_v\alpha u_v\right]+\frac{1}{g_c}\frac{\partial}{\partial z}\left[\rho_l(1-\alpha)u_l^2+\rho_v\alpha u_v^2\right]+\frac{dP}{\partial z}+F$$

$$\pm\left[\rho_l(1-\alpha)+\rho_v\alpha\right]\frac{g}{g_c}=0 \quad . \quad (3\text{-}115)$$

A positive sign for the final term indicates upward flow; a negative, downward; F is the frictional force per unit volume of fluid.

If the system remains at a nearly constant pressure, the equation of state can be written as

$$\rho_l \approx \rho_l(H_v) \tag{3-116}$$

$$\rho_v \approx \rho_v(H_v) \quad . \tag{3-117}$$

Note that in subcooled boiling the mixture density should be calculated on the basis of the amount of local boiling void but not on the basis of an energy balance.

The preceding equations may be simplified by introducing the quality defined as

$$\chi = \frac{w_v}{w_v + w_l} = \frac{\alpha \rho_v u_v}{\alpha \rho_v u_v + (1 - \alpha)\rho_l u_l} \quad . \tag{3-118}$$

If the local mass velocity is defined as

$$G = \alpha \rho_v u_v + (1 - \alpha)\rho_l u_l \quad , \tag{3-119}$$

the continuity balance becomes

$$\frac{\partial \bar{\rho}}{\partial t} + \frac{\partial G}{\partial z} = 0 \quad . \tag{3-120}$$

The volume weighted mean density $\bar{\rho}$ is given by Eq. (3-13), and the energy balance by

$$\bar{\rho}\, \frac{\partial H}{\partial t} - H_{fg} \frac{\partial \psi}{\partial t} + G\, \frac{\partial H}{\partial z} = q''' \quad . \tag{3-121}$$

The quantity ψ defined by

$$\psi = \rho_l \chi(1 - \alpha) - \rho_v \alpha(1 - \chi) \tag{3-122}$$

is a slip correction for the energy balance and is zero for nonslip flow. The mixing cup enthalpy H is defined by

$$H = H_l + \chi(H_v - H_l) \quad . \tag{3-123}$$

The momentum balance is

$$\frac{1}{g_c}\left[\frac{\partial G}{\partial t} + \frac{\partial}{\partial z}(v'G^2)\right] + \frac{\partial p}{\partial z} + F \pm \frac{\bar{\rho}g}{g_c} = 0 \quad , \tag{3-124}$$

where v', the "effective specific volume for spatial acceleration," is

$$v' = \frac{1}{G^2}\left[\rho_l u_l^2(1 - \alpha) + \rho_v u_v^2 \alpha\right] = \frac{\chi^2}{\alpha \rho_v} + \frac{(1 - \chi)^2}{(1 - \alpha)\rho_l} \quad . \tag{3-125}$$

This becomes $v' = 1/\bar{\rho}$ for nonslip flow, and equation of state may be written

$$\bar{\rho} = \bar{\rho}(H) \quad . \tag{3-126}$$

If the channel size is small (e.g., between fuel rods in a PWR core) and the vapor quality is sufficiently low so that bubbly flow exists, slip is negligible at high pressures. This is particularly true during a flow oscillation, since the void distribution changes as the flow changes from accelerating to decelerating.

Linearization and Laplace Transformation. When we consider a steam generator consisting of a large number of boiler tubes, each generating approximately the same amount of steam, it is usually adequate to consider the steam generator as a single channel. If we utilize the technique of small perturbations, the variables in Eqs. (3-113) to (3-116) can be described by

$$G(z,t) = G(z,0) + \Delta G(z,t)$$

$$H(z,t) = H(z,0) + \Delta H(z,t)$$

$$\bar{\rho}(z,t) = \bar{\rho}(z,0) + \Delta\bar{\rho}(z,t)$$

$$q'''(z,t) = q'''(z,0) + \Delta q'''(z,t) \quad , \tag{3-127}$$

where $\Delta G(z,t)/G(z,0) \ll 1$, etc. If these variables are substituted into the aforementioned equations and the second order terms are ignored, the equations can be linearized to yield

$$\frac{\partial \Delta G}{\partial z} = - \frac{\partial \Delta \rho}{\partial t} \tag{3-128}$$

$$\Delta q''' = G \frac{\partial \Delta H}{\partial z} + \Delta G \frac{\partial H}{\Delta z} + \rho \frac{\partial \Delta H}{\partial t} \tag{3-129}$$

$$\frac{1}{g_c} \left[\frac{\partial \Delta G}{\partial t} + \frac{\partial}{\Delta z} \left(\frac{2G \Delta G}{\rho} - \frac{G^2}{\rho^2} \Delta \rho \right) \right]$$

$$+ \frac{\partial \Delta P_{\text{channel}}}{dz} + \Delta \rho \frac{g}{g_c} + \frac{fG}{g_c D_c \rho} \Delta G - \frac{fG^2}{2g_c D_c \rho^2} \Delta \rho = 0 \tag{3-130}$$

$$\Delta \rho = \frac{\partial \rho}{\partial H} \Delta H + \frac{\partial \rho}{\partial G} \Delta G + \frac{\partial \rho}{\partial q'''} \Delta q''' \quad . \tag{3-131}$$

A Laplace transformation of the above is used to obtain a transfer function of the inlet flow variation with respect to a variation of the heat input as

$$G(s) = \frac{\Delta G(s)}{\Delta q'''(s)} = - \frac{as^2 + bs + c}{s^2 + ds + \omega_n^2} \quad , \tag{3-132}$$

where the coefficients a, b, c, d, and ω_n contain the system parameters. When $d = 0$, the flow will oscillate with the frequency ω_n. For

$d > 0$, the oscillations introduced by a disturbance in heat flux vanish for large values of time. Quandt[98] has suggested that $d = 0$ be used as a stability criterion, but the validity of this procedure is limited to small oscillations due to the linearization approximation.

The linearized STABLE-3 program[99] has been compared with the existing data (Refs. 92, 100-103) by Neal and Zivi,[92] who found that STABLE-3 predicts the data within 20% for about 70% of the tests. Recently Jain[104] showed that STABLE-3 predicts the data within 20% for 90% of his experiments. However, a limitation of the STABLE-3 program is that it requires prior knowledge of the steady-state flow rate for a given power level.

Nonlinear approaches to this problem have been considered by Randles,[105] Garlid,[106] and Nahavandi and Von Hollen.[107] The last investigators analyzed the stability of U-tube steam generators considering only the dimensions of length along the flow path and time. The differential conservation equations were solved numerically by means of a ''Modified-Euler'' integration process combined with appropriate iteration procedures. Nahavandi and Von Hollen believe that this procedure avoids the approximations inherent in linearized techniques.

Momentum Integration. The stability problem in a reactor core, where heat flux varies markedly both axially and radially, is more complex. This is especially true for those designs, such as in a pressure tube reactor, where the parallel channels are connected only at the inlet and exit. Here, the total flow to the core may remain essentially constant but oscillations in the flow to some channels may occur.

To solve the nonlinear transient-momentum equations simultaneously for several parallel channels, one must integrate the momentum equation along each channel. The fluid properties are obtained from the energy equation and the equation of state, and then the integrated equations are solved simultaneously. These techniques have been incorporated into the HYDNA computer code[108] that predicts the flow oscillation in parallel channels. For the description of the computational method of HYDNA, we shall again follow Tong.[21]

It is useful to separate the inlet mass velocity and the instantaneous axial mass flow rate distribution. If $\phi(z,t)$ is the axial mass flow rate distribution in the channel and $G(0,t)$ is the inlet mass flow rate, which can vary with time, we have

$$G(z,t) = G(0,t)\phi(z,t) \quad . \tag{3-133}$$

Substitution of this where $G(z,t)$ is the mass velocity as a function of z and t into the momentum balance over the channel length gives

$$\frac{dG(0,t)}{dt}$$

$$= -\frac{\Delta P + \int_0^L F\,dz + \int_0^L \pm \rho dz + \frac{1}{g_c}\Delta(v'G^2) + \frac{1}{g_c}G(0,t)\int_0^L \frac{\partial\phi}{\partial t}\,dz}{\frac{1}{g_c}\int_0^L \phi\,dz}\ ,$$

(3-134)

where ΔP is the pressure difference between the common plenums and $v' = 1/\rho$ for homogeneous flow. The factor $\int_0^L \phi dz$, which accounts for the effect of the axial variation of the mass velocity, comes close to unity for a slow transient if G remains nearly constant throughout the passage. However, $\partial\phi/\partial t$ vanishes if the shape of $G(z)$ remains constant. All terms of Eq. (3-134) except $dG(0,t)/dt$ and ΔP can be easily determined. Let C and B be given as

$$C = -\frac{1}{\frac{1}{g_c}\int_0^L \phi\,dz}$$

(3-135)

and

$$B = -\frac{\int_0^L F\,dz + \int_0^L \pm \rho\,dz + \frac{1}{g_c}\Delta(v'G^2) + \frac{1}{g_c}G(0,t)\int_0^L \frac{\partial\phi}{\partial t}\,dz}{\frac{1}{g_c}\int_0^L \phi\,dz}\ .$$

(3-136)

Substitution into the momentum balance yields

$$\frac{dG(0,t)}{dt} = C\,\Delta P + B\ .$$

(3-137)

Equation (3-137) can be written for each of n parallel channels

$$\frac{dG_1(0,t)}{dt} = C_1\Delta P + B_1$$

$$\frac{dG_2(0,t)}{dt} = C_2\Delta P + B_2$$

. . . .

$$\frac{dG_n(0,t)}{dt} = C_n\Delta P + B_n\ .$$

(3-138)

With a given total inlet flow rate $W(t)$

$$A_1G_1(0,t) + A_2G_2(0,t) + \ldots + A_nG_n(0,t) = W(t)\ ,$$

(3-139)

where $A_1, A_2, \ldots, A_n$ are the respective flow areas of channels 1, 2, $\ldots, n$. Differentiation of Eq. (3-139) gives

$$A_1 \frac{dG_1(0,t)}{dt} + A_2 \frac{dG_2(0,t)}{dt} + \ldots + A_n \frac{dG_n(0,t)}{dt} = \frac{dW}{dt}$$

or

$$A_1(C_1 \Delta P + B_1) + \ldots + A_n(C_n \Delta P + B_n) = \frac{dW}{dt}. \qquad (3\text{-}140)$$

The latter equation can be used to evaluate the pressure drop that is common to all channels; i.e.,

$$\Delta P = \frac{(dW/dt) - \Sigma B_n A_n}{\Sigma C_n A_n}. \qquad (3\text{-}141)$$

Equation (3-140) can be used to predict the pressure drop as a function of time by iterating upon it along with the n simultaneous equations of Eq. (3-138). The steps in the calculation for a small time increment are given by Tong[21] with a method that can predict the thermal and hydraulic behavior of the system in response to a specified variable inlet flow rate or a given variable power input to the channel.

3-3.4 Recommended Methods of Analysis

The recommended methods of analysis for various types of flow instabilities are:

1. The onset of density wave or dynamic instability in a uniformly heated boiling channel can be properly predicted by a linearization of the basic equations, such as in STABLE-3.[99]

2. For a parallel boiling channel with nonuniform heat flux distributions, a momentum integration such as used in HYDNA[108] should be used.

3. The static stability of a natural or forced circulation loop can be determined by the Ledinegg Criterion[90] with a lumped-pressure drop.

4. The analysis for predicting the onset of flow pattern instability has not been well established. An experimental determination is recommended.

5. To predict the onset of thermal oscillation, empirical correlations[94] are suggested.

3-4 LIQUID ENTRAINMENT, VAPOR CARRY-UNDER, AND STEAM SEPARATION

Liquid entrainment during evaporation, vapor carry-under in a natural circulation loop, and steam separation are closely related because they are all controlled by the buoyancy force. Although they are usually considered to be in the province exclusive of the boiling water reactor, they must be understood for steam generator design and system behavior during a loss-of-coolant accident.

3-4.1 Liquid Entrainment

Liquid Injection. Liquid droplets injected into a gas stream by the burst of bubbles have been studied by Mitsuishi et al.,[109] who found:

1. The liquid drop spray is injected almost perpendicularly to the liquid surface.

2. The liquid injected is largely from bubbles with diameters of 2 mm or less, and

$$D_p \propto D_b^{3/2} \quad , \tag{3-142}$$

where D_p is the diameter of droplet and D_b is the diameter of bubble.

3. Variation in the surface tension of liquid has little effect on the drop size. An increase in the viscosity of liquid brings about a decrease in the drop diameter and lower jetting height.

The injection velocities and jetting heights obtained by Mitsuishi et al.[109] are shown in Figs. 3.21 and 3.22, respectively. They also found that liquid entrainment increased rapidly after the vapor mass velocity increased above 800 lb/(h ft²) (about 6 ft/sec) at atmospheric pressure.

Newitt et al.[110] reported that the generation of drops by bursting bubbles is influenced by the depth of bubble generation, by the bubble diameter, and by the physical properties of the liquid. They found that large liquid drops can be eliminated by increasing the vapor space in an evaporator or by increasing the plate spacing in a plate column. The number of large drops is usually few for bubbles generated at very shallow depths. Sterman[111] provides an expression for determining the minimum diameter D at which entrainment is independent of vessel size:

$$\frac{D[\rho_v/(\rho_l - \rho_v)]^{-0.2}}{[\sigma/(\rho_l - \rho_v)]^{1/2}} \geq 260 \quad , \tag{3-143}$$

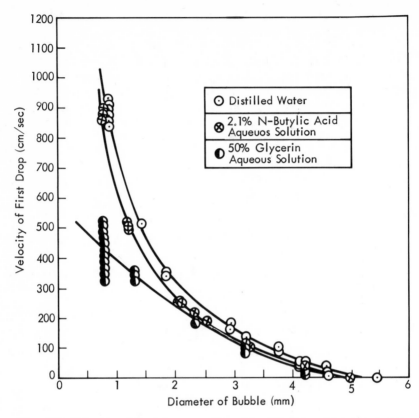

Fig. 3.21 Velocity of first drop vs diameter of bubble. (From Ref. 109.)

where

σ = surface tension (lb/ft)

ρ_l = liquid density (lb/ft^3)

ρ_v = vapor density (lb/ft^3)

D = diameter (ft).

Carry-Over. As indicated in Fig. 3.22, the height to which droplets are carried by rising steam increases with increasing steam velocity. This is most clearly seen in the insert of Fig. 3.23. The height at which water droplets are observed gradually increases until a critical "carry-over" steam velocity is reached where the entrained liquid remains with the steam and good surface separation can no longer be achieved.

Carry-over at high pressures has been studied by Davis[112] and

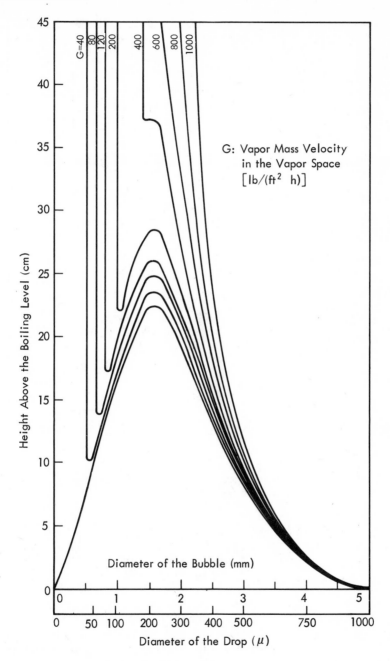

Fig. 3.22 Height of drop entrained above the boiling liquid level. (From Ref. 109.)

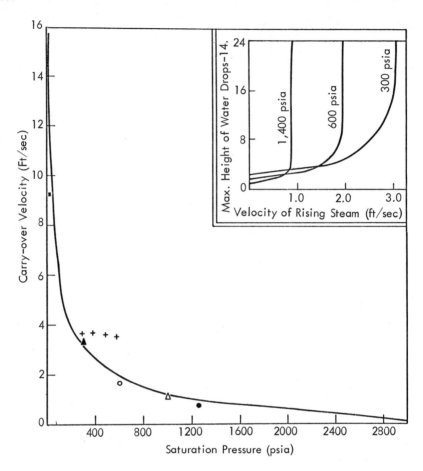

Fig. 3.23 Surface disengagement carryover velocities.

Notation: Curves by Davis, Ref. 112.
+ Allis Chalmers, 33-in. sep. ht.
△ General Electric, 32-in. sep. ht.
▲ Combustion Engineering, 50-in. sep. ht.
○ Combustion Engineering, 30-in. sep. ht.
● Combustion Engineering, 24-in. sep. ht.
■ Mitsuishi et al., Ref. 109.

various investigators on USAEC sponsored programs. The carry-over velocity as a function of pressure is plotted in Fig. 3.23, where the insert shows that, at high pressures, carry-over occurs much more suddenly and at a much lower steam velocity. The data of Wilson and McDermott[113] may be used in evaluating carry-over in small flow channels with cold walls.

3-4.2 Carry-Under

Carry-under, the entrainment of bubbles of vapor in the liquid stream leaving a separating surface, is the inverse of carry-over. Carry-under in both steam-water and air-water separations has been studied by Petrick,[33] whose air-water data were obtained using riser radii of 3.25 and 5.5 in., respectively, and whose steam-water data were taken at pressures of 600, 1000, and 1500 psia. He also obtained data from the Experimental Boiling Water Reactor (EBWR) at 300 and 600 psia and has suggested two carry-under equations: For $\chi_D/\chi_R = 3$ to 64,

$$\frac{\chi_D}{\chi_R} = -0.04 \log \left[\frac{\left(\frac{V_g}{V_e}\right)\left(\frac{\sigma^{2/3}}{G^2\mu}\right)\left(\frac{\rho_l}{\rho_v}\right)^{1/2}\left(\sqrt{\frac{D}{H}} + \sqrt{\frac{H}{D}}\right)}{64} \right]. \quad (3\text{-}144)$$

For $\chi_D/\chi_R = 0.1$ to 3,

$$\frac{\chi_D}{\chi_R} = -0.6 \log \left[\frac{\left(\frac{V_g}{V_e}\right)\left(\frac{\sigma^{2/3}}{G^2\mu}\right)\left(\frac{\rho_l}{\rho_v}\right)^{1/2}\left(\sqrt{\frac{D}{H}} + \sqrt{\frac{H}{D}}\right)}{3.7} \right], \quad (3\text{-}145)$$

where

χ_D = steam quality in the downcomer

χ_R = steam quality in the riser

V_g = vapor velocity in the riser, ft/sec

V_e = velocity of entrained gas in the downcomer, ft/sec

D = riser diameter

H = interface height

σ = surface tension, lb/ft

μ = viscosity of liquid, lb/(sec ft)

G = liquid mass velocity in the downcomer, lb/(sec ft^2).

Petrick[33] also has suggested a correlation for calculating the slip ratio in downflow

$$\frac{V_v}{V_l} = 0.63 \left(\frac{\bar{V}^2}{gD}\right)^{0.4} \left(\frac{\chi}{1-\chi} \frac{\rho_l}{\rho_v}\right)^{0.2}, \quad (3\text{-}146)$$

where $\bar{V}$ = average velocity of mixture.

3-4.3 Steam Separation

Separation by Surface Disengagement. Surface disengagement is effective when the steam velocity is low enough for water droplets to return to the two-phase interface by gravitational force. In designing this type of steam separator, the data in Fig. 3.23 can be used. The increase in vapor density with pressure initially overcomes the decrease in escape velocity, so that the allowable steam release rate reaches maximum at 1750 psia. This allowable steam release rate determines the maximum power output of a boiler relying solely on surface disengagement for its steam separation.

Separation by Centrifugal Force. This mechanism is encountered in a radial or vane type of steam separator. For analysis in the range of interest, the effects of gravity force, slip, and turbulence can be neglected, and the dynamic equation of a bubble becomes

$$\frac{C_d \pi D^2}{4} \rho_l \frac{u^2}{2g_c} = \frac{1}{6} \pi D^3 \frac{(\rho_l - \rho_v)}{g_c} \frac{v^2}{R} , \qquad (3\text{-}147)$$

where

C_d = drag coefficient, dimensionless

D = bubble diameter, ft

R = radius of separator, ft

u = radial velocity, ft/sec

v = tangential velocity, ft/sec .

Rearranging the above equation, it becomes

$$u^2 = \frac{4 v^2 D}{3 R C_d} . \qquad (3\text{-}148)$$

For a vane separator, design equations can be written by equating the time required for the bubble to separate

$$\frac{R\theta}{v} = \frac{b}{u} , \qquad (3\text{-}149)$$

where b is the water-annulus thickness, which the bubble travels and θ is the angle the bubble travels along the vane before separation. If we combine Eqs. (3-148) and (3-149), we get the condition of bubble separation:[114]

$$\frac{b^2}{R\theta} = \frac{4D}{3C_d} . \qquad (3\text{-}150)$$

It can be seen from Eq. (3-149) that the maximum inlet velocity v (i.e., maximum mixture rate) can be increased by increasing R and by decreasing b. The vane arc θ should be large but not more than 130 to 180 deg to allow space for the separated water to leave the vane.

REFERENCES

1. L. F. MOODY, "Friction Factors for Pipe Flow," *Trans. ASME*, **66**, 671 (1944).

2. W. M. KAYS and A. L. LONDON, *Compact Heat Exchangers*, The National Press, Palo Alto, California (1955).

3. V. L. STREETER, *Handbook of Fluid Dynamics*, John Wiley & Sons, New York (1961).

4. S. McLAIN and J. H. MARTENS, Eds., *Reactor Handbook*, 2nd ed., Vol. IV, Interscience Publishers, New York (1964).

5. E. N. SIEDER and G. E. TATE, "Heat Transfer and Pressure Drop of Liquid in Tubes," *Ind. Eng. Chem.*, **28**, 1429 (1936).

6. W. H. ESSELMAN, I. H. MANDIL, S. J. GREEN, P. C. OSTERGAARD, and R. A. FREDRICKSON, "Thermal and Hydraulic Experiments for Pressurized Water Reactors," *Proc. 2nd U.N. Intern. Conf. Peaceful Uses At. Energy*, **7**, 758, Geneva (1958).

7. B. W. LeTOURNEAU, R. E. GRIMBLE, and J. E. ZERBE, "Pressure Drop for Parallel Flow Through Rod Bundles," *Trans. ASME*, **79**, 483 (1957).

8. O. J. MENDLER, A. S. RATHBUN, N. E. VAN HUFF, and A. WEISS, "Natural Circulation Tests with Water at 800 to 2000 psia Under Non-boiling, Local Boiling, and Bulk Boiling Conditions," *Trans. ASME, Ser. C, J. Heat Transfer*, **83**, 261 (1961).

9. W. M. ROHSENOW and J. A. CLARK, "Heat Transfer and Pressure Drop Data for High Heat Flux Densities to Water at High Sub-Critical Pressures," *1951 Heat Transfer and Fluid Mechanics Institute*, Stanford University Press (June 1951).

10. R. G. DEISSLER and M. F. TAYLOR, "Analysis of Axial Turbulent Flow and Heat Transfer Through Banks of Rods or Tubes," USAEC Report TID-7529, Reactor Heat Transfer Conference, Part 1, Book 2, p. 416, U.S. Atomic Energy Commission (1957).

11. R. G. DEISSLER, "Analysis of Turbulent Heat Transfer, Mass Transfer, and Friction in Smooth Tubes at High Prandtl and Schmidt Numbers," NACA Report 1210, National Advisory Committee for Aeronautics (1955).

12. R. G. DEISSLER, "Analytical and Experimental Investigation of Adiabatic Turbulent Flow in Smooth Tubes," NACA Report TN-2138, National Advisory Committee for Aeronautics (1953).

13. J. LAUFER, "The Structure of Turbulence in Fully Developed Pipe Flow," NACA Report TN-2954, National Advisory Committee for Aeronautics (1953).

14. P. MILLER, J. J. BYRNES, and D. M. BENFORADO, "Heat Transfer to Water Flowing Parallel to a Rod Bundle," *A.I.Ch.E. J.*, **2**, 226 (1956).

15. J. L. WANTLAND, "Compact Tubular Heat Exchangers," USAEC Report TIC-7529, Part 1, Book 2, p. 525, U.S. Atomic Energy Commission (1957).

16. D. A. DINGEE and J. W. CHASTAIN, "Heat Transfer from Parallel Rods in Axial Flow," USAEC Report TID-7529, Part 1, Book 2, p. 462, U.S. Atomic Energy Commission (1957).

17. R. G. DEISSLER and M. F. TAYLOR, "Analysis of Turbulent Flow and Heat Transfer in Non-Circular Passages," NACA Report TN-4384, National Advisory Committee for Aeronautics (1958).

18. R. T. BERRINGER and A. A. BISHOP, "Model Study of the Pressure Drop Relationships in a Typical Fuel Rod Assembly," USAEC Report YAEC-75, Westinghouse Atomic Power Division (1959).

19. A. N. De STORDEUR, "Drag Coefficients for Fuel-Element Spacers," *Nucleonics*, **19**, *6*, 74 (1961).

20. A. A. BISHOP, P. A. NELSON, and E. A. McCABE, Jr., "Thermal and Hydraulic Design of the CVTR Fuel Assemblies," USAEC Report CVNA-115, Westinghouse Atomic Power Division (1962).

21. L. S. TONG, *Boiling Heat Transfer and Two-Phase Flow*, John Wiley & Sons, New York (1965).

22. G. W. MAURER, "A Method of Predicting Steady-State Boiling Vapor Fraction in Reactor Coolant Channels," USAEC Report WAPD-BT 19, Bettis Technical Review, p. 59, Bettis Atomic Power Laboratory (1960).

23. R. W. BOWRING, "Physical Model, Based on Bubble Detachment, and Calculation of Steam Voidage in the Subcooled Region of a Hot Channel," OECD Halden Reactor Project Report HPR-29, Halden, Norway (1962).

24. J. R. S. THOM, W. M. WALKER, T. A. FALLOW, and G. F. S. REISING, "Boiling in Subcooled Water During Flow up Heated Tubes or Annuli," *Proc. Inst. ME, 1965-1966*, 180, Part 3C (1966).

25. L. S. TONG, "Two-Phase Flow in Nuclear Reactors, and Flow Boiling and Its Crises," Lecture Notes for University of Michigan Short Course (Summer 1968).

26. S. G. BANKOFF, "A Variable Density Single-Fluid Model for Two-Phase Flow with Particular Reference to Steam-Water Flow," *Trans. ASME, Ser. C, J. Heat Transfer*, **82**, 265 (1960).

27. G. E. KHOLODOVSKI, "New Method for Correlating Experimental Data for the Flow of a Steam-Water Mixture in Vertical Pipes," *Teploenergetica*, **4**, *7*, 68 (1957).

28. G. A. HUGHMARK, "Holdup in Gas-Liquid Flow," *Chem. Eng. Prog.*, **58**, 62 (1962).

29. N. ZUBER and J. A. FINDLAY, "Average Volumetric Concentration in Two-Phase Flow System," ASME Annual Winter Meeting, New York (December 1964).

30. P. GRIFFITH and G. B. WALLIS, "Two-Phase Slug Flow," *Trans. ASME, Ser. C, J. Heat Transfer*, **83**, 307 (1961).

31. T. HARMATHY, "Velocity of Large Drops and Bubbles in Media of Infinite and of Restricted Extent," *A.I.Ch.E. J.*, **6**, 281 (1960).

32. J. F. MARCHATERRE and B. M. HOGLUND, "Correlation for Two-Phase Flow," *Nucleonics*, **20**, *8*, 142 (1962).

33. M. PETRICK, "A Study of Carry-Under Phenomena in Vapor Liquid Separation," *A.I.Ch.E. J.*, **9**, *2*, 253 (1963).

34. R. C. MARTINELLI and D. B. NELSON, "Prediction of Pressure Drops During Forced Circulation Boiling of Water," *Trans. ASME*, **70**, 695 (1948).

35. J. R. S. THOM, "Prediction of Pressure Drop During Forced Circulation Boiling of Water," *Intern. J. Heat and Mass Transfer*, **7**, 709 (1964).

36. W. L. OWENS, Jr., "Two-Phase Pressure Gradients," *Intern. Developments Heat Transfer*, Part II, ASME, pp. 363-368 (1961).

37. C. J. BAROCZY, "A Systematic Correlation for Two-Phase Pressure Drop," NAA-SR-Memo-11858, North American Aviation (March 1966).

38. R. W. LOCKHART and R. C. MARTINELLI, "Proposed Correlation of Data for Isothermal Two-Phase, Two-Component Flow in Pipes," *Chem. Eng. Prog.*, **45**, 39 (1949).

39. W. ZERNIK, H. B. CURRIN, E. ELYASH, and G. PREVETTI, "THINC—A Thermal Hydraulic Interaction Code for a Semi-Open or Closed Channel Core," WCAP-3704, Westinghouse Atomic Power Division (1962).

40. D. S. ROWE, "Cross-Flow Mixing Between Parallel Flow Channels During Boiling, Part I," USAEC Report NBWL-371P71, Pacific Northwest Laboratory (March 1967).

41. J. WEISMAN, A. H. WENZEL, L. S. TONG, D. FITZSIMMONS, W. THORNE, and J. BATCH, "Experimental Determination of the Departure from Nucleate Boiling in Large Rod Bundles at High Pressures," *Chem. Eng. Prog. Symp. Ser.*, **64**, *82*, 114 (1968).

42. W. H. BELL and B. W. LeTOURNEAU, "Experimental Measurements of Mixing in Parallel Flow Rod Bundles," WAPD-TH-381, Bettis Atomic Power Laboratory (1960).

43. R. J. SEMBLER, "Mixing in Rectangular Nuclear Reactor Channels," WAPD-T-653, Bettis Atomic Power Laboratory (1960).

44. E. D. WATERS, "Fluid Mixing Experiments with a Wire-Wrapper 7-Rod Bundle Fuel Assembly," HW-70178 Rev, USAEC Research and Development Report, Hanford Laboratory, General Electric Co. (1963).

45. P. A. LOWE, "Two-Dimensional Turbulent Flow Mixing Model for Parallel Flow Rod Bundles," *Nucl. Sci. Eng.*, **32**, 1 (1968).

46. M. A. GROLMES and H. K. FAUSKE, "Comparison of the Propagation Characteristics of Compression and Rarification Pressure Pulses in Two-Phase, One-Component Bubble Flow," *Trans. Am. Nucl. Soc.*, **11**, 683 (1968).

47. V. V. DVORNICHENKO, *Teploenergetika*, **13**, *10*, 72 (1966). Also available in Eng. translation, "The Speed of Sound in the Two-Phase Zone," *Thermal Eng.*, **13**, *10*, 110 (1966).

48. R. E. HENRY, M. A. GROLMES, and H. K. FAUSKE, "Propagation Velocity of Pressure Waves in Gas-Liquid Mixtures," Gas-Liquid Flow Symposium at Waterloo University, Waterloo, Ontario (1968).

49. R. E. COLLINGHAM and J. C. FIREY, "Velocity of Sound Measurements in Wet Steam," *Ind. Eng. Chem. Process Design and Development*, **3**, 197 (1963).

50. W. G. ENGLAND, J. C. FIREY, and O. E. TRAPP, "Additional Velocity of Sound Measurements in Wet Steam," *Ind. Eng. Chem. Process Design and Development*, **5**, 198 (1966).

51. M. E. DEICH, G. A. FILIPPOV, E. V. STEKOL'SHCHEKOV, and M. P. ANISIMOVA, "Experimental Study of the Velocity of Sound in Wet Steam," *Thermal Eng.*, **14**, 4, 59 (1967).

52. V. J. DEJONG and J. C. FIREY, "Effect of Slip and Phase Change on Sound Velocity in Steam-Water Mixtures and Relation to Critical Flow," *Ind. Eng. Chem. Process Design and Development*, **7**, 3, 454 (1968).

53. A. R. EDWARDS, "Conduction Controlled Flashing of a Fluid and the Production of Critical Flow Rates in a One-Dimensional System," UKAEA Report AHSB(S)R 147, United Kingdom Atomic Energy Authority, Risley, England (1968).

54. H. K. FAUSKE, "Contribution to the Theory of Two-Phase, One-Component Critical Flow," USAEC Report ANL-6633, Argonne National Laboratory (1962).

55. S. M. ZIVI, "Estimation of Steady-State Steam Void Fraction by Means of the Principle of Minimum Entropy Production," *Trans. ASME, Ser. C, J. Heat Transfer*, **86**, 247 (1964).

56. J. E. CRUVER and R. W. MOULTON, "Critical Flow of Liquid-Vapor Mixture," *A.I.Ch.E. J.*, **13**, 52 (1967).

57. F. J. MOODY, "Maximum Flow Rate of Single Component, Two-Phase Mixture," *Trans. ASME, Ser. C, J. Heat Transfer*, **87**, 1, 134 (1965).

58. F. J. MOODY, "Maximum Two-Phase Vessel Blowdown from Pipes," ASME Paper No. 65-WA/HT-1 (1965).

59. H. K. FAUSKE, "What's New in Two-Phase Flow," *Power Reactor Tech.*, **9**, 1, 35 (1966).

60. A. A. ARMAND, "The Resistance During the Movement of a Two-Phase System in Horizontal Pipes," U.K. Report No. AERE-Trans. 828, Atomic Energy Research Establishment, Harwell, England (1959).

61. Nuclear Safety Quarterly Report, November 1967–January 1968, for Nuclear Safety Branch of USAEC Div. of Reactor Development, USAEC Report BNWL-816, Pacific Northwest Laboratory (September 1968).

62. F. R. ZALOUDEK, "The Low Pressure Critical Discharge of Steam-Water Mixtures from Pipes," USAEC Report HW-68934, Rev., Hanford Works (1961).

63. J. G. BURNELL, "Flow of Boiling Water Through Nozzles, Orifices, and Pipes," *Engineering*, **164**, 572 (1947).

64. J. L. BRIGGS, "Maximum Superheating of Water as a Measure of Negative Pressure," *J. Appl. Phys.*, **26**, 1001 (1955).

65. P. LIEBERMAN and E. A. BROWN, "Pressure Oscillations in a Water Cooled Nuclear Reactor Induced by Water-Hammer Waves," *Trans. ASME, Ser. D, J. Basic Eng.*, **82**, 901 (1960).

66. V. L. STREETER and E. B. WYLIE, *Hydraulic Transients*, McGraw-Hill Book Co., New York (1967).

67. W. D. BAINES and E. G. PETERSON, "An Investigation of Flow Through Screens," *Trans. ASME*, **73**, 467 (1951).

68. D. R. MILLER, "Critical Flow Velocities for Collapse of Reactor Parallel Plate Fuel Assemblies," *Trans. ASME, Ser. A*, **82**, 83 (1960).

69. R. J. SCAVUZZO, "An Experimental Study of Hydraulically Induced Motion in Flat Plate Assemblies," WAPD-BT-25, p. 37, Bettis Atomic Power Laboratory (1962).

70. F. J. REMICK, "Hydraulically Induced Deflection of Flat Parallel Fuel Plates," PhD thesis, Pennsylvania State University (1963).

71. M. W. WAMBSGANSS, "Second Order Effects as Related to Critical Coolant Flow Velocities and Reactor Parallel Plate Fuel Assemblies," *Nucl. Eng. Design*, **5**, *3*, 268 (1967).

72. D. R. MILLER and R. G. KENNISON, "Theoretical Analysis of Flow Induced Vibration of a Blade Suspended in a Flow Channel," Paper No. 66-WAINE-1, presented at December 1966 ASME Annual Meeting.

73. M. W. WAMBSGANSS, "Flow Induced Vibration in Reactor Internals," *Power Reactor Technology and Reactor Fuel Processing*, **10**, *1*, 2 (1966-1967).

74. A. ROSHKO, "Experiments on Flow Past a Circular Cylinder at Very High Reynolds Number," *J. Fluid Mech.*, **10**, 345 (1961).

75. H. ROUSE, "Cavitation and Energy Dissipation in Conduit Expansion," Int. Ass'n. for Hydraulic Research, 11th Congress, Leningrad, Vol. 1, Paper 1.28 (1965).

76. G. J. BOHM, "Natural Vibration of Reactor Internals," *Nucl. Sci. Eng.*, **22**, 143 (1965).

77. D. BURGREEN, J. J. BYRNES, and D. M. BENFORADO, "Vibration of Rods Induced by Water in Parallel Flow," *Trans. ASME*, **80**, 991 (1958).

78. E. P. QUINN, "Vibration of Fuel Rods in Parallel Flow," GEAP-4059, General Electric Co. (1962).

79. H. SOGREAH, "Study of Vibrations and Load Losses in Tubular Clusters," Initial Special Report No. 3, EURATOM Report EURAEC-288, Société Grenobloise d'Etude et d'Applications Hydrauliques, Grenoble, France (1962).

80. R. T. PAVLICA and R. C. MARSHALL, "Vibration of Fuel Assemblies in Parallel Flow," *Trans. Am. Nucl. Soc.*, **8**, 599 (1965).

81. M. P. PAIDOUSSIS, "The Amplitude of Fluid-Induced Vibration of Cylinders in Axial Flow," AECL-2225, Atomic Energy of Canada Ltd. (March 1965).

82. A. E. MORRIS, "A Review on Vortex Streets, Periodic Wakes, and Induced Vibration Phenomena," *Trans. ASME, Ser. C, J. Basic Eng.*, **85**, *1*, 185 (1964).

83. M. P. PAIDOUSSIS, "An Experimental Study of the Vibration of Flexible Cylinders Induced by Axial Flow," *Trans. Am. Nucl. Soc.*, **11**, 352 (1968).

84. Y. N. CHEN, "Flow Induced Vibration and Noise in Tube-Bank Heat Exchangers Due to Von Harman Sheets," ASME Vibration Conf., Paper No. 67-VIBR-48, Boston, Massachusetts (1967).

85. M. RUDDICK, "An Experimental Investigation of the Heat Transfer at High.Rates Between a Tube and Water with Conditions at or near Boiling," PhD thesis, University of London (1953).

86. W. H. LOWDERMILK, C. D. LANZO, and B. L. SIEGEL, "Investigation of Boiling Burnout and Flow Stability for Water Flowing in Tubes," NACA Report TN-4382, National Advisory Committee for Aeronautics (1958).

87. F. MAYINGER, O. SHAD, and E. WEISS, "Research on the Critical Heat Flux (Burnout) in Boiling Water," Final Report, EURATOM Report EURAEC-1811 (1967).

88. G. B. WALLIS, "Some Hydrodynamic Aspects of Two-Phase Flow and Boiling," *Intern. Developments Heat Transfer, Part II, ASME* (1961).

89. D. H. WEISS, "Pressure Drop in Two-Phase Flow," USAEC Report AECU-2180, U.S. Atomic Energy Commission (1952).

90. M. LEDINEGG, "Instability of Flow During Natural and Forced Circulation," AEC-tr-1861, U.S. Atomic Energy Commission, Transl. from *Die Warme*, **61**, 891 (1938).

91. H. H. STENNING and T. N. VEZIROGLU, "Flow Oscillation Modes in Forced Convection Boiling," *Proc. 1965 Heat Transfer and Fluid Mechanics Inst.*, Stanford University Press, Stanford, California (1965).

92. L. G. NEAL and S. M. ZIVI, "Hydrodynamic Stability of Natural Circulation Boiling System, Vol. 1: A comparative Study of Analytical Models and Experimental Data," USAEC Report STL 372-14 (1), TRW Systems, Redondo Beach, California (1965).

93. M. J. SAARI, J. A. HELLER, R. G. DORSCH, P. L. STONE, H. G. HURRELL, M. V. GATSTEIN, and C. H. HAUSER, "Topics in Rankine Cycle Power Systems Technology," *Selected Technology for the Electric Power Industry*, NASA-SP-5057, pp. 35-90, National Aeronautics and Space Administration (1968).

94. F. J. EDESKUTZ and R. S. THURSTON, "Similarity of Flow Oscillation Induced by Heat Transfer in Cryogenic Systems," Symposium on Two-Phase Flow Dynamics, Eindhoven, Holland (1967).

95. A. J. CORNELIUS and J. D. PARKER, "Heat Transfer Instabilities near the Thermodynamic Critical Point," *Proc. of Heat Transfer and Fluid Mechanics Inst.*, Stanford University Press, Stanford, California (1965).

96. B. J. WALKER and D. G. HARDEN, "Heat Driven Pressure and Flow Transients in the Supercritical Thermodynamics Region," ASME Paper No. 64-WA/HT-37 (1964).

97. A. E. BERGLES, P. GOLDBERG, and J. S. MAULBETSCH, "Acoustic Oscillations in a High Pressure Single Channel Boiling System," Symposium on Two-Phase Flow Dynamics, Eindhoven, Holland (1967).

98. E. QUANDT, "Analysis and Measurement of Flow Oscillations," *Chem. Eng. Prog., Symp. Ser.*, 57, **32**, 111 (1961).

99. A. B. JONES and A. G. DIGHT, "Hydrodynamic Stability of a Boiling Channel, Part II," USAEC Report KAPL-2208, Knolls Atomic Power Laboratory (1962).

100. C. L. SPIGT, "On the Hydraulic Characteristics of a Boiling Water Channel with Natural Circulation," WW016-R92, Technological University of Eindhoven (1966).

101. R. P. ANDERSON, L. T. BRYANT, J. C. CARTER, and J. F. MARCHA-TERRE, "Transient Analysis of Two-Phase Natural Circulation Systems," USAEC Report ANL-6653, Argonne National Laboratory (1962).

102. E. S. BECKJORD and S. LEVY, "Hydraulic Instability in a Natural Circulation Loop with Net Steam Generation at 1000 psia," GEAP-3215, General Electric Co. (1959).

103. K. BECKER, R. MATHISEN, O. EKLIND, and B. NORMAN, "Measurements of Hydrodynamic Instabilities, Flow Oscillations, and Burnout in a Natural Circulation Loop," S-316, EAES Symposium on Two-Phase Flow, Studsvik, Sweden (1963).

104. K. C. JAIN, "Self-Sustained Hydrodynamic Oscillations in a Natural Circulation Two-Phase Flow Boiling Loop," PhD thesis, Northwestern University, Evanston, Illinois (1965).

105. J. RANDLES, "Kinetics of Boiling Hydraulic Loops," AEEW-R87, Atomic Energy Establishment, Winfrith, Dorchester, England (1961).

106. K. L. GARLID, "Theoretical Study of Transient Operation and Stability of Two-Phase Natural Circulation Loop," PhD thesis, University of Minnesota, Minneapolis, Minnesota (1961).

107. A. N. NAHAVANDI and R. F. VON HOLLEN, "Flow Stability in Large Vertical Steam Generators," ASME Paper 64-10 A/AUT-11 (December 1964).

108. H. B. CURRIN, C. M. HUNIN, L. RIVLIN, and L. S. TONG, "HYDNA-Digital Computer Program for Hydrodynamic Transients in a Pressure Tube Reactor or a Closed Channel Core," USAEC Report CVNA-77, U.S. Atomic Energy Commission (1961).

109. N. MITSUISHI, S. SAKATA, Y. MATSUDA, Y. YAMAMOTO, and Y. OYAMA, "Studies on Liquid Entrainment," AEC-tr-4225, U.S. Atomic Energy Commission (1961).

110. D. M. NEWITT, N. DOMBROWSKI, and F. H. KNELMAN, "Liquid Entrainment 1. The Mechanism of Drop Formation from Gas or Vapor Bubbles," *Proc. Trans. Inst. Chem. Eng.*, **32,** 244 (1954).

111. L. STERMAN, "Theory of Steam Separation," *I. Tech. Physics* (USSR), **28,** 7 (1958).

112. R. F. DAVIS, "The Physical Aspect of Steam Generation at High Pressures and the Problem of Steam Contamination," *Proc. I. Mech. E.*, **144,** 1198 (1940).

113. J. WILSON and M. McDERMOTT, "Moisture-De-Entrainment Tests in Two and Four Inch Diameter Test Sections," ACNP-5921, Allis Chalmers Mfg. Co. (1959).

114. W. L. HABERMAN and R. K. MORTON, "An Experimental Investigation of the Drag and Shape of Air Bubbles Rising in Various Liquids," DTMB-802, David W. Taylor Model Basin (1953).

4

Heat Transfer and Transport

The reactor coolant removes heat from the core by transferring heat from the fuel elements through convection or boiling, and then transporting the energy to the steam generator. Since the rate of heat transfer depends on the enthalpy of the fluid as well as on the heat flux, we first examine the determination of fluid enthalpy. Expressions useful in describing the axial heat-flux distribution in a reactor core are developed and are then used to compute the amount of heat transported by the coolant as a function of distance through the core. The heat transfer mechanisms that apply during single-phase and two-phase flow are presented, and the cooling of solid moderator and core structure is considered. Extensive tables of water and steam properties are available elsewhere[1,2] and are not repeated here.

4-1 HEAT TRANSPORT

4-1.1 Steady-State Enthalpy Rise Along a Coolant Channel

The axial power distribution of an unperturbed cylindrical reactor core was shown in Chap. 1 to follow a cosine curve; therefore, the local flux q'' can be expressed as a function of q''_{max}, the peak flux. As shown in Fig. 4.1, we define

L_0 = length between $\theta = 0$ and $\theta = \pi$ (half of cosine cycle length)

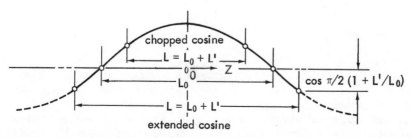

Fig. 4.1 Approximate axial-flux distribution within thermal reactor cores.

181

$L = L_0 + L' = $ actual core length

$L' = $ difference between actual core length and half of cosine cycle length (negative for a chopped cosine)

$Z = $ axial distance from center line.

When $F_Z^N \leq 1.57$, we have

$$q'' = q''_{max} \cos \theta = q''_{max} \cos (\pi Z / L_0) \ . \tag{4-1}$$

Then, by our previous definition for the axial hot-channel factor F_Z^N, we obtain for a chopped cosine distribution

$$F_Z^N = \cfrac{1}{\cfrac{2}{L} \int_0^{L/2} \cos \cfrac{\pi Z}{L_0} dZ} = \cfrac{\pi \left(1 + \cfrac{L'}{L_0}\right)}{2 \sin \cfrac{\pi}{2} \left(1 + \cfrac{L'}{L_0}\right)} \ , \tag{4-2}$$

where $-L/2 \leq Z \leq L/2$ and L' is negative.

For cosine heat flux distribution with reported axial hot-channel factors in excess of 1.57 ($\pi/2$), L' becomes positive. The flux is assigned a value of zero at $Z = \pm L/2$, and we then have

$$q'' = q''_{max} \cfrac{\cos \cfrac{\pi Z}{L_0} - \cos \cfrac{\pi}{2} \left(1 + \cfrac{L'}{L_0}\right)}{1 - \cos \cfrac{\pi}{2} \left(1 + \cfrac{L'}{L_0}\right)} \ , \tag{4-3}$$

where $-L/2 \leq Z \leq L/2$.

Hence, for an extended cosine distribution,

$$F_Z^N = \cfrac{1 - \cos \cfrac{\pi}{2} \left(1 + \cfrac{L'}{L_0}\right)}{\cfrac{2}{L} \int_0^{L-2} \left[\cos \cfrac{\pi Z}{L_0} - \cos \cfrac{\pi}{2} \left(1 + \cfrac{L'}{L_0}\right)\right] dZ}$$

$$= \cfrac{1 - \cos \cfrac{\pi}{2} \left(1 + \cfrac{L'}{L_0}\right)}{\cfrac{2}{\pi \left(1 + \cfrac{L'}{L_0}\right)} \sin \cfrac{\pi}{2} \left(1 + \cfrac{L'}{L_0}\right) - \cos \cfrac{\pi}{2} \left(1 + \cfrac{L'}{L_0}\right)} \ . \tag{4-4}$$

The values of L'/L_0 corresponding to the assigned value of F_Z^N are plotted in Fig. 4.2. Note, since two separate equations are used for defining F_Z^N, there is a change in slope at $L'/L_0 = 0$.

The heat absorbed by the coolant at location Z can be evaluated by taking a heat balance around a differential element and then integrating along the core to obtain

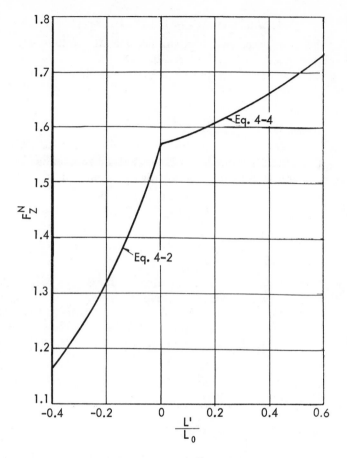

Fig. 4.2   Plot of F_Z^N vs. L'/L_o.

$$\left(D_e/4\right)G\,\Delta H = \int_{-L/2}^{Z} q''_{\max} \cos\left(\pi Z/L_o\right)dZ \ , \tag{4-5}$$

where ΔH = enthalpy at location Z, and inlet enthalpy and D_e and G have their previous meanings.   If the cumulative fraction F of heat absorbed by the coolant is defined as the ratio of heat absorbed at location Z to the total heat generated in the channel, then F can be evaluated by

$$F = \frac{\int_{-L/2}^{Z} q''_{\max} \cos\left(\pi Z/L_0\right)dZ}{\int_{-L/2}^{+L/2} q''_{\max} \cos\left(\pi Z/L_0\right)dZ} \ . \tag{4-6}$$

With this definition of F, the enthalpy of the fluid H at location Z is given by

$$H = H_{in} + [4 \; q''_{max} L/(F_Z^N \; De \; G)] \; F \quad , \tag{4-7}$$

where H_{in} is the inlet enthalpy. The values of F at various distances along a reactor channel are plotted in Fig. 4.3.

As noted in Sec. 1-2.3, a better approximation of an axial flux distribution that has been skewed by rod insertion is sometimes given by

$$q'' = [A + (BZ/L)] \cos(\alpha_0 Z/L) \quad . \tag{4-8}$$

The heat flux is assumed to go to zero at $Z/L = \pi/2\alpha_0$. By assuming that the slope of the flux curve is also zero at this value of Z/L, the constants A and B may be solved for in terms of q''_{max}, and we obtain

$$q'' = 0.54954 \; q''_{max} \left(\frac{\pi}{2} - \frac{\alpha_0 Z}{L} \right) \cos \left(\frac{\alpha_0 Z}{L} \right) \tag{4-9}$$

and

$$F_Z^N = (1.1585) \; \alpha_0/\sin \alpha_0 \quad . \tag{4-10}$$

Equation (4-10) may be used to determine α_0 from the value of F_Z^N. If a distribution skewed toward the top of the core is being considered, the above relations apply with each value of Z/L replaced by its negative value. The foregoing applies so long as F_Z^N is less than 1.82. At higher values, negative fluxes at the core ends will be encountered.

4-1.2 Transient Heat Transport

For a single closed channel, the partial differential equation describing the change in coolant enthalpy H with position Z and time t is again readily obtained by an energy balance around a differential control volume. This yields for a constant ρ

$$\rho \; \frac{\partial U}{\partial t} + G \; \frac{\partial H}{\partial Z} = \frac{q'p}{A} \quad , \tag{4-11}$$

when

$q'' = $ heat flux, Btu/(h ft^2)

$A = $ channel flow area, ft^2

$p = $ heated perimeter of the channel, ft

$\rho = $ fluid density, lb/ft^3

$U = $ internal energy at position Z, Btu/(lb ft^3).

When the system pressure remains constant, Eq. (4-11) may be simplified to

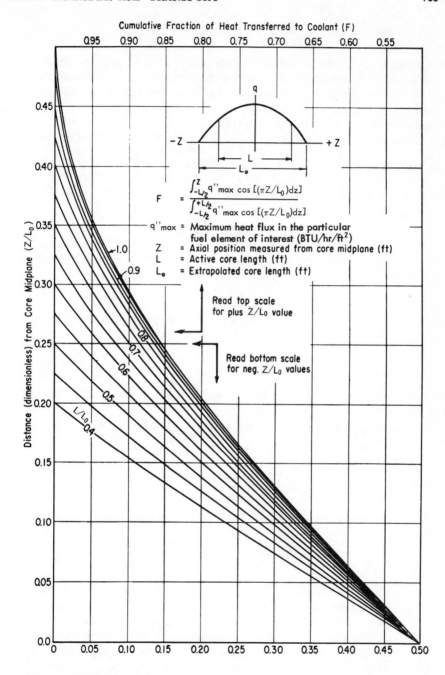

Fig. 4.3 Heat absorbed by coolant along reactor channel. (From *Nucleonics*, **18**, *11*, 170, 1960.)

$$\rho \frac{\partial H}{\partial t} + G \frac{\partial H}{\partial Z} = \frac{q''p}{A} \quad . \qquad (4\text{-}12)$$

For most situations, ρ varies significantly with H, and an analytic solution is not feasible. The usual procedure is to express Eqs. (4-11) or (4-12) in finite difference form in order to obtain a numerical solution. When the coolant remains substantially subcooled, density changes may be negligible, and an analytical solution for flow transients is then possible using the method of "characteristics."

Simple Flow and Power Transients. The method of "characteristics" is applicable to first-order linear partial differential equations of the form

$$S \frac{\partial z}{\partial x} + Q \frac{\partial z}{\partial y} = R \quad , \qquad (4\text{-}13)$$

where S, Q, and R are functions of x and y. It can be shown that the general solution of Eq. (4-13) is of the form

$$F(U_1 U_2) = 0 \quad , \qquad (4\text{-}14)$$

where $U_1 (x,y,z) = C_1$ and $U_2 (x,y,z) = C_2$ are any two independent solutions of

$$\frac{dx}{S} = \frac{dy}{Q} = \frac{dz}{R} \quad . \qquad (4\text{-}15)$$

The intersection of U_1 and U_2 is a characteristic curve whose tangent has the direction numbers $S{:}Q{:}R$.

Let us consider a flow transient where the mass velocity G varies in accordance with

$$G = G_0/(1 + t), \quad t > 0 \quad , \qquad (4\text{-}16)$$

where G_0 is a constant, and both heat flux and inlet enthalpy remain constant with time t. The basic differential equation is given by Eq. (4-12); therefore, our auxiliary equation, which is analogous to Eq. (4-15), is

$$\frac{dt}{\rho} = \frac{dZ}{G} = dH/(q''p/A) \quad . \qquad (4\text{-}17)$$

There are two solutions to this differential equation. We may first consider the behavior of a packet of fluid within the reactor when the transient began. It may be described in terms of the position Z_0, which it had when the transient began. The subsequent positions such a given packet (e.g., Z_{0_1}) will hold are shown by the appropriate lines of Region I in Fig. 4.4. A packet of fluid that had not yet entered the reactor when the transient began may be described in terms of the time t_0, measured from the beginning of the transient

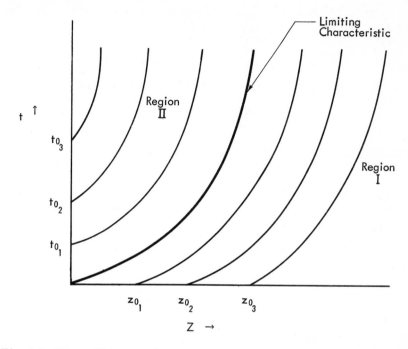

Fig. 4.4   Time—distance relationships during a hypothetical flow transient.

at which the packet does enter the reactor. The position vs time history of a designated packet is shown by a line within Region II of Fig. 4.4. The equations describing the solutions for Regions I and II may be expected to be different. The two regions are separated by the limiting characteristic corresponding to the history of the fluid packet that was just at the reactor inlet when the transient began. We find the solution for Region I by first integrating

$$dt/\rho = dZ/G \tag{4-18}$$

to obtain

$$Z - Z_0 = \int_0^t \frac{G_0}{\rho(1 + t)} \, d\theta = \frac{G_0}{\rho} \ln (1 + t) \ , \tag{4-19}$$

where Z_0 is the axial position of the fluid packet at time zero. From the integration of $dZ/G = dH/(q''p/A)$ we obtain

$$H - H_0 (Z_0) = \int_{Z_0}^{Z} \frac{(1 + t)}{G_0} \left(\frac{q''p}{A} \right) dZ \ , \tag{4-20}$$

where $H_0 (Z_0)$ is the coolant enthalpy at zero time and axial position

Z_0. We may evaluate this quantity from steady-state conditions, and, substituting into Eq. (4-20), we obtain

$$H_{(Z)} = H_{in} + \frac{p}{AG_0} \int_0^{Z_0} q'' dZ + \frac{p}{AG_0} \int_{Z_0}^{Z} (1 + t) q'' dZ \quad , \qquad (4\text{-}21)$$

where H_{in} is the inlet enthalpy. From Eq. (4-19), we have

$$(1 + t) = \exp[\rho/G_0 (Z - Z_0)] \quad , \qquad (4\text{-}22)$$

therefore,

$$H_{(Z)} = H_{in} + \frac{p}{AG_0} \int_0^{Z_0} q'' dZ + \frac{p}{AG_0} \int_{Z_0}^{Z} q'' \exp[\rho/G_0(Z - Z_0)] dZ. \qquad (4\text{-}23)$$

Integration of the equation for the desired flux shape and substitution of the value of Z obtained from Eq. (4-19) provides the desired solution for Region I.

To obtain the solution for Region II, we again begin by integrating Eq. (4-18), but now we consider the fluid that first entered the reactor after the transient began. Since t_0 is the time at which a given packet enters the reactor, we have

$$Z = (G_0/\rho) \int_{t0}^{t} dt/(1 + t) = (G/\rho) \ln[(1 + t)/(1 + t_0)] \quad , \qquad (4\text{-}24)$$

and by rearrangement

$$(1 + t) = (1 + t_0) \exp(\rho Z/G_0) \quad . \qquad (4\text{-}25)$$

Now, from

$$dZ/G = dH/(q'' p/A) \qquad (4\text{-}26)$$

$$H_{(Z)} - H_{in} = [p/(AG_0)] \int_0^{Z} q''(1 + t) dZ \qquad (4\text{-}27)$$

and by substitution for $(1 + t)$, we obtain

$$H_{(Z)} = H_{in} + \frac{p}{G_0 A} \frac{(1 + t_0)}{\exp(\rho Z/G_0)} \int_0^{Z} \exp(\rho Z/G_0) q'' dZ. \qquad (4\text{-}28)$$

The limiting characteristic is obtained by replacing G in terms of G_0 and t in Eq. (4-18) and integrating the resultant equation for both Z and t:

$$\int_0^{T} \frac{dt}{1 + t} = \int_0^{Z} \frac{\rho}{G_0} dZ$$

$$\ln (1 + t) = \frac{\rho Z}{G_0} \quad . \qquad (4\text{-}29)$$

For $t \geq T$, the Region I solution [Eq. (4-23)] holds; for $t \geq T$, the Region II solution [Eq. (4-28)] holds.

Complex Transients. Application of the previous approach requires
a knowledge of the coolant flow as a function of time. This pre-
supposes transient conditions such that the flow through the system
is unaffected by the fluid properties. In many transient situations,
particularly in a loss-of-coolant accident, we cannot assume this
decoupling, and we must consider simultaneously the conservation
of energy, momentum, and mass.

If we assume one-dimensional, homogeneous flow, we may write
the conservation of mass equation as

$$\rho \frac{\partial V}{\partial Z} + \frac{\partial \rho}{\partial t} + V \frac{\partial \rho}{\partial Z} = 0 \qquad (4\text{-}30)$$

and the conservation of momentum as

$$\frac{\partial V}{\partial t} + V \frac{\partial V}{\partial Z} + \frac{g_c}{\rho} \frac{\partial P}{\partial Z} + g_c F = 0 \quad , \qquad (4\text{-}31)$$

where

V = fluid velocity, ft/sec

F = frictional head loss per foot of length (lb force/lb mass ft)

P = pressure, lb/ft^2

and other symbols are as defined previously.

The $\partial P / \partial Z$ may be replaced by recalling that the velocity of sound
a can be obtained from

$$a^2 = g_c \, \partial P / \partial \rho \quad . \qquad (4\text{-}32)$$

For the momentum balance, we then have

$$\frac{\partial V}{\partial t} + V \frac{\partial V}{\partial Z} + \frac{a^2}{\rho} \frac{\partial \rho}{\partial Z} = 0 \quad . \qquad (4\text{-}33)$$

In adiabatic single-phase flow, we would have $a^2 = \rho^{\gamma-1}$ where $\gamma = c_P/c_V$. In actuality, two-phase flow will be encountered under non-
adiabatic conditions. At any given pressure, a is a function of ρ;
therefore, over a narrow pressure and enthalpy range, we can make
the approximation

$$a^2 = \rho^K \quad , \qquad (4\text{-}34)$$

where K = constant. We then can transform the mass and momentum
conservation equations to

$$a \frac{\partial V}{\partial Z} + \frac{2}{K} \left(\frac{\partial a}{\partial t} + V \frac{\partial a}{\partial Z} \right) = 0 \qquad (4\text{-}35)$$

$$\frac{\partial V}{\partial t} + V \frac{\partial V}{\partial Z} + \frac{2A}{K} \left(\frac{\partial a}{\partial Z} \right) + g_c F = 0 \quad . \qquad (4\text{-}36)$$

Our energy equation is now more complex than previously, since ρ may no longer be assumed constant, and we obtain

$$\frac{q''p}{A} = \frac{\partial}{\partial Z}\left[G\left(H + \frac{v^2}{2g}\right)\right] + \frac{\partial}{\partial t}\left[\rho\left(U + \frac{v^2}{2g}\right)\right] \quad . \tag{4-37}$$

If we replace U in terms of H, ρ, and P and use the conservation of mass, Eq. (4-37) may be transformed to

$$\frac{q''p}{A\rho} - \frac{1}{J\rho}\left(\frac{\partial P}{\partial t}\right) = \frac{\partial H}{\partial t} + V\frac{\partial H}{\partial Z} + \left[\frac{V}{2g_c}\left(\frac{\partial V^2}{\partial Z}\right) + \frac{1}{2g_c}\left(\frac{\partial V^2}{\partial t}\right)\right] \quad , \tag{4-38}$$

where J equals the mechanical equivalent of heat, Btu/(ft lb). If the work due to friction may be considered negligible in relation to the other terms in Eq. (4-38), the sum of the terms within the brackets at the right may be shown to be zero; therefore,

$$\frac{q''p}{A\rho} - \frac{1}{J\rho}\left(\frac{\partial P}{\partial t}\right) \approx \frac{\partial H}{\partial t} + V\frac{\partial H}{\partial Z} \quad . \tag{4-39}$$

We may observe that the three conservation equations are quasi-linear partial differential similar to those for which we found the method of characteristics applicable. Indeed, Courant and Friedrichs[3] have shown how the notion of characteristic directions can be extended to n quasi-linear partial differential equations in two independent variables. Although an analytical solution is not possible under general conditions, Lister[4] has shown how the method of characteristics may be used to obtain numerical solutions for flow transients, and Fabic[5] has used the method for analysis of a loss-of-coolant accident.

Let us follow Lister[4] and first consider Eq. (4-35), designated L_1, and Eq. (4-36), designated L_2, assuming a value for K is ~~shown~~ known. We form the linear combination L, where

$$L = \lambda_1 L_1 + \lambda_2 L_2 \quad , \tag{4-40}$$

therefore

$$L = \frac{\partial V}{\partial Z}(a\lambda_1 + V\lambda_2) + \frac{\partial V}{\partial t}(\lambda_2) + \frac{\partial a}{\partial z}(V\lambda_1 + a\lambda_2)(2/K) + \frac{\partial a}{\partial t}\left(\frac{2}{K}\lambda_1\right)$$

$$+ g_c F\lambda_2 = 0 \quad . \tag{4-41}$$

Now let us choose values for λ_1 and λ_2 such that

$$\frac{dt}{dz} = \frac{\lambda_2}{a\lambda_1 + V\lambda_2} = \frac{\lambda_1}{V\lambda_1 + a\lambda_2} \quad . \tag{4-42}$$

Next, we multiply both sides of Eq. (4-41) by dt

$$L\,dt = (\lambda_2)\left(\frac{\partial V}{\partial Z}dZ + \frac{\partial V}{\partial t}dt\right) + \left(\frac{2}{K}\lambda_1\right)\left(\frac{\partial a}{\partial Z}dZ + \frac{\partial a}{\partial t}dt\right) + g_c F\lambda_1 dt \quad , \tag{4-43}$$

But, since $V = V(Z,t)$ and $a = a(z,t)$,

$$dV = \frac{\partial V}{\partial Z} dZ + \frac{\partial V}{\partial t} dt \quad , \quad da = \frac{\partial a}{\partial Z} dZ + \frac{\partial a}{\partial t} dt \quad , \qquad (4\text{-}44)$$

therefore,

$$L\, dt = \lambda_2 dV + \left[(2/K)\lambda_1\right] da + g_c F \lambda_1 dt \quad . \qquad (4\text{-}45)$$

In the expression for L in Eq. (4-41), the derivatives of V and a have been combined to be in the same direction. This direction (dz/dt) is called the "characteristic direction" and is given the symbol ζ. Equation (4-43) can be solved for the ratio λ_1/λ_2

$$-\frac{\lambda_1}{\lambda_2} = \frac{dZ - Vdt}{-adt} = \frac{-adt}{dZ - Vdt} \quad , \qquad (4\text{-}46)$$

hence

$$dZ^2 - 2VdZdt + (V^2 - a^2)dt^2 = 0 \quad . \qquad (4\text{-}47)$$

There are two real solutions for dZ/dt

$$\frac{dZ}{dt} = \zeta_+ = (V + a) \quad , \quad \frac{dZ}{dt} = \zeta_- = (V - a) \quad . \qquad (4\text{-}48)$$

Equation (4-48) defines two families of characteristic curves (designated C_+ and C_-) in the z,t plane. Since ζ_+ and ζ_- are functions only of Z and t, we may substitute these into Eq. (4-46) and combine the results with Eq. (4-41) to obtain

$$dV + (2/K) da - g_c F dt = 0 \qquad (4\text{-}49)$$

and

$$-dV + (2/K) da - g_c F dt = 0 \qquad (4\text{-}50)$$

as the two characteristic equations.

The energy equation must also be written as a total differential equation. We may rewrite Eq. (4-39) to eliminate the pressure term and obtain

$$\frac{q''p}{A\rho} - \frac{a^2}{J\rho g_c} \left(\frac{\partial \rho}{\partial t}\right) = \frac{\partial H}{\partial t} + V \frac{\partial H}{\partial Z} \quad . \qquad (4\text{-}51)$$

If we were to assume temporarily that $(\partial \rho/\partial t)$ is a constant, Eq. (4-51) would be in the form of Eq. (4-13), and we then can make use of Eq. (4-15) to obtain

$$dt = dZ/V \qquad (4\text{-}52)$$

or

$$V = dZ/dt \quad . \qquad (4\text{-}53)$$

Substitution for V in Eq. (4-51) yields

$$\left[\frac{q''p}{A\rho} - \frac{-a^2}{J\rho g_c}\left(\frac{\partial\rho}{\partial t}\right)\right] = \frac{\partial H}{\partial t} + \left(\frac{dZ}{dt}\right)\frac{\partial H}{\partial Z} \quad . \tag{4-54}$$

Upon multiplication by dt, we find the right hand side to be the total differential dH

$$\left[\frac{q''p}{A\rho} - \frac{a^2}{J\rho g_c}\left(\frac{\partial\rho}{\partial t}\right)\right] dt = dH \quad . \tag{4-55}$$

This may be considered a third characteristic equation whose characteristic direction is equal to V.

Lister[4] indicates that numerical solutions can be obtained by using a grid of characteristics or by the method of specified time intervals. The latter appears more easily adaptable to the complex geometries encountered in any real problem. Let us assume that we have divided our system into a series of axial segments of length ΔZ and that we know the values of V, H, ρ and a at the grid locations at time t (points A, B, and C of Fig. 4.5). Now we wish to find the values of the problem parameters at a given location and time $t + \Delta t$ (point P of Fig. 4.5). The curves ζ_+ and ζ_- are two of the characteristic curves through P. Then, if R and S are the intersections of the characteristics with the horizontal line through time t, we have from Eq. (4-48)

$$(Z_p - Z_R) = \zeta_+ (\Delta t)$$

$$(Z_p - Z_S) = \zeta_- (\Delta t) \quad . \tag{4-56}$$

We need the values of V, a, (Z_R,t), and (Z_S,t), which may be estimated by linear interpolation from the values at A, C, and B. We then use a finite difference form of Eq. (4-49) and (4-50) to obtain V and a at point P:

$$(V_P - V_R) + (2/K)(a_P - a_R) - g_c F (t_p - t_R) = 0 \tag{4-57}$$

$$(V_P - V_S) + (2/K)(a_P - a_R) - g_c F (t_p - t_S) = 0 \quad . \tag{4-58}$$

The value of a_p is then used to obtain an updated value for ρ from Eq. (4-34), $\Delta\rho/\Delta t$ and $\Delta P/\Delta t$.

Our energy equation, Eq. (4-55), is the third characteristic ϕ through point P. The position Z_q at which this curve intersects the line through t is obtained from the finite difference form of Eq. (4-53).

$$Z_p - Z_q = V (\Delta t) \quad . \tag{4-59}$$

The enthalpy at point Q is obtained by linear interpolation and used to obtain H_p

$$H_p = \left[\frac{q''p}{A\rho} - \frac{a^2}{J\rho g_c}\left(\frac{\Delta\rho}{\Delta t}\right)\right]\Delta t + H_Q \quad . \tag{4-60}$$

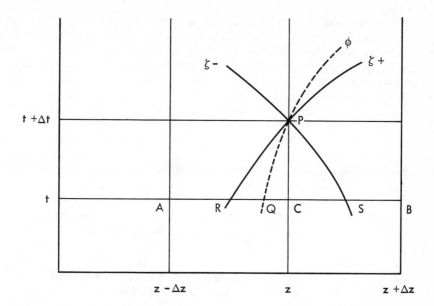

Fig. 4.5   Characteristic curves with grid of specified time intervals.

The new values of ρ, P, and H may then be used to update K, and if necessary, the calculation may be repeated using an improved average value of K. If the change has been small, the calculation proceeds to the next grid point to be evaluated.

The characteristic curves have a direct physical interpretation. The ζ curves may be thought of as compression and rarefaction waves traveling through the system at near sonic velocities, and the ϕ curve represents the transport of thermal energy through the system, which occurs at a rate determined by the fluid velocity. Once we have divided the system into a series of increments, we are no longer completely free in our choice of time step Δt, and it must be such that

$$\Delta t \leqq \Delta Z / (a_{max}) \ , \tag{4-61}$$

where a_{max} represents the maximum value the acoustic velocity has anywhere in the system. Without this restriction, we could not obtain the properties on the characteristic curve at time t by interpolation between the properties at adjacent nodes. In this interpolation, we have assumed that the characteristic curves are linear while in reality they are not. For improved accuracy, quadratic interpolation procedures may be used[4] for determining conditions at points R, Q, and S (see Fig. 4.5).

The method of characteristics is based on the concept of using a series of control volumes for representing the system, and the equations for conservation of mass, energy, and momentum are written for each control volume. An alternate approach is represented by the "node and branch" concept: In electrical and mechanical systems, it is usual to represent a distributed parameter system by a series of nodes connected to each other through a mechanical or electrical resistance. When applied to fluid dynamics, it is assumed that we have a series of spacial elements (nodes) that have capability for energy and mass storage only. The nodes are connected by "branches" that contain the flow resistance and inertance. Thus, the momentum equation is written for each branch while the energy and continuity equations are written for each node. The numerical integration procedures required here are considerably more complicated than those of the method of characteristics.[6]

4-2 FORCED CONVECTION HEAT TRANSFER IN SINGLE-PHASE FLOW

Since we have established the means for determining fluid enthalpy along the reactor core, we now are able to determine the existing heat-transfer regimes. Single-phase forced convection heat transfer is encountered in the inlet and low-power regions of a PWR core where fluid enthalpy is below that of the saturated liquid. It is also encountered on the tube side of the steam generators. The conditions for the onset of boiling are described in detail in Sec. 4-3.

4-2.1 Empirical Equations for Turbulent Heat Transfer

Despite marked progress in the understanding of turbulence, it is not yet possible to make accurate predictions of forced convection heat transfer coefficients from fundamental principles; therefore, empirical correlations must be used for design.

For flow of water inside conduits and annuli, the most extensively used correlation is that if Dittus and Boelter[7]:

$$\left(\frac{hD_e}{k}\right)_b = C \left(\frac{D_e G}{\mu}\right)_b^{0.8} \left(\frac{c_p \mu}{k}\right)_b^n , \qquad (4\text{-}62)$$

where

h = heat transfer coefficient, Btu/(h ft^2 °F)

D_e = equivalent diameter, ft

k = thermal conductivity of fluid, Btu/(h ft $^\circ$F)

c_p = specific heat of fluid, Btu/lb

G = mass velocity, lb/(h ft^2)

μ = fluid viscosity, lb/(h ft)

$C = 0.023$

$\left(\dfrac{D_e G}{\mu}\right) > 10\ 000$ and $L/D_e > 60$

b refers to bulk conditions.

The Dittus-Boelter correlation is also widely used for flow of water parallel to tube banks. The available experimental data indicate that the coefficient of Eq. (4-62) varies with the pitch-to-diameter ratio. The h values obtained from the Dittus-Boelter correlation are slightly conservative for the pitch-to-diameter ratios of interest to reactor designers. Weisman[8] correlated the available data for triangular-pitch lattices by using Eq. (4-62) with

$$C = 0.026\ (S/D) - 0.006 \qquad\qquad (4\text{-}63)$$

and the square-pitch lattice data with

$$C = 0.042\ (S/D) - 0.024\ , \qquad\qquad (4\text{-}64)$$

where

S = tube pitch

D = tube diameter.

The results for both types of lattices may be expressed as

$$C = 0.0333\ E + 0.0127\ , \qquad\qquad (4\text{-}65)$$

where

E = fraction of the total cross-sectional area in an infinite array taken up by the fluid.

Variations in the heat coefficients around the periphery of a rod have been found negligible for S/D ratios greater than 1.2.[9]

While all present PWR cores are designed with flow parallel to the fuel elements, some consideration has been given to the use of cross flow. Cross flow, which provides higher heat transfer coefficients than attainable at the same mass flow rate in parallel flow, is now encountered on the shell side of a once-through steam generator. The heat-transfer data for flow of liquids normal to banks of unbaffled tubes have also been correlated by Weisman.[10] For staggered tube banks, he found

$$\left(\frac{hD}{k}\right) E^{\phi b} = 0.38 \left(\frac{DG_s}{\mu E}\right)_f^{0.61} \left(\frac{c_p \mu}{k}\right)_f^{0.4}, \qquad 300 < \left(\frac{DG_s}{\mu E}\right) < 40\,000 \quad (4\text{-}66)$$

$$\left(\frac{hD}{k}\right) E^{\phi b} = 0.051 \left(\frac{DG_s}{\mu E}\right)_f^{0.8} \left(\frac{c_p \mu}{k}\right)_f^{0.52}, \qquad 80\,000 < \left(\frac{DG_s}{\mu E}\right) < 800\,000, \quad (4\text{-}67)$$

where f refers to film conditions, G_s is the superficial mass velocity based on total cross-section area,

$$b = 0.175\ (DG_s/\mu E)^{-0.07} \quad,$$

and ϕ, which depends on S_t/S_l, the ratio of the tube pitch transverse to the flow to the pitch parallel to the flow direction, is obtained from Fig. 4.6. For in-line tube banks, Weisman obtained

$$\left(\frac{hD}{k}\right) E^{\phi b} = 0.101 \left(\frac{DG_s}{\mu E}\right)_f^{0.745} \left(\frac{c_p \mu}{k}\right)_f^{0.4}, \qquad 2000 < \left(\frac{DG_s}{\mu E}\right) < 30\,000 \ . \quad (4\text{-}68)$$

Again, ϕ is obtained from Fig. 4.6.

Based on data obtained in conduits and annuli, the following correlation of Bishop et al.[11] is recommended for steam at moderately high pressures and Reynolds numbers in parallel flow situations:

$$\left(\frac{hD_e}{k}\right)_f = 0.0073 \left(\frac{D_e G}{\mu}\right)_f^{0.886} \left(\frac{c_p \mu}{k}\right)_f^{0.61} \left(1 + \frac{2.76}{L_h/D_e}\right), \qquad (4\text{-}69)$$

where

L_h = heated length = 30 - 385 ft

P = 1000 - 3190 psi

$$\frac{D_e G}{\mu} = 100\,000 - 0.6 \times 10^6$$

$$\frac{c_p \mu}{k} = 0.88 - 2.38$$

f refers to film conditions $[T = (T_w + T_b)/2]$.

For water flowing in a conduit under supercritical conditions, the Bishop et al. equation[12] is recommended:

$$\left(\frac{hD_e}{k}\right)_b = 0.0069 \left(\frac{D_e G}{\mu}\right)_b^{0.90} \left(\frac{\overline{c_p} \mu}{k}\right)_b^{0.66} \left(\frac{\rho_w}{\rho_b}\right)^{0.43} \left(1 + \frac{2.4}{L/D_e}\right), \quad (4\text{-}70)$$

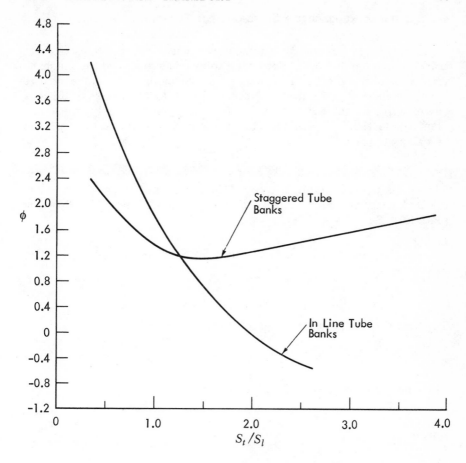

Fig. 4.6 Arrangement coefficients for heat transfer to fluids flowing normal to tube banks. (From *A.I.Ch.E.J.*, **1**, 342, 1955.)

where

$\bar{c}_p = (H_w - H_b)/(T_w - T_b)$ and b and w refer to bulk and wall conditions, respectively.

This correlation was developed from data in the following range:

$q'' = 0.1 \times 10^6$ to 1.1×10^6 Btu/(h ft^2)

$G = 0.5 \times 10^6$ to 2.7×10^6 lb(h ft^2)

$De = 0.10$ to 0.20 in.

$T_b = 561$ to $976°$F

$T_w = 666$ to $1172°$F.

4-2.2 Surface Roughness Effects on Heat Transfer

Most of the reported surface roughness effects on the heat transfer are empirical.[13] However, Kolar[14] has analyzed the mechanism of heat transfer in rough tubes by recognizing that the change in resistance is due to the production of local vortices. Since a vortex will contact the heating surface only momentarily, the transient conduction between the vortex element and the solid wall can be calculated from

$$\partial T/(\partial t) = \alpha \ \partial^2 T/(\partial x^2) \ , \tag{4-71}$$

where α is the thermal diffusivity. The solution of the above equation for sudden temperature change at the surface of an infinitely thick plate is

$$\theta = [2/(\pi)^{1/2}] \ \theta_i \int_0^u \exp(-u^2) dw \ , \tag{4-72}$$

where

$$u = x/[2(\alpha t)^{1/2}] \quad \text{and} \quad \theta_i = (T_{\text{wall}} - T_{\text{vortex}})_{t=0}.$$

The heat flux at the interface ($x = 0$) is then given by

$$q'' = -k \ \frac{\partial \theta}{\partial x} = -k \ \frac{\partial \theta}{\partial u} \frac{\partial u}{\partial x} = -\frac{k\theta_i \ \exp[-x^2/(4\alpha t)]}{(\pi \alpha t)^{1/2}} = \frac{k\theta_i}{(\pi \alpha t)^{1/2}} \ . \tag{4-73}$$

The heat transfer coefficient at a time τ is thus

$$h = q''/\theta_i = k/(\pi \alpha \tau)^{1/2}, \tag{4-74}$$

where

$$\tau = \lambda_0/v_\lambda$$

in which λ_0 is the size of vortex and is called the local degree of turbulence and v_λ is the velocity in fluctuation. At maximum energy dissipation ($v_\lambda = \nu/\lambda_0$) where ν is kinematic viscosity μ/ρ, Eq. (4-74) can be rewritten as

$$h = k(\nu/\alpha)^{1/2}/(\pi^{1/2} \ \lambda_0). \tag{4-75}$$

According to Kolmogorov[15] and Laufer,[16] the value of λ_0 can be evaluated from

$$\lambda_0 = 28 \ \nu/u^* , \tag{4-76}$$

where

$$\nu = \mu/\rho$$

$$u^* = \bar{u} \ (f/8)^{1/2}$$

$$\bar{u} = \text{average fluid velocity.}$$

By substituting Eq. (4-76) into Eq. (4-75) and rearranging, we get

$$hD/k = 0.02 \ (u^*D/\nu) \ (c_p\mu/k)^{0.5} \ . \qquad (4\text{-}77)$$

Note that the above equation is derived for a certain time τ corresponding to that at which maximum energy dissipation occurs. The average heat-transfer coefficient can be determined from the data of Kolar,[14] who studied the effect of surface roughness by heating air and water in tubes 33 to 26 mm in diameter and with roughness ratios (tube radius/projection height) of 26.39, 13.5, and 9.15 as well as in a smooth tube of the same diameter. The roughness was obtained by machining with a 60° triangular thread on the surface. The Reynolds number was varied from 4.5×10^3 to 1.45×10^5 and the Prandtl number from 0.71 to 5.52. Based on his experimental data, Kolar[14] obtained the following equation with an uncertainty of less than 4% in the Re range from 2×10^3 to 1×10^5

$$(hD/k)_f = 0.0517 \ (u^*D/\nu)_f \ (c_p\mu/k)_f^{0.5} \ , \qquad (4\text{-}78)$$

where the subscript f refers to film temperature and

$$u^* = \bar{u} \ (f_f/8)^{1/2}$$

f_f = friction factor = $0.515 \ (e/D)^{0.63}$ for $Re_f > 3 \times 10^4$

e_{avg} = height of projections above surface.

More recently, Wilkie[13] has reported heat-transfer and pressure-drop data collected from annuli with heated roughened inner and unheated smooth outer surface. The various inner surfaces tested were roughened by transverse square and rectangular ribs. Rib heights varied from 0.1 to 1.6% of D_e and pitch to height ratios from 2.5 to 50. His results are presented as a series of curves.

4-2.3 Turbulence Promoter and Grid Spacer Effects

Although higher coolant-mixing rates and heat-transfer coefficients are induced by grids due to the promotion of turbulence, hot spots generally occur at grids or spacers. Wilkie and White[17] have reported that, in air flow, a 25% reduction in the local heat transfer coefficient is introduced by grids; the hot spot occurring immediately downstream of the grid. The reduction in the heat-transfer coefficient is caused by the local retardation of the flow over the heating surface. Owing to the complicated configuration of grid spacers, the local velocity profile is usually determined experimentally. The net benefit of a turbulence promoter or a grid spacer depends on the balance of the following benefits and penalties:

1. benefit from flow mixing between adjacent channels

2. benefit from the increase of the average heat transfer coefficient

3. benefit from the increase in the critical heat flux by wiping off the bubble layer

4. penalty of having a local hot spot

5. penalty of a higher pumping power

6. penalty of forming a flow stagnation point.

Therefore, the design of turbulence promoters should vary with geometry and flow conditions, and no general design criterion can now be established or followed.

4-3 BOILING HEAT TRANSFER

Although the earliest core designs were based on the assumption that surface boiling could not be allowed, this limitation was soon discarded, and boiling heat transfer is now one of the steady-state heat transfer mechanisms in the PWR core.

4-3.1 Flow Boiling Heat Transfer

Heating a liquid at a very high heat flux will bring the heater wall temperature above that of the liquid's saturation point. The liquid adjacent to the wall is then superheated and nucleation sites are activated. Bubbles are generated in patches while forced convection persists in the remaining area. This heat transfer region is referred to as "partial nucleate boiling." If the heat flux is increased, bubbles are generated over a larger part of the surface until, at "fully developed nucleate boiling," bubbles are generated over the entire surface. If the bulk of the liquid is subcooled, the nucleate boiling is called local boiling and the bubbles formed condense locally. If the liquid is saturated, the bubbles do not collapse and this is called "bulk boiling."

In fully developed nucleate boiling, the wall temperature is determined by the heat flux and pressure but not by the liquid velocity. This independence of liquid velocity is illustrated in Fig. 4.7. For subcooled water at pressures between 30 and 90 psia, McAdams[18] correlated the available data by

$$q'' = 0.074 \ (T_w - T_{sat})^{3.86}, \qquad (4\text{-}79)$$

where

$q'' = $ heat flux Btu/(h ft^2)

T_w = wall temperature, °F

T_{sat} = saturation temperature, °F.

For pressure between 500 and 2000 psia, Jens and Lottes[19] correlated subcooled boiling data by

$$(T_w - T_{sat}) = 60 \ (q''/10^6)^{1/4}/[\exp(P/900)] , \qquad (4\text{-}80)$$

where P is the pressure in psia. The correlation appears to hold for all geometries and both local and bulk boiling. Rohsenow[20] has also correlated nucleate boiling coefficients, but the correlation of Jens and Lottes appears to have been preferred by most workers in the field.

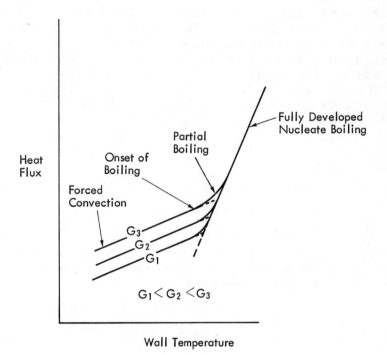

Fig. 4.7   Onset of boiling heat transfer.

More recently, there has been concern that the temperature differences predicted by the Jens-Lottes correlation are too low at high pressures. Thom et al.[21] concluded that their extensive data, at pressures from 750 to 2000 psia, were best correlated by

$$(T_w - T_{sat}) = 0.072 \ (q')^{1/2}/[\exp(P/1260)] .$$

The temperature differences predicted by this correlation tend to be higher than those obtained from Eq. (4-80).

McAdams[18] has defined the onset of fully developed nucleate boiling as the intersection of the fully developed boiling curve and the forced convection curve (Fig. 4.7). Kutateladze[22] has proposed a relationship between temperature and heat flux for the partial nucleate boiling region. However, the region is small, and, for most design purposes, it is adequate to take the onset of nucleate boiling as the condition where the forced convection wall temperature equals the fully developed nucleate boiling temperature.

At high-vapor fractions, the flow pattern in tubes is such that a vapor core exists surrounded by an annulus of water. The velocity of vapor in the core can be so high that the very high turbulence at the vapor-liquid interface causes the heat-transfer mechanism to change character. Evaporation now occurs at the liquid-vapor core interface, and, as is characteristic of non-boiling heat transfer, the heat transfer coefficient varies strongly with flow. This heat transfer region has been referred to as "forced convection vaporization."

The suppression of nucleate boiling occurs at high values of the liquid Reynolds numbers Re and $1/X_{tt}$, where X_{tt} is the Lockhart-Martinelli parameter,

$$1/X_{tt} = \left[\chi/(1 - \chi) \right]^{0.9} \left[\rho_l /(\rho_v) \right]^{0.5} (\mu_v/\mu_l)^{0.1} \qquad (4\text{-}81)$$

and

χ = steam quality

ρ_l, ρ_v = density of liquid and vapor

μ_l, μ_v = viscosity of liquid and vapor.

Chen[23] proposed a correlation where the heat-transfer coefficient h in this region is the sum of a nucleate boiling component and a forced convection component; thus,

$$h = S\,(0.00122)\, \frac{k_l^{0.79}\, c_l^{0.45}\, \rho_l^{0.49}\, g_c^{0.25}\, \Delta T^{0.24}\, \Delta P^{0.75}}{\sigma^{0.5}\, \mu_l^{0.29}\, H_{fg}^{0.24}\, \rho_v^{0.24}}$$

$$+\, F(0.023)\, \mathrm{Re}_l^{0.8}\, \mathrm{Pr}_l^{0.4}\, k_l/D_e \qquad (4\text{-}82)$$

c_l = specific heat of liquid

D_e = equivalent diameter

g_c = gravitational conversion factor

ΔP = difference in saturation pressures corresponding to wall superheat

H_{fg} = heat of vaporization

Re$_l$ and Pr$_l$ = Reynolds and Prandtl numbers, respectively, based on liquid properties

k_l = conductivity of liquid

$\Delta T = (T_{wall} - T_{sat})$, wall superheat

σ = surface tension.

The left-hand term represents the nucleate boiling component, and S, given by Fig. 4.8, is the nucleate boiling suppression factor. The right-hand term is the forced convection component, and it varies with F, which is a function of $1/X_{tt}$(Fig. 4.9).

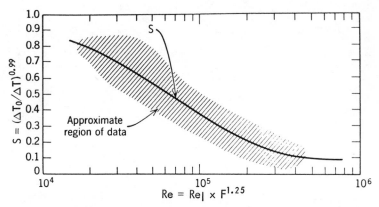

Fig. 4.8 Suppression factor S for Chen correlation. (From Tong, *Boiling Heat Transfer and Two-Phase Flow*, John Wiley & Sons, New York, 1965.)

4-3.2 The Boiling Crisis

The nucleate boiling heat flux cannot be increased indefinitely. At some critical flux, the steam produced forms an insulating layer over the surface and raises the surface temperature. This is the "boiling crisis." Immediately after the critical flux has been reached, boiling is unstable and partial film boiling or transition boiling occurs. Here, the surface is successively covered by a vapor film and a liquid layer. The surface temperature finally increases sufficiently to cause the formation of a stable vapor layer, which produces "stable film boiling."

The term "boiling crisis" is not in universal use. The phenomenon is also referred to as "burnout" because early tests detected the crisis by the physical failure of electrically heated test elements. The boiling crisis may be classified as "departure from nucleate

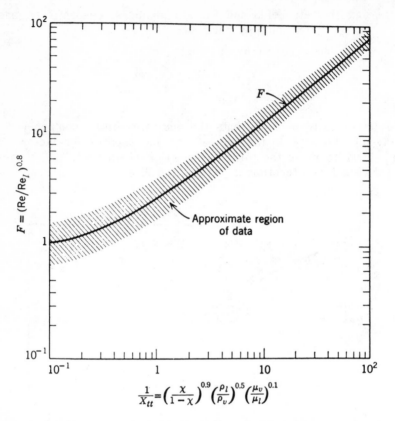

Fig. 4.9 Reynolds number factor F for Chen correlation. (From Tong, *Boiling Heat Transfer and Two-Phase Flow*, John Wiley & Sons, New York, 1965.)

boiling" (DNB) in the subcooled or low-quality region and "dryout" in the high-quality region.

The behavior of the boiling crisis is dependent on flow conditions. In the subcooled or low-quality region, the crisis occurs at a relatively high heat flux and appears to be associated with the cloud of bubbles, adjacent to the surface, that reduces the amount of incoming water. When this crisis occurs, the surface temperature rises rapidly to a high value.

In the high-quality region, the crisis occurs at a lower heat flux. The flow pattern is usually annular, and the surface is normally covered by a liquid layer. When the evaporation rate is high enough, the liquid layer may develop a dry patch when the boiling crisis occurs. Since the velocity in the vapor core is high, the heat transfer is much better than for the low quality cases, and wall temperature rises are lower and less rapid.

Design Correlation. Various attempts have been made to develop analytical approaches for predicting the boiling crisis, and the greatest success has been obtained when the boiling crisis is at high-quality annular flow. Here, the models are based upon the prediction of a dryout of the liquid film on the wall.[24-26] However, no model to date has lead to correlations entirely satisfactory for design use at the qualities expected during PWR operation. Reliance must still be placed on empirical correlations of experimental data.

For the range of interest of most power reactor designs, Tong[27] has developed the following correlation for uniformly heated chan-nels:

$$\frac{q''_{DNB,\,EU}}{10^6} = \{(2.022 - 0.0004302P) + (0.1722 - 0.0000984P)$$

$$\times \exp[(18.177 - 0.004129P)\chi]\}$$
$$\times [(0.1484 - 1.596\chi + 0.1729\chi\,|\chi\,|)\,G/10^6 + 1.037]$$
$$\times [1.157 - 0.869\chi] \times [0.2664 + 0.8357\,\exp(-3.151D_e)]$$
$$\times [0.8258 + 0.000794\,(H_{sat} - H_{in})]\,, \tag{4-83}$$

where

$$P = 1000 \text{ to } 2300, \text{ psia}$$
$$G = 1.0 \times 10^6 \text{ to } 5.0 \times 10^6, \text{ lb/(h ft}^2)$$
$$D_e = 0.2 \text{ to } 0.7, \text{ in.}$$
$$\chi_{loc} \leqq 0.15$$
$$H_{in} \geqq 400 \text{ Btu/lb}$$
$$L = 10 \text{ to } 144, \text{ in.}$$
$$\frac{\text{heated perimeter}}{\text{wetted perimeter}} = 0.88 \text{ to } 1.00$$
heat flux is in Btu/(h ft^2) .

Tong was able to extend this correlation to channels with a nonuniform axial flux distribution by

$$q''_{DNB,\,N} = q''_{DNB,\,EU}/F\,, \tag{4-84}$$

where

$q''_{DNB,N}$ = DNB heat flux for the nonuniformly heated channel

$q''_{DNB,EU}$ = equivalent uniform DNB flux from Eq. (4-83)

and

$$F = \frac{C}{q''_{local} \left[1 - \exp(-Cl_{DNB,EU})\right]} \int_0^{l_{DNB}} q''(z) \, \exp[-C \, (l_{DNB,N} - z)] dz$$

$$C = 0.44 \frac{(1 - \chi_{DNB})^{7.9}}{(G/10^6)^{1.72}} \text{ in.}^{-1} \tag{4-85}$$

l_{DNB} = axial location at which DNB occurs, in.

This approach successfully correlates a wide variety of nonuniform flux distribution data.

Tong[28] notes there is theoretical justification for this approach since the flow, particularly the boundary-layer region, coming from the upstream region carries superheat and bubbles with it when it contacts the downstream surface. The upstream heat-flux distributions thus affect the boundary layer at the DNB position. This "memory effect" is conveyed by means of the F factor. In the subcooled region, where the value of C in Eq. (4-85) will be large, the F factor will be small and the local heat flux determines the boiling crisis. At high qualities, C is small and the memory effect high, and the average heat flux, or enthalpy rise, primarily determines the boiling crisis.

Other investigators have generally assumed that the boiling crisis is determined solely by local conditions. Janssen and Levy[29] have proposed for 1000 psia,

$$\frac{q''_{crit}}{10^6} = 0.705 + 0.237 \, (G/10^6) \qquad \text{for } \chi < x_1 \tag{4-86}$$

$$\frac{q''_{crit}}{10^6} = 1.634 - 0.270 \, (G/10^6) - 4.710\chi \text{ for } x_1 < \chi < x_2 \tag{4-87}$$

$$\frac{q''_{crit}}{10^6} = 0.605 - 0.164 \, (G/10^6) - 0.653\chi \text{ for } x_2 < \chi , \tag{4-88}$$

where
$$\chi = \text{quality}$$
$$x_1 = 0.197 - 0.108 \, (G/10^6)$$
$$x_2 = 0.254 - 0.026 \, (G/10^6) , \tag{4-89}$$

and, for other pressures,

$$q''_{crit} \text{ (at } P) = q''_{crit} \text{ (at 1000 psia)} + 440 \, (1000 - P) . \tag{4-90}$$

The parameter ranges are

$P = 600$ to 1450 psia

$G = 0.4 \times 10^6$ to 6.0×10^6 lb/(h ft^2)

χ = negative to +0.45

D_e = 0.245 to 1.25 in.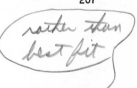

L = 29 to 108 in.

These design equations are stated to be a lower envelope of the data. More recently, Healzer et al.[30] have presented a revised set of lower envelope curves.

For subcooled boiling conditions, Bernath[31] has developed a correlation of the boiling crisis data based on the concept of turbulent mixing. He considered the heat-transfer mechanism to be convection across a homogeneous mixture as given by

$$q''_{crit} = h_{crit} (T_{w, \, crit} - T_{bulk}) , \qquad (4\text{-}91)$$

and he developed a correlation for both the critical wall temperature $T_{w, \, crit}$ and the critical heat-transfer coefficient h_{crit}:

$$T_{w, \, crit} = 1.8 \left\{ 57 \ln P - 54 \left[P/(1 + 15) \right] - V/4 \right\} + 32 \qquad (4\text{-}92)$$

$$h_{crit} = 10\ 890 \left[D_e/(D_e \pm D_i) \right] + 48V/(D_e^{0.6}) \quad \text{for } D_e \leqq 0.1 \text{ ft} , \quad (4\text{-}93)$$

where

P = system pressure (psi)

V = coolant velocity (ft/sec)

T = temperature (°F)

h = heat transfer coefficient $[\text{Btu}/(\text{h ft}^2 \text{ °F})]$

D_e and D_i = the hydraulic and inner diameter (ft).

The range of parameters covered is

P = 23 to 3000 psia

V = 4.0 to 54 ft/sec

D_e = 0.143 to 0.66 in.

The correlation of h_{crit} has been extended to fluids other than water with good success.

The Bettis Atomic Power Laboratory[32] has developed a design equation for water flowing in the narrow (approximately 0.1 in.) rectangular channels used in the Shippingport core. This critical heat flux $[\text{Btu}/(\text{h ft}^2)]$ is given by

$$q''_{crit} /10^6 = K[(H' - H)^{1/2}/(H' - H_0)]^{1/2}, \qquad (4\text{-}94)$$

where

$$K = 0.84 \left\{ 1 + \left[(2000 - P)/800 \right]^2 \right\}$$

$H_0 = 655 - 0.004 \, (2000 - P)^{1.63}$

$H' = H_v - 0.275 \, H_{fg} - 0.725 \, H_{fg} \, (300/H_{fg})^{10^6/G}$

and

H_{fg} = heat of vaporization, Btu/lb

H_v = enthalpy of saturated vapor, Btu/lb

P = pressure, psia.

Additional design correlations used in the United States have been proposed by Wilson and Ferrell,[33] and Bell.[34] The Wilson and Ferrell correlation is

$$q''_{crit} = F_p A \left[(G/B) \, (S/L)^n \right] \exp \left[a + b \, (\Delta T_{sub})_{in} + c \, (\Delta T_{sub})^2_{in} \right] , \quad (4\text{-}95)$$

where $(\Delta T_{sub})_{in}$ is the subcooling at the inlet to the heated section.

The constants depend on whether one has a round tube or rectangular channel:

$$F_p = (1.83 - 0.000415 \, P), \quad 800 \leqq P) \leqq 2000 \text{ psia} .$$

	Rectangular Channel	*Round Tube*
A	150 000	90 000
B	90	240
n	1.2	1.0
a	0.44	0.3987
b	0.00073	0.001036
c	0	-1.027×10^6
S	width	i.d.

The Bell correlation for all enthalpies is

$$\frac{q''_{crit}}{10^6} = 0.427 \left(2.59 + \frac{G}{10^6} \right)^{1.81} \left(\frac{H_v - H_{crit}}{10^3} \right)^{1.77} \left(\frac{G}{10^6} \right)^{0.406} , \qquad (4\text{-}96)$$

for $H \geqq$ Btu/lb

$$\frac{q''_{crit}}{10^6} = 1.37 \left(1.19 + \frac{G}{10^6} \right)^{1.44} \left(\frac{H_v - H_{crit}}{10^3} \right)^{1.67} \left(\frac{G}{10^6} \right)^{0.474} , \qquad (4\text{-}97)$$

where

P = 2000 psia

G = 0.2 to 5.0×10^6 lb/(h ft^2)

H_{crit} = 540 to 1000 Btu/lb.

Numerous other empirical correlations have been proposed, and a full review of these is provided by Tong.[28]

Cross Flow. Since heat transfer coefficients in cross flow are higher than in parallel flow, one might expect a similar effect for the critical heat flux. Coffield et al.[35] examined critical heat fluxes in a crossed-rod matrix cooled by Freon 113, and they found the critical flux to be about 200% higher than those obtained in parallel flow at the same mass velocity and liquid subcooling.

Kezios et al.[36] studied critical heat fluxes with flow normal to a single heated rod in contact with a matrix of unheated rods and correlated their data by

$$q''_{crit} = 7.37 \times 10^3 \, (G/3600)^{0.53} \, \Delta T_{sc} \, (S/D)^{-0.4} \, , \qquad (4\text{-}98)$$

where

G = mass velocity, $lb/(h \, ft^2)$

ΔT_{sc} = local subcooling, °F

(S/D) = rod pitch/rod diameter.

Transient Effects. The investigations upon which the previous correlations are based have all been steady state. The application of steady-state data to the prediction of transient data has been investigated by Martenson,[37] who found that his measured points fell above the predictions of the Bernath correlation.[31] Transient critical heat fluxes were also examined by Schrock et al.[38] for water flowing at 1 ft/sec at pressures of 1000 and 500 psia. In each case, the electrical power to the rod was increased in accordance with a known exponential period τ. Redfield[39] suggested a transient boiling crises based on these data and Bernath's correlation. He proposed

$$q''_{crit} = [12\,300 + (67 \, V/D_e{}^{0.6})] \, \{102.5 \ln P - 97 \, [P/(P + 15)] + 32 - T_{bulk}\}$$
$$\times \, [\exp(4.25/\tau)] \, , \qquad (4\text{-}99)$$

where all terms are as previously defined.

More recently, Cermak et al.[40] examined the applicability of steady-state data to simulated blowdown runs. Their study was conducted using a 21-rod bundle and covered pressures between 750 and 1500 psia, inlet temperatures from 480 to 540°F, and mass velocities from 1×10^6 to $3 \times 10^6 \, lb/(h \, ft^2)$. They found their transient and steady-state data to be in good agreement provided the comparisons were made using the transient enthalpy, flow, and pressure. They concluded that predictions based on steady-state data provided conservative estimates of the transient observations since, in most cases, their data were equal to, or slightly greater than, the predictions obtained from a steady-state correlation.

Film Boiling. As previously noted, the heat-transfer regime that exists after the critical heat flux has been exceeded is referred to as film boiling. If the critical heat flux were to be exceeded at full reactor power, the low film-boiling heat-transfer coefficients would cause the fuel cladding temperature to rise rapidly to its melting point. Since every precaution is taken to ensure that the design conditions are well below those at which the critical heat flux occurs, the onset of film boiling at normal power is very unlikely.

In the analysis of accident situations, particularly the loss-of-coolant accident, the possibility of film boiling must be considered. Since the reactor is shut down promptly after initiation of the accident, the power level of the reactor may be reduced significantly when the critical flux is exceeded. Film-boiling heat-transfer coefficients must be computed in order to estimate the temperature rise of the cladding. Under proper conditions, the reactor heat flux may be sufficiently reduced so that nucleate boiling conditions may be restored before damage to the fuel occurs. This phenomenon is referred to as "return to nucleate boiling" (RNB).

At the onset of film boiling, an unstable mix of nucleate and film boiling exists, and this is referred to as "partial film boiling." Sparse data exist applicable to the partial film-boiling regime. Most designers have assumed conservatively that stable film boiling begins as soon as the critical heat flux is exceeded. Tong[41] has proposed a simplified correlation of transition boiling-heat transfer to water at a pressure of 2000 psia

$$h = h_{FB} + 16\ 860\ \exp[-0.01\ (T_{\text{wall}} - T_{\text{sat}})]\ ,\qquad (4\text{-}100)$$

where

T_{wall} , T_{sat} = wall and saturation temperatures, respectively

h_{FB} = stable film-boiling heat-transfer coefficients obtained from applicable correlation of succeeding paragraphs.

When the heat-transfer surface is entirely covered by a stable steam film, we have what is called "stable film boiling." At fairly low wall temperatures, it is possible for droplets to wet the surface. At the "Leidenfrost point," the surface becomes so hot that the rapidly evaporating steam between the liquid droplet and heater forms a vapor cushion that supports the drops and keeps the liquid away from the surface.

Flow Film Boiling. If there is a high-velocity flow, such as in the early stages of a loss-of-coolant accident, it is to be expected that liquid droplets will strike the wall. If the droplets can wet the wall, the heat transfer will be enhanced. Thus, Parker and Grosh[42] noted that, with a steam-water mixture at 30 psia and a wall superheat of less than 50°F, the heat-transfer coefficient was three to six times the value for dry steam flowing at the same conditions. Above

50°F superheat, they observed heat-transfer coefficients almost identical to those for pure steam. From these data and those of Bennet et al.[43] and Bertoletti et al.[44] it appears that the Leidenfrost point increases from about 300°F at 30 psia to about 560°F at 250 psia and to 750 to 800°F at 1000 psia. Thus, the allowable wall superheat increases from about 50°F at 30 psia to 160°F at 250 psia and to about 250°F at 1000 psia.

For film boiling at high-mass velocities, particularly when the wall temperature is below the Leidenfrost point, the following correlation of Bishop et al.[45] is suggested:

$$\left(\frac{hD_e}{k}\right)_f = 0.0193 \left(\frac{D_e G}{\mu}\right)_f^{0.80} \left(\frac{c_p \mu}{k}\right)_f^{1.23} \left(\frac{\rho_v}{\rho_{\text{bulk}}}\right)^{0.68} \left(\frac{\rho_v}{\rho_{l\,\text{sat}}}\right)^{0.068}, \qquad (4\text{-}101)$$

where f refers to film temperature, which equals $(T_w + T_b)/2$; v refers to the vapor phase; and l_{sat} to the saturated liquid. This correlation was developed from data in the following ranges:

$q'' = 0.11 \times 10^6$ to 0.61×10^6 Btu/(h ft^2)

$G = 0.88 \times 10^6$ to 2.5×10^6 lb/(h ft^2)

$P = 580$ to 3190 psia

$D_e = 0.10$ to 0.32 in.

$T_b = 483$ to 705°F

$T_w = 658$ to 1100°F.

For lower mass velocities, the following correlation, suggested by Tong and reported by Bishop et al.[46], is recommended:

$$hD_e/(K_{w,v}) = 0.005 \left[D_e \, V_m \, \rho_{w,v}/(\mu_{w,v})\right] \left[c_p \mu/(k_{w,v})\right]^{1/2}, \quad (4\text{-}102)$$

where

V_m = mixture velocity

$\mu_{w,v}$ = vapor viscosity at wall temperature

$k_{w,v}$ = vapor thermal conductivity at wall temperature

$\rho_{w,v}$ = vapor density at wall temperature.

The range of parameters used in developing the correlation were

$$500 \leqq \text{Re} \leqq 50\,000$$

$$1500 \leqq P \leqq 2200 \text{ psia} .$$

At lower pressures and low flows the correlation of Bertoletti et al.[44] may be used. They correlated the film boiling data at 1000 psia by

$$q'' \left[(2.54 \, D_e)^{0.2}/(0.000135 \, G\chi)^{0.8}\right] = 34 \, \Delta T_{\text{sat}}^{0.921}, \qquad (4\text{-}103)$$

where χ equals quality, $\Delta T_{sat} \geqq 360°F$, and $0.1 < G/10^6 < 0.74$ lb/ (h ft^2).

Polomik et al.[47] correlated the film-boiling data obtained during the annular flow regime at pressures from 800 to 1400 psia by

$$(hD_e/k)_f = 0.0036 \left[\text{Re}_f \left[(1 - x)/x \right] \right]^{0.853} \left[\alpha/(1 - \alpha) \right] (\text{Pr}_f)^{1/3}, \quad (4\text{-}104)$$

where all properties are evaluated at the film temperature.

At very high qualities, the coolant may be considered a mist. If the wall temperature is definitely above the Leidenfrost temperature, any droplet touching the wall will "sputter" away from the surface. Little error is introduced by evaluating the heat-transfer coefficient considering the steam flow only. A correlation for steam film coefficients such as that of McEligot et al.[48] may be used. They recommended

$$h = 0.020 \, (k/D_e) \, (\text{Re}_b)^{0.8} \, (\text{Pr}_b)^{0.4} \, (T_b/T_w)^{0.5}, \quad (4\text{-}105)$$

where b indicates bulk steam temperature and w, the wall temperature. Reynolds number, Prandtl number, and k would all be based on steam flow and properties only.

Pool Boiling. When the core is recovered at the end of a loss-of-coolant accident, the liquid mass-flow rates are low. At that point, the heat-transfer mechanism may be considered to be that of pool-film boiling. At pressures significantly above atmospheric, the following laminar-film boiling correlation of Borishanski and Fokin[49] is recommended:

$$h = (Fk_v/\delta_v) \left\{ (k_v g \delta_v^3/\nu_v) \left[(\gamma_l - \gamma_v)/\gamma_v \right] \right\}^n, \quad (4\text{-}106)$$

where

k_v = thermal conductivity of vapor

γ_l = specific gravity of liquid

γ_v = specific gravity of vapor

ν_v = kinematic viscosity of vapor

δ_v = mean vapor film thickness

$\quad = 31[\sigma/(\gamma_l - \gamma_v)]^{0.5} \left[q'' \mu/(H_{fg} \gamma_v \, \sigma) \right]^{0.53}$

H_{fg} = latent heat of vaporization

σ = surface tension

μ = viscosity of vapor

q'' = heating rate

and

$$\left. \begin{array}{l} F = 2.8 \\ n = 0.33 \end{array} \right\} \quad \text{for} \quad 2 \times 10^4 \left[\frac{g\delta_v^3}{\nu_v} \left(\frac{\gamma_l - \gamma_v}{\gamma_v} \right) \right] < 1.4 \times 10^6$$

$$F = 0.0094 \atop n = 0.57 \Bigg\} \quad \text{for } 1.4 \times 10^6 < \left[\frac{g \delta_v^3}{\nu_v} \left(\frac{\gamma_l - \gamma_v}{\gamma_v} \right) \right] < 1.5 \times 10^7 \quad .$$

Bromley[50] correlated the data for pool boiling at low pressures by an equation that was later modified slightly by Hsu and West-water[51], for vertical surfaces

$$h = 0.7 \left\{ \left[k_v^3 \, \rho_v \, (\rho_l - \rho_v) g H_{fg} \right] / (L \, \Delta T \, \mu_v) \right\}^{0.25} \quad , \qquad (4\text{-}107)$$

where

H_{fg} = heat of vaporization, Btu/lb

L = heated length, ft

$\Delta T = T_{\text{wall}} - T_{\text{bulk}}$

and the subscripts

v = vapor property

l = liquid property.

The equation is similar to that derived theoretically by Ellion.[52]

Radiative Heat Transfer. For film boiling conditions, the surface temperature may rise to the point where radiative heat transfer is significant. The foregoing equations describe the convective heat transfer only, but the radiation coefficient appropriate to the geometry should be included. For this purpose the empirical method of Hottel[53] is recommended.

For the simple geometry of a circular pipe, we may write

$$q''_{\text{total}} = h_c \, (T_w - T_{\text{sat}}) + \epsilon \; 1.73 \times 10^{-9} \, (T_w^4 - T_{\text{sat}}^4) \quad , \qquad (4\text{-}108)$$

where

h_c = appropriate convective heat transfer coefficient

ϵ = effective emissivity $= \left\{ \dfrac{1}{\epsilon_w} + \left[\dfrac{1}{\epsilon_v \alpha + (1-\alpha)\epsilon_l} \right] - 1 \right\}^{-1}$

α = void fraction

ϵ_w = emissivity of wall

ϵ_v = emissivity of steam

ϵ_l = emissivity of liquid.

4-3.3 Effects of Crud Deposition

During the operation of any water system at high temperatures, corrosion products are generated. The metallic ions rapidly hydrolyze to form insoluble hydroxides that partially decompose to the oxides. This insoluble material is referred to as "crud." Most of the crud is removed by the purification system, but a portion is deposited on loop and core surfaces. There is some evidence that it is deposited preferentially on the surfaces with the highest heat flux, and the effect of the crud deposition on core heat transfer naturally concerns the thermal designer.

A comparison of convective and nucleate boiling-heat transfer from clean and crudded vertical surfaces at atmospheric pressure is illustrated in Fig. 4.10. The data were obtained from crudded surfaces formed under conditions believed to simulate those of a PWR.[54] It will be noted that a decrease in convective heat transfer was observed and that nucleate boiling began at lower wall temperatures. The results obtained may be expected to depend on conditions under which the crud was deposited. Weisman et al.[55] observed that a crud deposit can form an insulating layer on heater rods; however, the crud contained an appreciable quantity of magnesium oxide from a ruptured preheater and was deposited on rods bearing an electric potential. Such conditions are not representative of those in a reactor core.

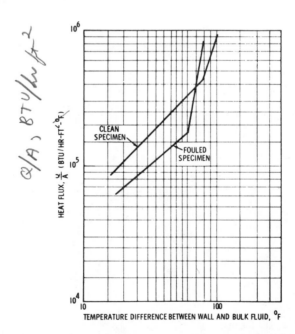

Fig. 4.10 Effect of subcooling on heat transfer from clean and crudded electrically heated cylindrical specimens. (From *Trans. ASME, Ser. C, J. Heat Transfer,* **89,** 242, 1967.)

The effect of crud deposition on the boiling crisis was tested by Cohen and co-workers[56] using a 45-in. long 0.375-in. electrically heated tube. To establish a basis for comparison, tests were also conducted before the application of crud. Although the effects of crud were small, the results seemed to indicate a slight increase in the DNB heat flux.

Goldstein[57] has reported on the results of high-pressure boiler tests in which contaminants were added to the water. He observed that under some conditions deposition of contaminants resulted in DNB where nucleate boiling had been obtained with clean surfaces. The effect was found to be temporary with conditions returning to normal over a period of several hours after the contaminant was added.

The effect of crud deposition on the flow through the core is probably of most concern. After loading a new core, observation of the CVTR reactor[58] indicated a small decrease in core flow attributed to crud deposition. If highly preferential crud deposition were to take place in a core having very narrow passages (e.g., plate type cores), flows to some core channels could be significantly reduced. Coolant conditions must be maintained to prevent this from occurring.

4-4 HEAT TRANSFER IN STEAM GENERATORS

4-4.1 Heat Transfer Rate

Most steam generators are natural circulation units, and the heat transfer area for such units may be estimated using an overall heat transfer coefficient U and the log mean temperature difference (LMTD). Lewis et al.[59] estimate that the normal range for U in a natural circulation boiler is between 600 and 900 Btu/(h ft^2 °F). For a more precise area calculation, consideration should be given to the fact that the secondary side water entering the tube bundle is subcooled. Figure 4.11 shows the temperature change in primary and secondary fluid as a function of the fluid enthalpies for a typical straight-through design. It is obvious that the use of an LMTD taking the secondary fluid to be at saturation is conservative. The situation may be handled by computing the LMTDs for the subcooled and bulk-boiling regions separately. In the case shown, areas for the two regions would be computed. When a once-through superheating unit is designed, the superheating section must be considered separately.

The overall resistance to heat transfer is the sum of the resistance of the primary-coolant film, the tube wall, fouling, and the

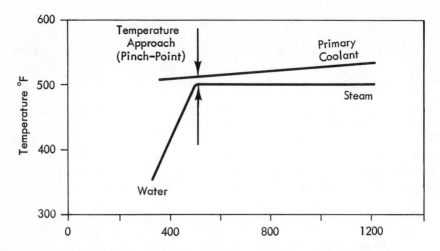

Fig. 4.11 Temperature variation in a typical steam generator.

boiling-film coefficient. If we base the calculations on the outer, or steam side area, we have

$$\frac{1}{U} = \frac{1}{h_i}\frac{A_o}{A_i} + \frac{r_o - r_i}{k_w}\frac{A_o}{A_m} + f + \frac{1}{h_o} \, , \qquad (4\text{-}109)$$

where

h_i = primary coolant film coefficient, Btu/(h ft^2 °F)

h_o = secondary side, boiling film coefficient

A_o, A_i, A_m = outside, inside, and mean surface areas

r_o, r_i = outside and inside radii

k_w = thermal conductivity of tube wall, Btu/(h ft^2 °F)

f = fouling factor, (°F ft^2 h)/Btu.

The primary-side coefficient may be computed from Eq. (4-62) or another available correlation for a low-viscosity fluid flowing tur-bulently inside a tube. The maximum value of h is usually deter-mined by the highest mass velocity tolerable from a pumping power standpoint. This limit, which has been in the neighborhood of 10 to 15 ft/sec, is encountered before reaching velocities at which erosion is a problem.

The correlations available for computing shell-side boiling-film coefficients have been discussed in Sec. 4-3.1. Both the Rohsenow and Jens-Lottes correlations have been used by designers. It should be noted that it is possible that a short section near the secondary-side inlet may not be in local boiling. An appropriate correlation for forced convection single-phase coefficients for flow parallel or across tube bundles should be used (see Sec. 4-2.1) for this portion of the exchanger. In the superheat region of a once-through unit, steam will be flowing across a baffled tube bank. Design of such cross-baffled exchangers is often handled using the method of Tinker.[60] Fouling factors may be considered to represent safety factors that increase the design area of a heat exchanger to compensate for possible scale buildup on the heat transfer surfaces. Since the primary coolant is maintained at extremely high purity levels, fouling on the primary side is usually negligible. Secondary system purity is lower and some fouling can occur. Lewis et al.[59] state that an allowance of 0.0003 ($^\circ$F ft^2 h)/Btu is generally accepted as reasonable.

Although it is unlikely that DNB will be encountered in a recirculating unit, it is possible for it to occur: (a) in the primary-coolant inlet region where temperature differences and heat fluxes are highest and (b) at the secondary-fluid exit where steam qualities are highest. The designer compares the expected local heat flux with the predicted DNB flux for those regions (Sec. 4-3.2) and attempts to maintain an adequate safety margin.

Since DNB is of greater importance in a once-through boiler, reasonable costs can be achieved only if most of the heat is transferred by means of nucleate boiling. Davies[61] states that it is possible to maintain nucleate boiling up to the position where the quality is in excess of 85% if the low mass flow rates [below 400 000 lb/(h ft^2)] and heat fluxes under 150 000 Btu/(h ft^2) are used. At higher qualities, heat transfer may be assumed to be to steam. Baffling is used to provide flow velocities that yield acceptable heat-transfer coefficients.

4-4.2 Circulation Rate

A natural circulation loop is established in each recirculating steam generator design. A differential head is produced by the difference in density between the water in the downcomer and the two-phase mixture in the risers or tube bundle. The circulation rate is determined by equating the differential head to the pressure losses of the system.

A crude measure of the adequacy of secondary-coolant flow through the tube bundle is the "circulation ratio," which is defined as the weight of water circulating in the exchanger per unit weight of steam generated. A small circulation ratio indicates a large fraction of steam in the tube bundle and the possibility of poor heat transfer on the shell side. In addition, a low-circulation ratio can lead to flow instability. In the past, units have been designed with circulation ratios such that the steam quality at the exit of the bundle does not exceed 20 to 25%. For operation with 600 psia steam, this requires a circulation ratio of about 40.

A low circulation ratio can lead to flow oscillations that cause periodic uncovering of a portion of the heat exchanger surface. This "chugging" phenomenon reduces the heat-transfer efficiency, and flow oscillations of sufficient amplitude can lead to large fluctuations in the water level or steam-flow rate.

Experience has shown that flow stability can be achieved by keeping the steam quality in the tube bundle low, or equivalently, by keeping the recirculation ratio high. This necessitates a low-pressure drop on the shell side that can be accomplished by increasing the size of the flow paths and hence the steam generator vessel. This is undesirable for large units since it may lead to an uneconomic design. In modern practice, an attempt is made to predict the dynamic response of the system using the technique discussed in Sec. 3-3.

4-5 COOLING OF STRUCTURE AND SOLID MODERATOR

4-5.1 Temperature Distribution Within Core Structure

Section 1.5 indicated that the heat distribution in a flat plate due to the absorption of uncollided γ flux follows a distribution of the form

$$q_x''' = q_1''' \exp(-ax) \quad , \tag{4-110}$$

where

q_x''' = volumetric heat flux at distance x from surface

q_1''' = volumetric heat flux at surface adjacent to source.

An equation of this form is often used as an approximate representation of the total heat generation, the effect of buildup factors being approximately accounted for adjustment of the constant a. For this flux distribution, the general solution for the temperature distribution, when the heat transferred from each surface of the plate is not the same, is given by

$$T_x - T_c = \left[q_1''' / (ka^2) \right] \exp(-ax) - C_1 x + C_2 \quad , \tag{4-111}$$

where

$$C_1 = \left[\frac{-q_1'''}{ka} \left(\frac{k}{h_1} + \frac{1}{a} + \frac{ke^{-aL}}{h_2} - \frac{e^{-aL}}{a} \right) \right] \bigg/ \left(\frac{k}{h_1} + \frac{k}{h_2} + L \right)$$

$$C_2 = \frac{kC_1}{h_1} + \frac{q_1'''}{h_1 a} + \frac{q_1'''}{ka^2}$$

and

T_c = temperature of coolant

k = thermal conductivity of plate, Btu/(h ft °F)

h_2, h_1 = heat transfer coefficients at surfaces $x = L$ and $x = 0$, Btu/(h ft² °F)

L = thickness of plate, ft

q_1''' = volumetric heat flux at surface $x = 0$, Btu/(h ft³).

In a cylindrical shell with a central source, such as a portion of the vessel or thermal shield, the heat-generation rate falls more rapidly than in a plate. Since the incident flux varies inversely with the radius μ, the heat-generation rate is then given by

$$q_x'' = (R_1/\mu) \, q_1''' \, \exp[-a \, (r - R_i)] \, , \qquad (4\text{-}112)$$

where

R_i = the inside radius.

The temperature distribution then becomes

$$T - T_0 = [(R_i q_1 \exp(-aR_i)/(ak)] \{E_i[-aR_i (1 + (L/R_i) L_1)] - E_i(-aR_i)$$
$$- \exp(-aR_i) (1 + (L/R_i) L_m) \ln(1 + (L/R_i) L_1)\} \, , \qquad (4\text{-}113)$$

where

E_i = exponential integral

L = wall thickness

$L_1 = r - R_i/L$

L_m = thickness at which maximum temperature occurs

T_0 = temperature at $x = 0$.

Equation (4-112) is rarely used for temperature evaluation due to its complexity. Fortunately, for most structural units encountered, the ratio of a wall thickness to cylinder diameter is low enough so that a good approximation is obtained by using the solution for a plate. Equation (4-111) may then be used where a simple exponential distribution offers a good approximation of the heat-flux distribution. In most instances, a better approximation of the heat generation is provided by

$$q_x''' = q_1''' \exp(-a_1 x) + q_2''' \exp(-a_2 x) + \ldots \, q_m''' \exp(-a_m x) \, .$$
$$(4\text{-}114)$$

Thus, one may allow for the various energy groups. When the plate is heated from both sides, terms of the form $q_i \exp[-a_i(L-x)]$ may be included, and they can be rewritten as

$$q_i \left[\exp(-a_i L)\right] \exp(a_i x) = q_i' \exp(-a_i' x) \ , \qquad (4\text{-}115)$$

where

$$a_i = -a_i \ .$$

These are compatible with Eq. (4-114) and the subsequent development. By including rapidly decaying terms with negative q_i, one may also closely approximate the effect of buildup factors on heat generation in the region closest to the surface.

For heat generation following Eq. (4-114) in a plate cooled on both sides, the temperature distribution is given by

$$T - T_2 = - \frac{1}{k} \left[\frac{q_1''' \exp(-a_1 x)}{a_1^2} + \frac{q_2''' \exp(-a_2 x)}{a_2^2} \right.$$

$$\left. + \ldots \quad \frac{q_n''' \exp(-a_n x)}{a_n^2} \right] - C_1 x - C_2 \ , \qquad (4\text{-}116)$$

where

$$C_1 = \left[L + k \left(\frac{1}{h_1} + \frac{1}{h_2} \right) \right]^{-1} \left\{ \frac{q_1'''}{a_1} \left[\exp(-a_1 L) \left(\frac{1}{h_2} - \frac{1}{a_1 k} \right) + \frac{1}{h_1} + \frac{1}{a_1 k} \right] \right.$$

$$+ \frac{q_2'''}{a_2} \left[\exp(-a_2 L) \left(\frac{1}{h_2} - \frac{1}{a_2 k} \right) + \frac{1}{h_1} + \frac{1}{a_2 k} \right] + \ldots$$

$$\left. + \frac{q_n'''}{a_n} \left[\exp(-a_n L) \left(\frac{1}{h_2} - \frac{1}{a_n k} \right) + \frac{1}{h_1} + \frac{1}{a_n k} \right] + (T_2 - T_1) \right\} \qquad (4\text{-}117)$$

and

$$C_2 = \frac{C_1 k}{h_1} - \frac{q_1'''}{a_1} \left(\frac{1}{h_1} + \frac{1}{a_1 k} \right) - \frac{q_2'''}{a_2} \left(\frac{1}{h_1} + \frac{1}{a_2 k} \right) - \ldots - \frac{q_n'''}{a_n} \left(\frac{1}{h_1} + \frac{1}{a_n k} \right) \ ,$$

$$\qquad (4\text{-}118)$$

where

T_1 and T_2 = coolant temperatures at surfaces $x = 0$ and $x = L$, respectively

L = thickness of plate

h_1 = heat-transfer coefficient at surface $x = 0$

h_2 = heat transfer coefficient at surface $x = L$.

Since the constants C_1 and C_2 contain $1/h$ terms, it will be observed that the previous expressions cannot be used if one wall is insulated (one h is zero). In that event, we may write the constants C_1 and C_2 as

$$C_1 = \frac{q_1''' \exp(-a_1 L)}{a_1 k} + \frac{q_2''' \exp(-a_2 L)}{a_2 k} + \ldots \quad \frac{q_n''' \exp(-a_n L)}{a_n k} \quad (4\text{-}119)$$

$$C_2 = \frac{-q_t''}{hA} - \frac{1}{k} \left[\frac{q_1'''}{a_1^2} + \frac{q_2'''}{a_2^2} + \ldots \quad \frac{q_n'''}{a_n^2} \right] , \quad (4\text{-}120)$$

where

$$q_t'' = \int_0^L q_x''' \, dL \quad .$$

For very thin plates or tubes, it is adequate to use a uniform heat generation throughout. In this case, we assume the coolant temperature is the same on both sides of the plate and find

$$T - T_c = \frac{q_1'''x^2}{2k} + \frac{q_1'''x}{k} \left[-\frac{L}{2} + \frac{k}{h_2} + \left(\frac{kL/h_2 + L^2/2}{k/k_1 + k/h_2 + L} \right) \right.$$
$$\left. \times k \left(\frac{1}{xh_1} - \frac{1}{Lh_1} - \frac{1}{Lh_2} \right) \right] , \quad (4\text{-}121)$$

where T_c = coolant temperature.

4-5.2 Temperature Distribution Within a Solid Moderator

We have previously observed that, in a solid with internal heat generation, the temperature field must satisfy the partial differential equation

$$\nabla (k\nabla T) = q''' , \quad (4\text{-}122)$$

where q''' is the volumetric rate of heat generation. Normally the solid will be cooled by the series of parallel channels that contain the fuel elements. At each such channel we must satisfy the boundary condition

$$k(\partial T/\partial n) = k (T_f - T_w) , \quad (4\text{-}123)$$

where

n = the outward normal to the solid boundary

T_f = the fluid temperature

T_w = the temperature of the solid boundary.

A complete solution of the problem is highly complex since q''' may vary with location, k may be a function of temperature, and T_f may vary significantly along the channel. Under such conditions, a numerical solution is required. The heat conduction Eq. (4-122) is written in finite difference form, and an estimate of the heat removed by the coolant obtained. The flow distribution, coolant axial temperature rises, and pressure drops of the coolant can then be estimated, and revised coolant temperatures can then be used to obtain an improved estimate of the solid temperatures. The iteration is continued until the heat-flux distributions at the fluid-solid interfaces are compatable with both sets of equations. An example of a computer program for such an analysis is provided by Lee and Gallagher.[62]

Computation of the rate of gamma heating of a solid moderator is quite complex. Gamma heating of graphite moderated systems have been examined by Hanson and Busselman[63] using both a point-kernal shielding code[64] and a transport code.[65] The transport code appeared to supply the more reliable results.

For large graphite moderated cores, heat generation and coolant conditions may vary quite slowly with distance. A reasonable estimate of the radial temperature distribution in a region can then be obtained by considering a typical channel and the moderator surrounding it. Fend et al.[66] have obtained an approximate analytical solution in circular harmonics for a large, uniformly heated reactor with coolant holes at the vertices of equilateral triangles (Fig. 4.12). Since the region has $30°$ symmetry, only the area bounded by the adiabatic planes $\Theta = 0°$, $\Theta = 30°$, and $x = c$ need be considered. The temperature at the walls of the coolant channels $(r = a)$ will be taken as uniform.

An approximate solution is obtained in circular coordinates by satisfying the isothermal conditions at the coolant channel wall, satisfying the adiabatic conditions at $\Theta = 0$ and $30°$, and trying to meet the remaining adiabatic conditions at $x = c$ by setting $(\partial T/\partial x)_c = 0$ at some values of Θ and by assuming this condition along $x = c$.

If the axial temperature gradient is negligible, the temperature field satisfies

$$\frac{\partial^2 T}{\partial r^2} + \frac{1}{r}\frac{\partial T}{\partial r} + \frac{1}{r^2}\frac{\partial^2 T}{\partial \Theta^2} + \frac{q'''}{k} = 0 \ . \tag{4-124}$$

By substituting $T' = T + q''' r^2/4k$, this reduces to a cylindrical form of Laplace's equation

$$\frac{\partial^2 T'}{\partial r^2} + \frac{1}{r}\frac{\partial T'}{\partial r} + \frac{1}{r^2}\frac{\partial^2 T'}{\partial \Theta^2} = 0 \ . \tag{4-125}$$

One form of the general solution of Laplace's equation in terms of n'th degree circular harmonics is

$$T' = (A_0 + B_0 \ln r) + \sum_{n-1}^{\infty} + (A_n r^n + B_n r^{-n})(C_n \cos n\Theta + D_n \sin n\Theta). \tag{4-126}$$

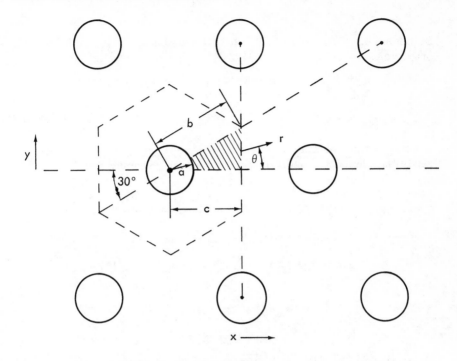

Fig. 4.12 Coolant passages in graphite moderated reactor.

The adiabatic conditions along the radial boundaries are satisfied by modifying the above for the conditions of symmetry: T must repeat itself in each 60° segment; therefore, the permissible eigenvalues are $n = 0$, 6, and 12. Also, since T must be an even function of Θ, only the cosine terms apply, giving

$$T = A_0 + B_0 \ln r - [q'''/(4k)] r^2 + \sum_{n-1}^{\infty} (A_{6n} r^{6n} + B_{6n} r^{-6n}) \cos 6 n \Theta \ .$$

(4-127)

Fend et al. evaluate B_0 by noting that the heat generated in the 30° volume must leave through the coolant channel between $\Theta = 0$ and 30°, thus

$$(q'''/12) (3 \sqrt{3}\ b^2/2 - \pi a^2) = \int_0^{\pi/6} h\ (ad\Theta)\ (\partial T/\partial r)_a = \pi/6\ (B_0 k - q'''\ a^2/2) \ ,$$

(4-128)

which gives

$$B_0 = 3 \sqrt{3}\ q'''\ b^2/(4\pi k) \ .$$

By observing that $T = T_a$ at $r = a$, they can choose $A_{6n} = - B_{6n} a - 12_n$, providing they set $A_0 = T_a + q''' a^2/4k - B_0 \ln_a$. This yields

$$T = T_a + [3\sqrt{q}''' b^2/(4\pi k)] \ln (r/a) - (q'''/4k) (r^2 - a^2)$$

$$+ \sum_{n-1}^{\infty} A_{6n} [(r^{12n} - a^{12n})/r^{6n}] \cos 6n\Theta \quad . \tag{4-129}$$

When a finite number of terms in the series are used, we can ratify the adiabatic condition along $x = c$ at as many points as there are series terms, the value of A_6 and A_{12} are found by setting $\partial T/\partial x = 0$ at Θ_1 and Θ_2. Fend et al. chose Θ_1 and Θ_2 as 12 and 30°, respectively, and obtained as a final approximate solution,

$$\frac{T - T_a}{q''' b^2/k} = \tfrac{1}{4} [(3\sqrt{3}/\pi)\ln (r/a) - (r/a)^2 + (a/b)^2]$$

$$- 0.01484 (r/b)^6 \cos 6\Theta - 0.00021 (r/b)^{12} \cos 12\Theta \quad . \tag{4-130}$$

REFERENCES

1. J. H. KEENAN and F. G. KEYES, *Thermodynamic Properties of Steam*, John Wiley & Sons, New York (1936).

2. C. R. TIPTON, Ed., *Reactor Handbook, Vol. I, Materials*, 2nd ed., Interscience Publishers, New York (1960).

3. R. COURANT and K. O. FRIEDRICHS, *Supersonic Flow and Shock Waves*, Interscience Publishers, New York (1948).

4. M. LISTER, "Numerical Solution of Hyperbolic Partial Differential Equations by the Method of Characteristics," *Mathematical Methods for Digital Computers*, A. RALSTON and H. WOLF, Eds., p. 165, John Wiley & Sons, New York (1967).

5. S. FABIC, "Westinghouse Atomic Power Department Computer Program for Calculation of Fluid Pressure, Flow and Density Transients During a Loss of Flow Accident," *Trans. Am. Nucl. Soc.*, **12**, 358 (1969).

6. A. NAHAVANDI, "Loss of Coolant Accident Analysis in Pressurized Water Reactors," *Nucl. Sci. Eng.*, **36**, 159 (1969).

7. F. W. DITTUS and L. M. K. BOELTER, University of California, Berkeley, *Pub. Eng.*, **2**, 433 (1930).

8. J. WEISMAN, "Heat Transfer to Water Flowing Parallel to Tube Bundles," *Nucl. Sci. Eng.*, **6**, 79 (1959).

9. D. A. DINGEE, W. B. BELL, J. W. CHASTAIN, and S. FAWCETT, "Heat Transfer from Parallel Rods in Axial Flow," USAEC Report BMI-1026, Battelle Memorial Institute (August 1955).

10. J. WEISMAN, "Effect of Void Volume and Prandtl Modulus on Heat Transfer in Tube Banks and Packed Beds," *A.I.Ch.E. J.*, **1**, 342 (1955).

11. A. A. BISHOP, F. J. KRAMBECK, and R. O. SANDBERG, "Forced Convection Heat Transfer to Superheated Steam at High Pressure and High Prandtl Numbers," ASME Paper 65-WA/HT-35 (1965).

12. A. A. BISHOP, R. O. SANDBERG, and L. S. TONG, "Forced Convection Heat Transfer to Water at Near-Critical Temperature and Supercritical Pressure," *Proc. A.I.Ch.E.—I. Chem. E., Joint Meeting, London Symp.*, No. 2, A.I.Ch.E., New York (1965).

13. D. WILKIE, "Forced Convection Heat Transfer from Surfaces Roughened by Transverse Ribs," *Proc. Third Intern. Heat Transfer Conf. Vol. 1*, Chicago, A.I.Ch.E., New York (1966).

14. V. KOLAR, "Heat Transfer in Turbulent Flow of Fluids Through Smooth and Rough Tubes," *Intern. J. Heat Transfer*, **8**, 639 (1965).

15. A. N. KOLMOGOROV, "The Local Structure of Turbulence in Incompressible Viscous Fluids for Very Large Reynolds Numbers," *Dokl. Akad. Nauk. SSR*, **30**, 301 (1941); "Dissipation of Energy in Locally Isotropic Turbulence," *Dokl. Akad. Nauk. SSR*, **32**, 16 (1941).

16. J. LAUFER, "The Structure Turbulence in Fully Developed Flow," NACA Tech. Report 1174, p. 17, National Advisory Committee on Aeronautics (1954).

17. D. WILKIE and L. WHITE, "Fuel Element Heat Transfer near Dimple Braces," *Nucl. Eng.*, **11**, 596 (1966).

18. W. H. McADAMS, W. E. KENNEL, C. S. MINDEN, R. CARL, P. M. PICORNELL, and J. E. DEW, "Heat Transfer at High Rates to Water with Surface Boiling," *Inst. Chem. Eng.*, **41**, 1945 (1949).

19. W. H. JENS and P. A. LOTTES, "Analysis of Heat Transfer, Burnout, Pressure Drop, and Density Data for High Pressure Water," USAEC Report ANL-4627, Argonne National Laboratory (1951).

20. W. M. ROHSENOW, *Heat Transfer, A Symposium*, University of Michigan Press, Ann Arbor (1953).

21. J. R. S. THOM, W. M. WALKER, T. A. FALLON, and G. F. REISING, "Boiling in Sub-Cooled Water During Flow up Heated Tubes or Annuli," *Proc. Inst. Mech. Eng.*, **180**, 226 (1965-66).

22. S. S. KUTATELADZE, "Boiling Heat Transfer," *Intern. J. Heat and Mass Transfer*, **4**, 31 (1961).

23. J. C. CHEN, "A Correlation for Boiling Heat Transfer to Saturated Fluids in Convective Flow," ASME Paper 63-HT-34 (1963).

24. R. G. VANDERWATER, "An Analysis of Burnout in Two-Phase Liquid-Vapor Flow," PhD thesis, University of Minnesota (1956).

25. L. TOPPER, "A Diffusion Theory Analysis of Boiling Burnout in the Fog Flow Regime," *Trans. ASME, Ser. C, J. Heat Transfer*, **85**, 284 (1956).

26. H. S. ISBIN, R. G. VANDERWATER, H. FAUSKE, and S. SINGH, "A Model for Correlating Two-Phase Steam-Water Burnout Heat Transfer Fluxes," *Trans. ASME, Ser. C, J. Heat Transfer*, **83**, 149 (1961).

27. L. S. TONG, "Prediction of Departure from Nucleate Boiling for an Axially Non-Uniform Heat Flux Distribution," *J. Nucl. Energy*, **6**, 21 (1967).

28. L. S. TONG, *Boiling Heat Transfer and Two-Phase Flow*, John Wiley & Sons, New York (1965).

29. E. JANSSEN and S. LEVY, "Burnout Limit Curves for Boiling Water Reactors," APE D-3892, General Electric Co. (1962).

30. V. M. HEALZER, J. E. HENSH, E. JANSSEN, and S. LEVY, "Design Basis for Critical Heat Flux Conditions in Boiling Water Reactors," USAEC Report APED-5286, General Electric Co. (1966).

31. L. BERNATH, "A Theory of Local Boiling Burnout and its Application to Existing Data," *Chem. Eng. Prog. Symp. Ser.*, **56**, *30*, 95 (1960).

32. "Pressurized Water Reactor (PWR) Project Technical Progress Report, April-June 1961," USAEC Report WAPD-MRP-92, Bettis Atomic Power Laboratory (1961).

33. R. H. WILSON and J. K. FERRELL, "Correlation of Critical Heat Flux for Boiling Water in Forced Circulation at Elevated Pressures," BAW-168, Babcock & Wilcox Co. (November 1961).

34. D. W. BELL, "Correlation of Burnout Heat Flux Data at 2000 psia," *Nucl. Sci. Eng.*, **7**, 245 (1960).

35. R. D. COFFIELD, Jr., W. M. ROHRER, Jr., and L. S. TONG, "An Investigation of the Departure from Nucleate Boiling in a Crossed Rod Matrix with Normal Flow of Freon 113 Coolant,' *Nucl. Eng. Design*, **6**, 147 (1967).

36. S. P. KEZIOS, T. S. KIM, and F. M. RAFCHIEK, "Burnout in Crossed-Rod Matrices and Forced Convection Flow of Water,' *International Developments in Heat Transfer, Part II*, ASME, p. 262 (1961).

37. A. J. MARTENSON, "Transient Boiling in Small Rectangular Channels," PhD thesis, Department of Mechanical Engineering, University of Pittsburgh (1962).

38. V. E. SHROCK, H. A. JOHNSON, A. GOPALAKRISHNAN, K. E. LAVEZZO, and S. M. CHO, "Transient Boiling Phenomena," USAEC Report SAN-1013, University of California, Berkeley (1966).

39. J. A. REDFIELD, "CHIC-KIN, A Fortran Program for Intermediate and Fast Transients in a Water Moderated Reactor," USAEC Report WAPD-TM-479, Bettis Atomic Power Laboratory (1965).

40. J. O. CERMAK, R. F. FARMAN, L. S. TONG, J. E. CASTERLINE, S. KOKOLIS, and B. MATZNER, "The Departure from Nucleate Boiling in Rod Bundles During Pressure Transients," Paper 70-HT-12, ASME, New York (1970).

41. L. S. TONG, "Heat Transfer Mechanisms During a Loss of Coolant Accident," ASME Symposium, Idaho Falls, Idaho (1967).

42. J. D. PARKER and R. J. GROSH, "Heat Transfer to a Mist Flow," USAEC Report ANL-6291, Argonne National Laboratory (1961).

43. A. W. BENNET, G. F. HEWITT, H. A. KEARSEY, and R. K. F. KEEYS, "The Wetting of Hot Surfaces by Water in a Steam Environment at High Pressure," UKAEA Report AERE-R 5146, Atomic Energy Research Establishment, Harwell (1966).

44. S. BERTOLETTI, J. LESAGE, C. LOMBARDI, G. PETERLONG, M. SILVESTRI, G. SOLDANI, and F. WECKERMANN, "Heat Transfer and Pressure Drop with Steam-Water Spray," CISE R-36, Centro Informazioni Studi Experimenze, Milan (1961).

45. A. A. BISHOP, R. O. SANDBERG, and L. S. TONG, "Forced Convection Heat Transfer at High Pressure after the Critical Heat Flux," ASME Paper 65-TH-31 (1965).

46. A. A. BISHOP, L. E. EFFERDING, and L. S. TONG, "A Review of Heat Transfer and Fluid Flow of Water in the Supercritical Region During Once-Through Operation," USAEC Report WCAP-2040, Westinghouse Atomic Power Division (1962).

47. E. E. POLOMIK, S. LEVY, and E. C. SAWOCHKA, "Heat Transfer Coefficients with Annular Flow During 'Once-Through' Boiling of Water to 100 Per Cent Quality at 800, 1100, and 1400 psi," USAEC Report GEAP-3703, General Electric Co. (1961).

48. D. M. McELIGOT, P. M. MAGEE, and G. LEPPERT, "Effect of Large Temperature Gradients on Convective Heat Transfer in the Downstream Region," *Trans. ASME, Ser. C, J. Heat Transfer*, **87**, 67 (1965).

49. V. M. BORISHANSKI and B. S. FOKIN, "Correlation of Heat Transfer Data in Stable Film Boiling on Vertical Surfaces in the Presence of Free Liquid Convection in Large Volumes," *Intern. Chem. Eng.*, **5,** *4*, 666 (1965).

50. L. A. BROMLEY, "Heat Transfer in Stable Film Boiling," *Chem. Eng. Prog.*, **46,** 221 (1950).

51. Y. Y. HSU and J. W. WESTWATER, "Approximate Theory for Film Boiling on Vertical Surfaces," *Chem. Eng. Prog. Symp.*, **56**, *30*, 15 (1962).

52. M. E. ELLION, "A Study of the Mechanism of Boiling Heat Transfer," Memo 20-88 CIT, Jet Propulsion Laboratory (1954).

53. H. C. HOTTELL, "Radiation Heat Transmission," in *Heat Transmission*, by W. H. McADAMS, Chap. 4, McGraw-Hill Book Co., Inc., New York (1954).

54. P. COHEN and G. R. TAYLOR, "Discussion of 'Boiling Heat Transfer Data at Low Heat Flux,' by W. C. Elrod et al.," *Trans. ASME, Ser. C, J. Heat Transfer*, **89**, 242 (1967).

55. J. WEISMAN, A. H. WENZEL, L. S. TONG, D. FITZSIMMONS, W. THORNE, and J. BATCH, "Experimental Determination of the Departure from Nucleate Boiling in Large Rod Bundles," *Chem. Eng. Symp. Ser.*, **64**, *22*, 114 (1968).

56. P. COHEN, Westinghouse Electric Corp., Personal Communication (1967).

57. P. GOLDSTEIN, "A Research Study on Internal Corrosion of High Pressure Boilers," *Trans. ASME, Ser. A, J. Eng. for Power,* **90,** 21 (1968).

58. "Carolina-Virginia Nuclear Power Associates, Inc. Quarterly Progress Report for April-June 1966," USAEC Report CVNA-267, p. 4 (1966).

59. G. T. LEWIS, Jr., M. ZIZZA, and P. De RIENZO, "Heat Exchangers for Water Cooled Reactors," *Nucleonics,* **19,** 7, 70 (1961).

60. A. Y. LEE and J. G. GALLAGHER, "A Program for Steady State Fluid Flow and Heat Conduction Coupled Calculations of Heat Generating Solids Cooled by Parallel Channels Using the MCAP and TOSS Codes," WANL-TME-967, Westinghouse Astronuclear Laboratory (October 1964).

61. D. K. DAVIES, "Nuclear Steam Generators," *Proc. Am. Power Conf.,* **27,** 310 (1965).

62. T. TINKER, "Shell Side Characteristics of Shell and Tube Heat Exchangers," *Proc. of the General Discussion on Heat Transfer,* Inst. of Mech. Eng., London, and ASME, New York (1951).

63. G. E. HANSON and G. J. BUSSELMAN, "Gamma Heating Calculations in Graphite Moderated Systems," USAEC Report BNWL-625, Battelle Northwest Laboratory, Richland, Washington (1967).

64. R. L. ENGEL, J. GREENBERG, and M. M. HENDRICKSON, "ISOHLD—A Computer Code for General Purpose Shielding Analysis," USAEC Report BNWL-236, Battelle Northwest Laboratory, Richland, Washington (1967).

65. W. W. ENGEL, Jr., "A User's Manual for ANISN—A One-Dimensional Discrete Ordinates Transport Code with Anisotropic Scattering," USAEC Report K-1693, Union Carbide Nuclear Division, Oak Ridge, Tennessee (1967).

66. F. A. FEND, E. M. BOROODY, and J. C. BELL, "An Approximate Calculation of the Temperature Distribution Surrounding Coolant Holes in a Heat Generating Solid," USAEC Report BMI-T-42, Battelle Memorial Institute, Columbus, Ohio.

Thermal and Hydraulic Performance of A Reactor Core

The thermal and hydraulic design of a core depends heavily on the expected performance of the core as indicated by its load follow characteristics, fuel burnup, and core life. This information is used to establish the relative heat-flux distribution within the core. The limiting power output of the core design is then determined by the maximum heat-removal capability in the hot channel or at the hot spot.

5-1 THERMAL DESIGN

5-1.1 Thermal Design Limitations

Clad integrity as well as economy determine the maximum allowable power output of a UO_2 fuel rod. The factors considered are:

1. no significant center melting to avoid excessive clad strain or failure

2. heat flux below a maximum value allowable by coolant conditions

3. ourrup and fission-gas release limited to avoid excessive internal pressure and clad creep or embrittlement

4. suitable power density (kW/kg of U) for a convenient refueling time and also for a reasonable fuel-fabrication cost.

Each of the first three limitations requires a knowledge of the most adverse heat-flux conditions in the core. We may determine the core radial location at which the flux distribution predicts the highest integrated power. We may also determine the location at which the local heat flux is a maximum. The actual heat fluxes may be higher than those obtained from nuclear considerations alone because of deviations from the ideal. We account for these deviations by use of the "hot-channel" and "hot-spot" concepts. The hot-channel concept compounds all pertinent adverse engineering effects into a single-flow channel having the highest integrated-power output. The hot-spot concept compounds all pertinent adverse engineering effects into a local hot spot having the highest local power output. The thermal conditions in the hot channel and at the hot spot must satisfy the design criteria under steady-state and transient conditions. By using these conservative concepts in a core design, one can ensure the safe operation of the rest of the core.

A single flow channel in a rod bundle fuel assembly is sometimes called a subchannel and is formed by four neighboring rods in a square lattice, or by three neighboring rods in a triangular lattice. The hot channel may be considered to be one such subchannel.

5-1.2 Design Approach

We shall illustrate the usual design procedure by consideration of the design of a rod bundle core. The basic thermal and hydraulic design approach evaluates the enthalpy rise in the hot channel by using a subchannel analysis. Such an analysis considers the interaction between the adjacent subchannels (hereafter simply called channels). The interaction between the parallel and laterally open-flow channels is produced by cross-flow and turbulent-flow mixing, and the amount of interaction depends on the local peaking conditions in the hot channel. Before the local hot channel in any hot assembly can be analyzed, the average flow conditions of the hot assembly must be known. The steps required for evaluation of the enthalpy rise in a hot channel are:

1. calculation of the "hot-assembly factor"* by superimposing the assembly power distribution on the assembly inlet-flow distribution with considerations of the cross flow and the turbulent mixing between the assemblies

2. calculation of the "local hot-cell factor"** by superimposing the local power distribution on the flow area of each channel in the hot assembly

3. calculation of the overall hot-channel factor by multiplying the hot-assembly factor and the local hot-channel factor.

Obviously this approach is too complicated for hand calculation and needs a digital computer code.

---

*The ratio of the hot-assembly enthalpy rise to the core average enthalpy rise.

**The ratio of the hot-channel enthalpy rise to the hot-assembly average enthalpy rise.

Preliminary estimates also require a simplified analysis that applies the estimated subfactors simultaneously to a single closed hot channel. The subfactors, which are either estimated from past experience or extrapolated from model tests, are: the fabrication tolerance, flow mixing, inlet plenum, and flow redistribution. The probability of occurrence of various hot-channel factors can be combined in the calculation, but the coupling effects of various subfactors remain. These coupling effects introduce repetition of design penalties. Thus, the simplified analysis may give an overly conservative design.

5-1.3 Fuel-Rod Design

In selecting a fuel-rod design, the independent variables of power density, rod diameter, fuel porosity, and total burnup must be considered. The primary constraint is, however, the design requirement that center fuel melting by avoided at the peak power expected. Usually this limitation is applied at the core hot spot considering the reactor to be operating at a level above its nominal power rating. The increased power assumption allows for the possibility that normal reactor control can allow small overpower conditions (e.g., 110 to 115% of nominal power) to exist for brief periods.

The computation of center fuel temperatures was discussed extensively in Chap. 2. It will be recalled that for a given pellet surface temperature, the power required to reach center melting is independent of rod diameter. The temperature difference producing center melting is directly proportional to the linear power rate [see Eq. (2-53)]. For similar coolant conditions, the center melting limitation can therefore be expressed as a limitation on the linear power output (kW/ft) of the fuel rod. The approximate interrelationship of the surface heat flux, the linear power rate, and the power density for a stainless clad UO_2 fuel rod is shown in Fig. 5.1. If the maximum heat flux is regarded as fixed by the coolant conditions, the rod size can be determined by a compromise between the fuel center temperature (i.e., kW/ft) and the power density. The selection process is actually an iterative procedure since coolant conditions may be revised to lead to an improved choice.

The maximum burnup of a UO_2 rod is primarily determined by the material problems of cladding corrosion, creep, and embrittlement. Cladding creep may be caused first by the external pressure and then by internal fission gas pressure and UO_2 swelling under irradiation. The porosity of sintered UO_2 can accommodate a part of the fuel swelling, and thus a relatively low density UO_2 pellet should be used for a high burnup fuel rod. The required initial fuel element void volume, including the pellet porosity and the gap between the clad and

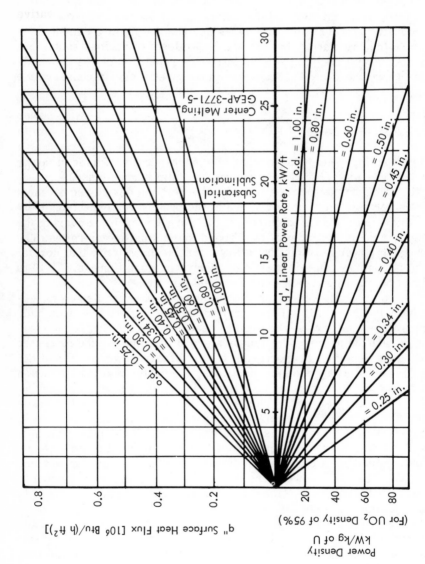

Fig. 5.1 Surface-heat flux and power density vs. linear power for various size UO₂ rods with stainless-steel cladding. (From *Nucl. Eng. Design*, **6**, 301, 1967.)

the pellet, has been plotted against the expected burnup with clad swelling in Fig. 2.1. This figure can be used for guidance in the selection of fuel density, but a detailed analysis, by means of a computer code such as CYGRO,[1] must be conducted to determine if the proposed design is satisfactory.

5-1.4 Core Arrangement

Establishment of the maximum allowable linear power density, rod diameter, water-to-fuel ratio, and nuclear hot-channel factors serves as a basis of the thermal and hydraulic design. We shall illustrate the effect of these parameters by further consideration of a pressure vessel reactor containing a rod-cluster core.

Average Power Output of a Fuel Rod. Since the average power output of a fuel rod strongly influences the fuel cost, it is one of the measurements of the effectiveness of a core design. By knowing the maximum linear power density q'_{max} and the hot-channel factor for heat flux F_q, one can determine the limiting average power output of a fuel rod:

$$q'_{avg} = q'_{max}/F_q \quad . \tag{5-1}$$

Fuel Rod Array. For a square lattice, the pitch S of the rod array is a function of the ratio of moderator to fuel M/F, and of the clad thickness t

$$\left(\frac{M}{F}\right)\left[\frac{\pi}{4}\ (D_o - 2t - 2g)^2\right] = S^2 - \frac{\pi}{4}\ D_o^2 \quad , \tag{5-2}$$

where

D_o = rod outside diameter

g = cold gap between fuel and clad

t = clad thickness

S = fuel-rod pitch (center to center distance).

In most stainless-steel clad PWR cores, S is approximately $1.3\ D_o$.

Assembly Size and Core Size. The following relationships determine the sizes of assembly and core:

First, the minimum fuel rod number is a function of core length L and the average heat flux

$$N = [Q][C_1/(L\ q'_{avg})] \quad , \tag{5-3}$$

where

   N = minimum number of fuel rods for the limiting q'_{avg}

   Q = thermal power output of the core

   C_1 = fraction of power generated in the fuel rod.

Second, the number of fuel assemblies should be determined by considering the axisymmetry in the core and a suitable period for fuel cycling. The actual fuel rod number, obtained by selecting the proper combination of the number of assemblies and the number of rods in each assembly, should be close to, but greater than, the minimum fuel-rod number calculated by Eq. (5-3).

Third, the equivalent core diameter D_{eq} is a function of the average core power density.

$$C_2 \frac{\pi}{4} L D^2_{eq} = \frac{Q}{q'''_{avg}} \quad , \tag{5-4}$$

where C_2 is a factor to account for clearance between assemblies and

$$q'''_{avg} = q'_{avg}/S^2 \quad .$$

Fourth, in order to provide reasonable core fabrication costs and neutron economy, the values of D_{eq} and L should satisfy the following relationship,

$$0.9 \leq (L/D_{eq}) \leq 1.5. \tag{5-5}$$

5-1.5 Determination of Coolant Requirements

The major limitation on the thermal design of a water-cooled reactor is the necessity to maintain an adequate safety margin between operating conditions and the critical heat flux (DNB). The core design criterion is generally stated in terms of a DNB ratio defined as

$$\text{DNBR} = \frac{\text{DNB heat flux predicted by applicable correlation}}{\text{reactor local heat flux}} \quad \cdot \tag{5-6}$$

The DNB ratio will vary along the channel since both the local heat flux and fluid enthalpy are varying. For a cosine heat flux, the minimum DNB ratio will be found at some portion past the midplane of the core. A typical situation is shown in Fig. 5.2, where the reactor heat flux and DNB heat flux are plotted vs the ratio of height to total (z/L). It will be observed that, in the region just past the midplane, the increased fluid enthalpy decreases the predicted DNB flux more rapidly than the local flux is decreasing.

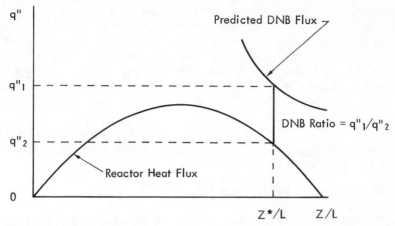

Fig. 5.2 DNB (departure from nucleate boiling) ratio evaluation. (From *Nucl. Eng. Design*, **6**, 301, 1967.)

It is, of course, the minimum DNB ratio (at $Z*/L$ in Fig. 5.2) in the hottest channel that is of concern to the designer. A typical PWR design criterion is that the minimum DNB ratio should be equal to or greater than 1.30 at the maximum overpower conditions. The probability of a PWR reaching the specified maximum overpower condition is very small. Even at the maximum overpower conditions, the number of fuel rods having DNBRs close to the value of 1.30 is again very small.

Sufficient coolant flow must be provided to maintain the desired minimum DNBR. At low qualities, increasing the mass velocity increases the critical heat flux; however, increased coolant flow acts primarily to reduce the coolant enthalpy rise and, hence, quality. As may be seen from the critical heat flux correlation of Eq. (4-83), a reduced quality substantially increases the predicted critical flux.

The determination of enthalpy rise along the hot channel requires a knowledge of the flow, which is effective in removing heat from the core. The effective flow rate is the total flow rate minus the by-pass flow rate. We then have

$$\Delta H_{\text{reactor}} = Q/W_{\text{total flow}} \tag{5-7}$$

$$\Delta H_{\text{core}} = Q/W_{\text{effective}} \tag{5-8}$$

$$\Delta H_{\text{hot channel}} = F_{\Delta H} \times \Delta H_{\text{core}} \quad , \tag{5-9}$$

where

Q = total heat output, Btu/h

W = flow, lb/h

$F_{\Delta H}$ = enthalpy rise hot-channel factor.

Thus, once the by-pass flow is determined and a value for $F_{\Delta H}$ has been assigned, we can obtain the hot-channel exit conditions. For a preliminary estimate of the enthalpy rise along the hot channel, it may be assumed that the hot channel is closed and that the value of $F_{\Delta H}$ is constant along its length. The enthalpy rise at any position along the channel is then obtained by multiplying the (ΔH) from Eq. (4-5), or its equivalent for flux distributions other than the cosine, by $F_{\Delta H}$.

For final core design, the more sophisticated approach briefly indicated in Sec. 5-1.2 is used. We shall consider this approach in more detail in the next section.

5-1.6 Hot-Channel Factor Evaluation

The total hot-channel factors for heat-flux and enthalpy rise include both nuclear effects and engineering uncertainties such as dimensional and flow variations. The effects of the engineering uncertainties are generally combined and expressed as engineering hot-channel subfactors for heat flux F_q^E and for enthalpy rise $F_{\Delta H}^E$. The total hot-channel factors for heat-flux and enthalpy rise can then be defined as follows:

$$F_q = \frac{\text{maximum heat flux at hot spot}}{\text{average heat flux in core}} = F_R^N \, F_Z^N \, F_q^E \qquad (5\text{-}10)$$

$$F_{\Delta H} = \frac{\text{maximum enthalpy rise in hot channel}}{\text{average enthalpy rise in core}} = F_R^N \, F_{\Delta H}^E \,. \qquad (5\text{-}11)$$

Note that the hot-channel factor for the temperature difference between the fuel surface and coolant is usually not significant in a PWR design due to the high heat-transfer coefficient.

Engineering Subfactors. The individual effects that must be included in the engineering hot-channel factors are usually expressed in terms of engineering subfactors. The most common hot channel subfactors are:

1. Fuel fabrication tolerance – accounts for the flow reduction due to a reduced pitch and a bowing of the fuel rod.

2. Fuel pellet diameter, density, and enrichment – account for the variation in the quantity of fissionable material in the fuel pellet.

3. Lower plenum – accounts for the effect of local flow maldistribution at the core inlet.

4. Flow redistribution – accounts for the reduction in flow in the hot channel due to the increase in pressure drop as a result of nucleate boiling.

5. Flow mixing – accounts for the flow mixing between parallel and laterally open channels.

6. By-pass flow percentage – accounts for flow leakage by-passing the core.

Originally, the overall engineering hot-channel factors F_q^E and $F_{\Delta H}^E$ were taken as the product of these individual subfactors. As previously indicated, this leads to an overly conservative design. The subfactors that are related to fuel fabrication tolerances (items 1 and 2) are stochastic in nature; hence, the probability that all fabrication effects are simultaneously adverse is low. To combine these effects properly, we must allow for the probability distributions associated with them. The subfactors relating to flow mixing and redistribution are all interrelated, and a true independent evaluation of each subfactor is not possible.

Statistical Evaluation of Fabrication Tolerance Subfactors: The influence of fuel rod dimensional deviations on thermal design is usually much less in a core of cylindrical rods than in a core of plate type fuel elements. This is so as the flow area in a plate assembly varies with a single gap, whereas the flow area of a rod bundle varies with the average of the four gaps. The engineering hot-channel subfactors for fuel element fabrication tolerances have been evaluated for fuel plates by LeTourneau and Grimble.[2] Chelmer and Tong[3] have evaluated these subfactors for fuel-rod cores using statistical concepts.

It is desirable at this point to review a few basic statistical relations. Random variations are distributed in accordance with the normal distribution curve as defined by the equation

$$f(x) = \frac{1}{\sigma\sqrt{2\pi}} \exp\left[-\frac{1}{2}\left(\frac{x-\mu}{\sigma}\right)^2 \right] \ , \tag{5-12}$$

where $f(x)$ is the relative frequency with which a value x occurs, μ is the mean or expected value, and σ is the standard deviation. The probability p that x is greater than a value, say a, is given by integrating the above expression from a to ∞:

$$p(x \geqq a) = \int_a^\infty \frac{1}{\sigma\sqrt{2\pi}} \exp\left[-\frac{1}{2}\left(\frac{x-\mu}{\sigma}\right)^2 \right] dx \ . \tag{5-13}$$

If the substitutions $t = (x - \mu)/\sigma$ and $t_a = (a - \mu)/\sigma$ are made, the result is

$$p(x \geqq a) = p(t \geqq t_a) = \frac{1}{\sqrt{2\pi}} \int_{t_a}^\infty \exp(-t^2/2)\,dt \ . \tag{5-14}$$

When nominal conditions exist, the engineering hot-channel factors cause no adverse effect. From Eqs. (5-10) and (5-11), we see that

they must then have a value of 1. Since nominal conditions are nothing
more than the expected conditions, the mean value of any engineering
hot-channel factor is 1. Thus, if x in Eq. (5-12) represents the value
of the hot-channel factor, μ equals 1.

We are concerned only with deviations from the nominal that cause
adverse effects; e.g., increased enrichment, higher pellet density,
etc. Deviations in the other direction are not harmful. Thus, we are
concerned only with hot-channel factors in excess of 1. The probability of exceeding any given value of the hot-channel factor is therefore found from Eq. (5-14).

As an example, consider the probability of exceeding a hot-channel
factor of $1 + 3\sigma$. Letting $a = 1 + 3\sigma$ gives $t_a = 3$ so that

$$p(x \geq 1 + 3\sigma) = p(t \geq 3) = \frac{1}{\sqrt{2\pi}} \int_3^\infty \exp(-t^2/2) \, dt = 0.00135 \quad . \qquad (5\text{-}15)$$

The numerical value is obtained from standard tables.[4] If a hot-
channel factor may be considered as a linear function of its governing
physical quantities, each of which is normally distributed, then it can
be shown[4] that the hot-channel factor will be normally distributed.
The value of σ may then be estimated from the relation

$$\sigma^2 \approx (\partial\phi/\partial x_1)^2 \, \sigma_1^2 + (\partial\phi/\partial x_2)^2 \sigma_2^2 + \dots (\partial\phi/\partial x_k)^2 \, \sigma_k^2 \quad , \qquad (5\text{-}16)$$

where the hot-channel factor expression is represented by $\phi(x_1, x_2,$
$\dots x_k)$: The x terms are the governing physical quantities; their
standard deviations are given by σ; and the partial derivatives are
evaluated at the mean x values.

To determine if the hot-channel factor may be considered linear in
the x terms, the following test suggested by Hald[4] may be applied.

$$\phi(\mu) - \phi(\mu - 2.58\sigma) = \phi(\mu + 2.58\sigma) - \phi(\mu) = 2.58\sigma \, (d\phi/dx)\big|_{x=\mu} , \qquad (5\text{-}17)$$

where ϕ is a function of the variable x having a mean and standard
deviation of μ and σ. If the equality is satisfied, the function may be
considered linear throughout 99% of the range of the variation in x.
This test may be applied for functions of more than one variable by
considering one at a time while holding the others constant.

The confidence level of a statistically determined relationship is
the fraction of the time the relationship is expected to be satisfied.
The aforementioned means and standard deviations are obtained from
a finite number of samples. To maintain a high confidence level that
the design hot-channel factors will not be exceeded, the following
procedure is adopted. We define m and s as the mean and standard
deviation determined from a sample of size n taken from a normal
distribution. The confidence parameter k is defined by the following
probability equation:

$$p(x < m + ks) = p_k \quad , \qquad (5\text{-}18)$$

where k values are listed in Ref. 5 for various confidence levels γ and resulting probabilities p_k. For an infinite sample size, the values of m and s will approach μ and σ respectively, so that

$$p(x < \mu + k_\infty \sigma) = p_k \quad , \tag{5-19}$$

where k_∞ is the value of k for $n = \infty$. Comparing the above two equations, we get

$$\sigma = (m + ks - \mu)/k_\infty \approx ks/k_\infty \quad . \tag{5-20}$$

We now use the value of σ, derived from the experimentally observed value of s, to establish design values for the engineering hot-channel factors which have very low probabilities of being exceeded. The engineering hot-channel factor for heat flux F_q^E is proportional to the pellet weight per unit length w' and the enrichment e. By assuming that the measurements of w' and e are abundant and that they are independent and normally distributed, we get

$$F_q^E = \left(\frac{w'_{\text{max local}}}{w'_{\text{nom}}}\right)\left(\frac{e_{\text{max local}}}{e_{\text{nom}}}\right) \tag{5-21}$$

$$\sigma_{F_q}^2 = (\sigma_w / \mu_{w'})^2 + (\sigma_e / \mu_e)^2 \quad , \tag{5-22}$$

where σ and μ are the standard deviation and mean, respectively. If a 99.87% probability of not exceeding the design hot-channel factor is required, the value of $(F_q^E)_{\text{des}}$ becomes

$$(F_q^E) = 1 + 3\sigma_{F_q} \quad . \tag{5-23}$$

The fabrication subfactor of the engineering hot-channel factor for enthalpy rise $F_{\Delta H, \text{fab}}^E$ is defined as

$$F_{\Delta H, \text{fab}}^E = \left(\frac{G_{\text{nom}}}{G_{\text{hot channel}}}\right)\left(\frac{\overline{w}'_{\text{hot channel}}}{\overline{w}'_{\text{nom}}}\right)\left(\frac{\overline{e}_{\text{hot rod}}}{\overline{e}_{\text{nom}}}\right) \quad , \tag{5-24}$$

where G is the flow rate in a channel, $\overline{w}'$ is the average pellet weight per length of the fuel rod, and $\overline{e}$ is the average enrichment of the fuel rod.

The parameters in Eq. (5-24) are assumed to be independent and normally distributed; thus

$$\sigma_{F_{\Delta H, \text{fab}}}^2 = (\sigma_G/\mu_G)^2 + (\sigma_{\overline{w}'}/\mu_{\overline{w}'})^2 + (\sigma_{\overline{e}}/\mu_{\overline{e}})^2 \quad . \tag{5-25}$$

A 99.87% probability of not exceeding the design value is again required, and

$$\left(F_{\Delta H, \text{fab}}^E\right)_{\text{des}} = 1 + 3\sigma_{F_{\Delta H, \text{fab}}} \quad . \tag{5-26}$$

By-Pass Flow and Core Flow Subfactors. To assemble the fuel assemblies and the reactor internals in the vessel, clearances must be provided to account for the fabrication tolerances. These clearances also provide passages for coolant to by-pass the core, such as:

- the gap between the baffle and outlet nozzle
- the gap between fuel assemblies
- the gap in control-rod slot or around control-rod thimbles
- the gap between the baffle and barrel.

These by-pass flows, which can be 4 to 8% of the total flow depending on the size of the design clearances, are not effective in removing heat from the core. Any reduction of these clearances directly increases the effective coolant flow.

The subfactors for core-flow conditions consist of the lower plenum, flow redistribution, and flow mixing. They cannot be evaluated statistically because the hot channels are not randomly distributed and the core-flow conditions are strongly dependent on geometrical dimensions and power distributions. The values of these subfactors can be obtained only from test data such as those from tests of an isothermal hydraulic model with geometrically similar to the reactor vessel. Better simulated models will give more realistic values of these subfactors. Table 5.1 lists typical engineering hot-channel factors for various existing PWRs, indicating the progress in development and testing.

Table 5-1

REDUCTIONS IN ENGINEERING HOT-CHANNEL FACTORS OF SOME PRESSURIZED WATER REACTIONS

Factors	Reactors		
	Yankee-Rowe	Selni-Sena	Others[a]
Rod diameter, pitch and bowing, pellet density, and enrichment	1.14	1.14	1.08[b]
Lower plenum subfactor	1.07	1.07	1.03[c]
Flow redistribution subfactor	1.05	1.05	1.05
Flow mixing subfactor	-	0.95	0.92[d]
Total engineering hot-channel factor for enthalpy rise, $F_{\Delta H}^E$	1.28	1.22[e]	1.08
Total engineering hot-channel factor for heat flux, F_q^E	1.08	1.04[e]	1.04

[a]Connecticut Yankee, San Onofre, Indian Point II, Zorita, Genna, Turkey Point, Point Beach; [b]Ref. 6; [c]Ref. 7; [d]Ref. 8; [e]Ref. 3.

Digital Computer Evaluation of Core Flow Subfactors. Since these flow subfactors were evaluated individually, a problem arises in applying them to a core design. We have observed that the use of the product of these subfactors usually introduces repetition; for instance, flow starvation at the inlet of a hot channel reduces the pressure drop in this channel. It will be repetitive if we apply the reduced inlet flow simultaneously with the flow redistribution subfactor to avoid excessive pressure drop in the same hot channel. Similarly, a reduced flow at the channel inlet may very well be the correct flow rate for a hot channel with a reduced pitch and bowing of fuel rods.

The effect on enthalpy rise can be charged to either of the above reasons, but not to both. A constant mixing subfactor assigned to all reactors with different power distributions is also not proper, because the effect of mixing on enthalpy rise depends on the radial thermal gradient between the channels (i.e., power distribution) as well as the flow conditions.

A more rigorous way to account for various hydraulic and nuclear effects on the enthalpy rise is first to calculate the "hot-assembly factor" by superimposing the power distribution among the assemblies on the inlet-flow distribution allowing for flow mixing between assemblies. A "hot-cell factor" is then calculated by superimposing the effect of local power distribution within the hot assembly on the effects due to the varying flow areas of the unit cells formed by the fuel-rod lattice and the boundary of the fuel assembly. An allowance is made for mixing between the channels. The total hot-channel factor is the product of a hot-assembly factor and a local hot-cell factor. Obviously this calculation is very complicated and digital computer codes are necessary.

In order to study the flow redistribution in a reactor core, a mathematical model of the core's physical configuration is established. Interchange of mass, heat, and momentum is allowed between neighboring assemblies, the amounts of this interchange being governed by conservation equations. In Sec. 3-1.3, a numerical technique for evaluating this core-wide flow redistribution (hot-assembly factor) was described. It was assumed that the inlet-pressure distribution was known on the basis of model studies and that the pressure across the upper plenum was uniform. With these boundary conditions it is possible to establish the average flow in each of the core assemblies as a function of axial position.

Several computer analyses[9-11] of the flow redistribution within a confined region, such as a fuel assembly, have been developed. Any of these methods allows a determination of the "hot-cell factor," and the common basis for the analyses may be illustrated by considering a single channel m and one neighboring channel n, as shown in Fig. 5.3.

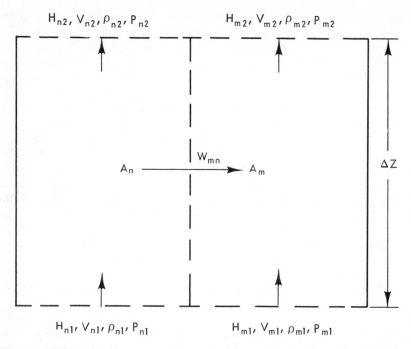

Fig. 5.3 Mathematical representation of flow redistribution with hot-channel factor superimposed.

In Fig. 5.3 H, V, ρ, and p represent the coolant enthalpy, velocity, density, and static pressure; A is the channel flow area; W_{mn}, the cross-flow between channels; and w', the flow exchange of diffusion mixing. The numbered subscripts refer to two different axial elevations in the core. Writing the mass, energy, and momentum balance equations for channel m between elevations 1 and 2 results in the following relationships, where W_{mn} has been considered to be positive in the direction from channel n into channel m:

Conservation of Mass

$$A_m V_{m1}\rho_{m1} + W_{mn} = A_m V_{m2}\rho_{m2} \tag{5-27}$$

Conservation of Heat

$$A_m V_{m1}P_{m1}H_{m1} + Q_{mz} + W_m \overline{H}_n + w'(H_n - H_m)\,\Delta Z = A_m V_{m2}\rho_{m2}H_{m2} \tag{5-28}$$

Conservation of Momentum

$$A_m P_{m1} + A_m \rho_{m1}V^2_{m1}/g_c + W_{mn}\overline{V}_n/g_c = A_m P_{m2} + A_m \rho_{m2}V^2_{m2}/g_c$$
$$+ K_{mz}A_m\overline{\rho}_m V^2_m/2g_c + \overline{\rho}_m\,\Delta Zg/g_c \quad,$$

$$\tag{5-29}$$

where

Q_{mz} = heat input into channel m in the interval ΔZ

W_{mn} = cross flow from channel n to channel m

$\overline{H}, \overline{\rho}, \overline{V}$ = mean values in ΔZ of enthalpy, density and velocity

w' = flow exchange rate per unit length

K_{mz} = pressure loss coefficient for channel m in the interval ΔZ

P = pressure.

The evaluation of ρ and K_{mz} requires the determination of void frac-tion and two-phase pressure drop as described in Chap. 3. The additional terms arising from the coupling of channel m to other surrounding channels are readily deduced.

A similar set of equations can be written for every other channel in the region studied. A simultaneous solution of all of these equa-tions is required to determine the fluid conditions at the exit of the length interval.

The various computer codes that have been used for solution of this problem differ primarily in the manner in which they handle di-version cross-flows and the mathematical techniques used to obtain a solution to the set of simultaneous nonlinear equations. For example, in HAMBO[10] the quantity of diversion cross-flow is determined by the pressure gradient between adjacent channels. A cross-flow is esti-mated on the basis of the conditions at the inlet of the segment and the axial pressure drop calculated. The revised pressure drops are used to calculate new cross-flows and the iteration continued until convergence is achieved. COBRA[9] also assumes that the cross-flow is determined by the pressure gradient. Conditions at the exit of the axial step are determined by a modified Euler method into which special provisions are incorporated to control the diversion cross-flow. The resulting nonlinear equations are linearized and solved iteratively. In contrast, THINC II[11] assumes that, since the assembly area is confined, no significant pressure differences exist across it. The cross-flows are then determined as those required to provide a laterally uniform pressure at each axial position considered.

5-2 STEADY-STATE PERFORMANCE ANALYSIS AND OPTIMIZATION

5-2.1 Thermal Efficiency and Coolant Performance

The production of high temperature steam is desirable as the plant thermodynamic efficiency obviously increases with increasing steam temperature. This is illustrated in Fig. 5.4 where the efficiency of a

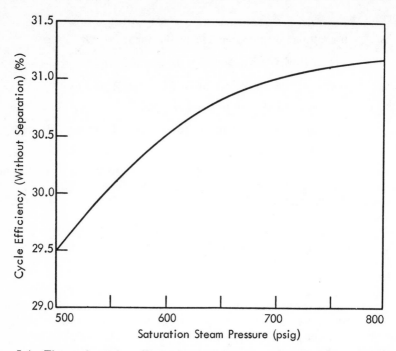

Fig. 5.4 Thermal cycle efficiency as a function of pressure. (From *Nucl. Eng. Design,* **6**, 301, 1967.)

saturated steam cycle is shown as a function of pressure. The effects of moisture separation and reheat are not included.

High steam temperatures require high primary coolant temperatures. The coolant conditions around the primary loop are shown schematically in Fig. 5.5. We may relate the primary coolant temperatures to the secondary steam temperatures through the log mean temperature difference ΔT_m, which can be defined as

$$\Delta T_m \; = \frac{\Delta T_H \; - \Delta T_C}{\ln(\Delta T_H / \Delta T_C)} \quad , \tag{5-30}$$

where ΔT_H and ΔT_C are defined in Fig. 5.5.

As we observed in Sec. 4-4, the heat transfer in the steam generator can be expressed approximately in terms of ΔT_m as

$$q \; = \; UA \, \Delta T_m \quad , \tag{5-31}$$

where

q = rate of heat transfer, Btu/h

U = overall coefficient of heat transfer, Btu/(h ft$^{2\circ}$F)

A = heat transfer area, ft^2.

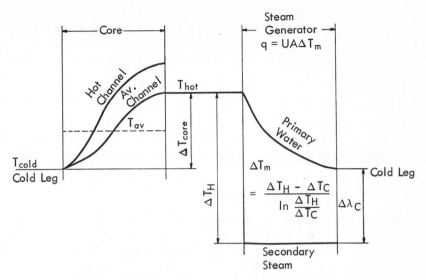

Fig. 5.5 Coolant performance. (From *Nucl. Eng. Design*, **6**, 301, 1967.)

Equation (5-31) shows that a higher log mean temperature difference reduces the required heat-transfer area in the steam generator.
Higher secondary steam temperature and pressure is possible if the
size of steam generator is kept constant. However, we are limited in
this regard, since a high coolant enthalpy will decrease the critical
heat flux and, hence, lead to a low maximum allowable heat flux. Thus,
the minimum flow rate and the maximum inlet temperature of a reactor are determined by the ability of the coolant to transfer the required heat safely. The effectiveness of PWR coolant systems can be
evaluated by comparing average enthalpy rises and the coolant temperatures at the core inlets. This evaluation should be performed in
conjunction with the evaluation of the average heat flux to show the
entire engineering effectiveness of the core design.

5-2.2 Effect of Core-Flow Arrangement on Core Performance

Multi-Pass vs Single-Pass Cores. In a multi-pass core, the core
is separated into regions through which the coolant flows successively.

The advantages of a multi-pass core are:

1. High coolant mass velocity increases the DNB margin.

2. High coolant mixing, occurring at core interpasses, reduces
   $F_{\Delta H}$. However, the benefit of mixing disappears as the radial
   power distribution becomes flat.

3. Since the coolant of a multi-pass core passes through both the high-power region and the low-power region, the total enthalpy rise in the hot channel does not change considerably even if the high-power and low-power regions interchange in later core life.

The disadvantages are:

1. Mechanical design is complicated and requires more structural material inside the core; this is especially significant in a small core.

2. Pressure drop across the core is greatly increased; this increases the pumping power or reduces the total flow rate.

Vaughan[12] has analyzed the thermal and hydraulic performance of a multi-pass core. He assumes the total flow rate has been constant and does not consider the additional cost to achieve the higher pressure drop. An equal-division, two-pass core is equivalent to an orificed core having eight times the pressure-loss coefficient of the one-pass core. If the primary pump were not changed, the total flow rate would be greatly reduced. Since large PWRs use nearly the largest pumps available, pumping capacity normally cannot be increased without adding additional pumps. This essentially nullifies the advantage of a two-pass core.

Orificing For Closed Assemblies And Pressure Tubes. An orificed core redistributes the flow so that more passes through the hot channel at the expense of an increased core pressure drop. The increase in the pressure drop depends mainly on the degree of orificing. For example, a PWR core with 40% additional flow passing through the hot assembly requires the other assemblies to be orificed to give the same pressure drop. Thus, an orificed core would have almost twice as much pressure drop as a similar but unorificed core, This high-pressure drop across an orificed core reduces the total flow rate to the core or increases the pump cost and the pump power. The shift of the power peak during the core life greatly reduces the benefit of orificing so that sometimes its cost exceeds its benefits.

Regional Inlet Velocity Control in an Open Core. When fuel assemblies are open laterally, it is not possible to set the inlet flow to each assembly in accordance with the assembly power. Marked assembly-to-assembly differences in inlet flow would lead to large pressure gradients and high lateral flows that could largely negate the effect of orificing. It may, however, be possible to control flow on a regional basis. If the outermost region were assigned one flow, the adjacent region another, and the innermost region a third flow, assembly-to-pressure differentials could be kept moderate. Although lateral flows would still occur, they would probably not be large enough to negate all the benefit of orificing.

The possible effects of regional velocity control are illustrated in Table 5.2 for the reactor having the configuration and power distribution shown in Fig. 5-6. To keep lateral pressure gradients at a reasonable level, the flow is only partially matched to the power. That is, although the relative power level in region 2 is 1.2, the flow is only 110% of nominal. If the flow in the hot assembly of region 2 is assumed to be 10% less than that assigned to that region, we still obtain an $F_{\Delta H}$ of 1.2. This would be a significant improvement over the $F_{\Delta H}$ of 1.27 that would be obtained without orificing.

TABLE 5-2

Effects of Regional Velocity Control

	Region 1	Region 2	Region 3
Normalized average power density, P	1.0	1.2	0.8
Assigned nominal inlet velocity	1.0	1.1	0.9
Assumed maximum velocity reduction in hot assembly	0.1	0.1	0.1
Minimum inlet velocity, W	0.9	1.0	0.8
Resulting $F_{\Delta H} = P/W$	1.1	1.2	1.0

5-2.3 Interaction of Thermal-Hydraulic and Nuclear Effects

The thermal and hydraulic design of a PWR core cannot be established alone. Many parameters have to be determined mutually by nuclear, thermal, mechanical, control, and material engineering considerations. However, the most complicated relationship is one with the nuclear design that has to be carried out iteratively. Before the thermal and hydraulic design can be initiated, the following nuclear information is required:

1. Power distributions during core life both in steady-state and transient operations. These distributions give the peak power that limits the reactor power output.

2. Water-to-fuel ratio and fuel-rod size for a most economical fuel utilization and suitable reactivity control. This information determines fuel-rod lattice and core size.

After a preliminary thermal and hydraulic design is made, the following information should be given to the nuclear designers for their evaluation:

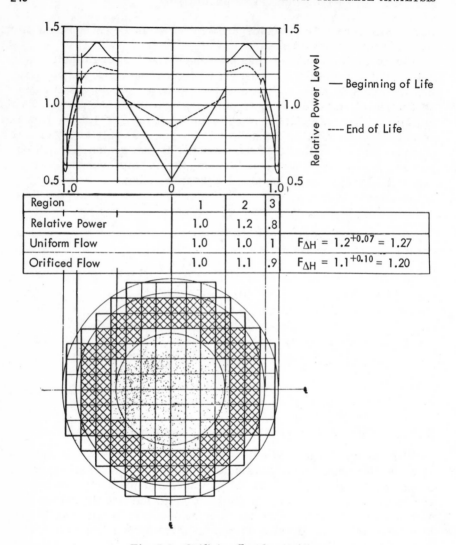

Region	1	2	3	
Relative Power	1.0	1.2	.8	
Uniform Flow	1.0	1.0	1	$F_{\Delta H} = 1.2^{+0.07} = 1.27$
Orificed Flow	1.0	1.1	.9	$F_{\Delta H} = 1.1^{+0.10} = 1.20$

Fig. 5.6   Orificing flow by regions.

1. Void distribution including local boiling void and bulk boiling void.   The void distribution can be used to refine the calculation of nuclear power distribution and to evaluate the reactivity loss due to voids in the core.

2. Average fuel temperature at various power levels.   These temperatures determine the core power coefficient through the Doppler effect.

Reduction of Local-Power Peaking. Reducing the local-power peaking is the most effective way to increase the average power density of the fuel without exceeding the material limitations. The local-power peaking in a water moderated reactor core is usually located adjacent to a vacant control-rod slot or the fuel-assembly boundary because of the large water gaps that cause a local increase in thermal flux. A uniform distribution of all water gaps is always helpful in reducing local-power peaking, which can also be reduced by a lower fuel enrichment or by a thicker clad. A fuel rod of lower enrichment can hardly be identified during assembly. However, a fuel rod of thicker clad can be identified, and the location of a fuel rod with thicker cladding at the corner of a square fuel-assembly is a common way of reducing local-power peaking.

Effect of Local-Boiling Void on Local Power. The void generated by local boiling reduces the local-moderator density and thus reduces the local-power level. This ability to use its own local-boiling void as an automatic power-peak limiter is a unique feature of the pressurized water reactor. This is even true for a chemical shim controlled PWR where boron is dissolved in the coolant. Although it is possible for the overall void coefficient to be positive, the local effect will reduce the thermal-neutron flux in the vicinity of the void. Creation of voids locally dilutes the poison and thus tends to increase the fast-neutron flux. However, in a channel having less than a four-inch radius, the local decrease in moderator density increases the flux leakage from the channel sufficiently to cause a decrease in local power. This self-limiting effect is most pronounced at the end of the core life where practically no boron is present in the moderator.

Evaluation of Local-Boiling Void. We have seen in Chap. 3 that the bubbles in subcooled local boiling are, for the most part, attached or flowing parallel to the heating surface. The bubbles generated in a bulk boiling behave quite differently. In a constant pressure system, the bulk-boiling void is related directly to the bulk-flow enthalpy with only a secondary effect resulting from mass-flow rate. Subcooled local-boiling void is not only a function of local subcooling, but also a strong function of mass-flow rate and local-heat flux. Thus, the density variation of the coolant mixture can be expressed in the following form:

$$\Delta\rho = \left.\frac{\partial\rho}{\partial T}\right|_{q'',G} \Delta T + \left.\frac{\partial\rho}{\partial q''}\right|_{T,G} \Delta q'' + \left.\frac{\partial\rho}{\partial G}\right|_{T,q''} \Delta G \quad . \qquad (5\text{-}32)$$

The voids in a PWR core are largely the result of subcooled local boiling and are generated in the high heat flux region of the core. Therefore, an accurate determination of the local-boiling void is of

prime importance in the calculation of the moderator coefficient of a
pressurized water reactor. We may determine the voids at a given
set of operating conditions using the void models of Sec. 3-1.2 in a
digital computer code, such as THINC-I (Sec. 3-1.3), which is capable
of computing core-wide flows. By repeating the process for a slightly
different value of one of the independent variables, the partial
derivative of density with respect to that variable may be established.
The rates of density changes $\partial\rho/\partial T$, $\partial\rho/\partial q''$, and $\partial\rho/\partial G$ at typical
PWR operating conditions are presented in Figs. 5.7 and 5.8.

Combined Thermal and Nuclear Calculations. Computer codes are
now available that can consider both thermal-hydraulic and nuclear-
spatial effects simultaneously. Minton[13] reports that the THUNDER

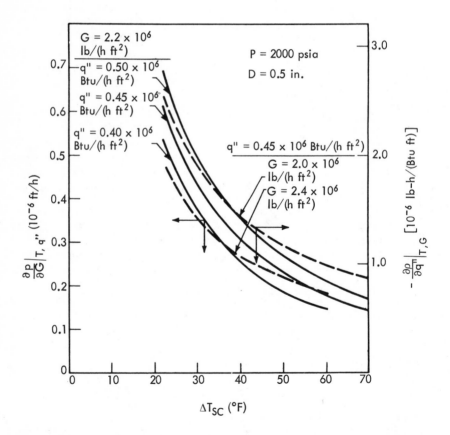

Fig. 5.7 Water-density change rate vs flow rate and heat flux. (From *Nucl.
Eng. Design,* **6**, 301, 1967.)

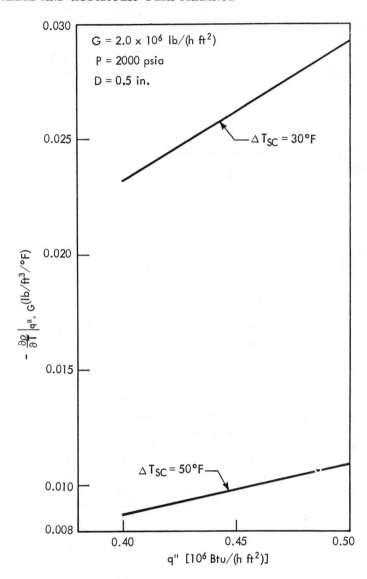

Fig. 5.8 Water-density change rate vs subcooling. (From *Nucl. Eng. De-sign*, **6**, 301, 1967.)

code utilizes an approximate heat flux distribution to obtain a void distribution. The void distribution is then used to modify the original power distribution, and the process is continued until convergence is obtained.

5-2.4 Thermal Performance Progress and Optimization

The advance in ratings of pressurized water reactors can be seen chronologically from Yankee's initial rating of 134 MW(e) in 1960 through units of over 1000 MW(e) now being built. By 1980, units of about 1500 MW(e) are expected to be on the line.

Many factors have contributed to the rapid development of the PWR and have made these larger plant sizes feasible from both engineering and economic standpoints. Continuing improvements in thermal performance of the plant represent a key development and these are particularly significant because they have been made within a comparatively limited temperature range—bounded by condenser cooling water temperature at the bottom and maximum allowable reactor coolant temperature at the top, both of which are relatively fixed. Thus, the reactor-coolant and the steam-turbine cycles must fit within this temperature range and must be assigned operating temperatures that result in optimum overall plant performance.

In a typical 1960 nuclear plant, the value of $F_{\Delta H}$ used was conservatively set at 3.36 because of the lack of previous operational data. By 1968, with the improvements in core design and more realistic calculation of the subfactors, this hot-channel factor was reduced to about 1.7. The thermal-performance improvements that have accompanied this reduction in the hot-channel factor are plotted in Fig. 5.9. A list of thermal parameters of various PWR cores indicating their progress is given in Table 5.3. However, the rapid advances in PWR plant ratings cannot be assigned to the improved thermal cycle alone; other contributing factors are higher operating pressures, increased coolant-flow rates, and greater heat-transfer area, to name a few. Within the manufacturing restrictions on the size of components at any given point in time, these variables are more often determined by engineering economics than by thermal-cycle improvements. Thus, within the allowable temperature range, an engineering economic study is required to determine the optimum choice of plant operating parameters and the size of components. In this optimization process, the thermal performance of the reactor core is a key factor.

With the development of modern optimization theory, the trend has been to consider the economic study to determine thermal-design parameters as a mathematical programming problem. In such a problem, one attempts to minimize or maximize a function, called the objective function, subject to a number of constraints. In this case, the objective function would be power costs, and the thermal constraints would be those cited in Sec. 5-1.1 (e.g., DNBR $\geq k$). Additional constraints are imposed by other engineering and physics requirements.

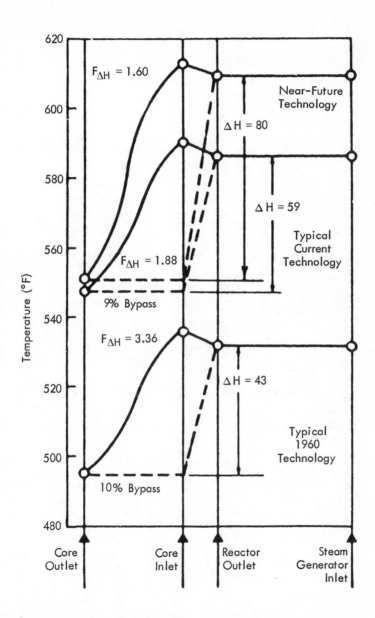

Fig. 5.9 Pressurized water reactor core performance advances since 1960.
(From *Nucl. Eng. Design*, **6**, 301, 1967.)

Table 5-3

THERMAL PARAMETERS OF TYPICAL PWR CORE DESIGNS

Year of Design →	58	64	62	64	64	66	66	67
Reactor →	Yankee Rowe	Yankee Rowe	SELNI	Conn-Yankee	San Onofre	Turkey Point	Indian Point II	Burlington No. 1
Thermal power, MW(th)	392	600	825	1473	1346	2097	2758	3083
Average heat flux, 10^3 Btu/(h ft^2)	86	128	130	136	143	164	175	196
Average reactor ΔT, °F	30	41.6	56.5	38.5	44.2	54	53	59.4
Maximum linear power, kW/ft	6.5	9.9	12.4	14.3	15.0	17.3	18.5	17.9
Core power density, kW/liter	58	89	64	66.6	72	79	85	84
Fuel power density, kW/kg of U	19	28.7	21	22.2	23.4	29.5	31.5	31.5

Mathematically, we may state our problem as:

minimize

$$C = \phi(y_1, y_2, \ldots y_n) \qquad (5\text{-}33)$$

subject to the constraints

$$f_1(y_1, y_2, \ldots y_n) = 0$$
$$f_j(y_1, y_2, \ldots y_n) \leqslant 0$$
$$f_k(y_1, y_2, \ldots y_n) \geqslant 0 \qquad (5\text{-}34)$$

where y_1, y_2, $\ldots y_n$ are the designer's decision variables, which may include the total flow to the core, core-inlet temperature, primary-system operating pressure, secondary-system pressure, fuel-rod diameter, number of fuel rods, etc.

Numerical solutions for large-size optimization problems can now be executed readily on modern computers. The procedures adaptable to problems of the type expected generally fall into two categories:

In the first, the problem is linearized by writing the objective function and each constraint as a Taylor's series expansion in which only the linear terms are retained. Thus, we would have

$$f_i(y_1, y_2, \ldots, y_n) \approx A_i + \left(\frac{\partial f_i}{\partial y_1}\right)\Delta y_1 + \left(\frac{\partial f_i}{\partial y_2}\right)\Delta y_2 + \ldots + \left(\frac{\partial f_i}{\partial y_n}\right)\Delta y_n .$$

$$(5\text{-}35)$$

This linear problem can then be solved by the well-known Simplex procedure. Since the linearization is applicable only over a small region, the full step predicted by the Simplex algorithm is not taken; the variables are moved in the predicted direction but the maximum Δy is limited. The procedure is then repeated for the succession of points indicated until an optimum solution is obtained. An operable example of this class of computer program is POP which has been described by Smith.[14]

In the second major class of methods, the constrained optimization is converted to an unconstrained problem. This may be done by forming a new objective function SN, such that, if we have m constraint functions,

$$SN = C + \sum_{i=1}^{m} \delta_i K_i [f_i(y_1, y_2, \ldots y_n)]^2 . \qquad (5\text{-}36)$$

The quantities δ_i are unity for the equality constraints. For inequality constraints, the δ_i are zero if the constraint is met and unity otherwise. The K_i are positive constants. It may be seen that the greater the violation of the constraint the higher the objective function. By attempting to minimize this revised function, we minimize the constraint violations. Solution of the problem for a series of increasing values of K_i leads to a condition where all constraints are finally satisfied.

To minimize the new unconstrained objective function SN, a search procedure may be used. An example of a computer program following this technique is the Optimal Search of Weisman et al.[15] Alternatively, the new unconstrained objective function may be minimized by following its gradient. An example of this technique is the SUMPT program of Fiacco and McCormick.[16] The SUMPT program also uses a somewhat different formulation of Eq. (5-36). For extensive reviews of nonlinear programming, the reader is referred to Hadley[17] and Zangwill.[18]

5-3 CORE RELIABILITY

5-3.1 Reliabilty Criterion

We may distinguish between system failures that could affect the health and safety of the public and those that would have little if any such effect. The former category is the concern of the safeguards analysis, while the latter determines system reliability.

The basic criterion in the design of a reactor core is assurance of the integrity of the fuel cladding under all operating conditions. Cladding failures do not in themselves cause a risk to public health or safety. A small number of failures can be tolerated, providing the leakage of fission products is within the cleanup capability of the system, but an excessive number of failures would require a plant shutdown to remove the defective fuel. Since the shutdown would occur at activity levels within the limits for which the plant was designed, we cannot consider that public safety would be compromised; however, excessive failures would obviously have adverse effects on plant reliability.

The reliability of a system may be defined as the probability that the system will not fail. The reliability of a core thermal design can therefore be evaluated from the total probability of fuel failure. The modes of fuel-cladding failure include (1) clad failure caused by exceeding the critical-heat flux (DNB) and (2) clad failure due to operation at an excessive linear-power rating. Experience has shown that both types of failures are local in nature and do not propagate throughout the core. If these modes of failure are considered to be independent, the total failure probability is the sum of the individual failure probabilities.

5-3.2 Reliability of Core Thermal Design

The safety margin incorporated in a core thermal design necessarily limits the power capability of the core. We have seen that the major design limitation on the power capability of a PWR core is the critical heat-flux phenomenon, or departure from nucleate boiling (DNB). By increasing the DNB safety margin, we obviously increase system reliability but decrease power capability. Thus, the parameter of most significance in a reliability analysis is the minimum-DNB ratio defined by Eq. (5-6). This section will deal with those parameters affecting DNB and the manner in which variations in the parameters are used to relate the DNB ratio to a reliability value. The items to be considered are:

- uncertainty in the DNB correlation

- engineering hot-channel factor distribution

- nuclear hot-channel factor distribution

- variations of operating pressure, temperature, and instrumentation error.

Reliability Based on Hot-Channel Analysis. There are several methods by which we can evaluate the reliability of a core thermal design. We may consider the hot channel alone and determine the probability of a failure there. To do so, we will define a design DNB ratio

$$\text{DNBR}_{\text{des}} = \frac{q''_{\text{DNB predicted}}}{q''_{\text{des}}} , \qquad (5-37)$$

where

q''_{des} = hot-channel heat flux, at location where DNB flux is minimum, obtained using design hot-channel factors

$q''_{\text{DNB predicted}}$ = DNB flux predicted by DNB correlation for assumed operating conditions.

There is variability associated with both the DNB flux and the hot-channel flux. We may therefore define an actual DNB ratio

$$\text{DNBR}_{\text{actual}} = \frac{q''_{\text{DNB}}}{q''_{\text{actual}}} , \qquad (5-38)$$

where

q''_{DNB} = actual flux at which DNB occurs

q''_{actual} = actual hot-channel flux at DNB location.

We can obtain the hot-channel heat fluxes in terms of the radial-nuclear factor F_R^N, heat flux F_q^E, and the heat flux in the average channel at the DNB location $q''_{\text{DNB}_{avg}}$; hence,

$$\frac{\text{DNBR}_{\text{actual}}}{\text{DNBR}_{\text{des}}} = \left[\frac{q''_{\text{DNB}}}{\left(q''_{\text{DNB}_{avg}}\right)\left(F_{R_{\text{act}}}^N\right)\left(F_{q_{\text{act}}}^E\right)}\right]\left[\frac{\left(q''_{\text{DNB}_{avg}}\right)\left(F_{R_{\text{des}}}^N\right)\left(F_{q_{\text{des}}}^E\right)}{q''_{\text{DNB}_{\text{predicted}}}}\right] \quad ,$$

$$(5\text{-}39)$$

where the subscripts "des" and "act" indicate design and actual values, respectively. Next, we solve for the actual DNB ratio

$$\text{DNBR}_{\text{actual}} = \left[\frac{\left(\text{DNBR}_{\text{des}}\right)\left(F_{R_{\text{des}}}^N\right)\left(F_{q_{\text{des}}}^E\right)}{\left(F_{R_{\text{act}}}^N\right)\left(F_{q_{\text{act}}}^E\right)}\right]\left[\frac{q''_{\text{DNB}}}{q''_{\text{DNB}_{\text{predicted}}}}\right] \quad . \qquad (5\text{-}40)$$

We now define

$$F^{\text{DNB}} = \frac{q''_{\text{DNB}_{\text{predicted}}}}{q''_{\text{DNB}}} \qquad (5\text{-}41)$$

then

$$\text{DNBR}_{\text{actual}} = \frac{\left(\text{DNBR}_{\text{des}}\right)\left(F_{R_{\text{des}}}^N\right)\left(F_{q_{\text{des}}}^E\right)}{\left(F_{R_{\text{act}}}^N\right)\left(F_{q_{\text{act}}}^E\right)\left(F^{\text{DNB}}\right)} \quad . \qquad (5\text{-}42)$$

Failure will occur when the actual DNB ratio is less than unity; therefore, it occurs when

$$F_{R_{\text{act}}}^N \; F_{q_{\text{act}}}^E \; F^{\text{DNB}} > \text{DNBR}_{\text{des}} \; F_{R_{\text{des}}}^N \; F_{q_{\text{des}}}^E \qquad (5\text{-}43)$$

Then the probability that no failure occurs is

$$p_{nf} = p\left[F_{R_{\text{act}}}^N \; F_{q_{\text{act}}}^E \; F^{\text{DNBR}} < \text{DNBR}_{\text{des}} \; F_{R_{\text{des}}}^N \; F_{q_{\text{des}}}^E\right] \quad , \qquad (5\text{-}44)$$

where $p(B)$ = the probability that (B) will occur.

The factors $F_{q_{\text{act}}}^E$, $F_{R_{\text{act}}}^N$, and F^{DNB} may all be described in terms of probability distribution functions. We have seen in Sect. 5-1.6 how a probability distribution can be determined for F_q^E. To determine a distribution function for F^{DNB}, we must compare the predictions of the DNB correlation with the experimental data available. The data are classified in accordance with the ratio F^{DNB}, and we fit a normal frequency function $f(F^{\text{DNB}})$ to the resulting histogram. A distribution function $\phi(X)$ can then be obtained from

$$\phi(X) = \int_{-\infty}^{x} f(F^{\text{DNB}})d(F^{\text{DNB}}) \qquad (5\text{-}45)$$

Note that for any specified value of F^{DNB}, say A,

$$\phi(A) = p(F^{DNB} < A) \quad . \tag{5-46}$$

The available DNB data may be considered a sample of all the data that could be obtained. Another sample would give a different histogram, and, to account for this uncertainty, a set of tables[5] that enable the determination of probabilities based on sample parameters at a given confidence level γ is used. The tables may be regarded as providing a correction factor for Eq. (5-45). After the correction has been applied, we may say that, at most, a proportion p of the normal population is less than the value specified with confidence level γ. A value of 95% is usually assumed for γ.

To obtain the distribution function for $F_{R_{act}}^N$, the values of F_R^N obtained from an appropriate nuclear-design code are plotted in terms of the fraction of the total number of channels having F_R^N values less than that stated. A function is then fitted to the resultant curve.

To obtain the combined probability that design conditions will not be exceeded, we must convolute the individual distributions. If we have two independent variables X and Y having distribution functions ϕ_1 and ϕ_2, the probability that the product XY is less than a given value A is given by

$$p[XY < A] \leqslant \sum_i [\phi_1(X_{i+1}) - \phi_1(X_i)][\phi_2(A/X_i)] \quad . \tag{5-47}$$

By assuming a series of values for A, we may determine the distribution function for (XY). This function may then be convoluted with additional variables.

Core-Wide Reliability Analysis. In confining attention to the hot channel alone, we tacitly make the assumption that non-failure probability elsewhere is also one. A more reasonable assumption is that a failure is possible in any channel of the core. One method for determining core-wide reliability has been proposed by Antognetti et al.[19] and Businaro and Pozzi.[20] They divided the core into a large number of regions and performed a full set of thermal-design calculations in each region based on values of the randomly varying parameters drawn from their distributions by a Monte-Carlo technique. Distributions for the maximum clad temperature or other desired quantities can thus be obtained for the entire core. The method is, however, quite cumbersome and requires considerable computer time.

Tong[21] has indicated how the previous hot-channel analysis can be extended core-wide. We shall illustrate the extended method by applying it to the Brookwood reactor core,[22] and by estimating the number of rods that might reach DNB at the maximum overpower condition for a reactor having a limiting DNB ratio of 1.3. The engineering hot-channel factors will be omitted for simplicity.

The local heat flux q'' at any radial position in the reactor can be expressed by the equation

$$q'' = \overline{q}''_{\text{reactor avg}} \times \frac{q''_{\text{rod avg}}}{\overline{q}''_{\text{reactor avg}}} \times F_Z^N \quad , \qquad (5\text{-}48)$$

where

q'' = local flux in a rod

$\dfrac{q''_{\text{rod avg}}}{\overline{q}''_{\text{reactor avg}}}$ = rod power in fraction of average rod power (value varies with radial position)

F_Z^N = axial hot-channel factor (fixed for all rods).

The plots of rod power distributions labeled as the best fit and the worst cases are shown in Fig. 5.10, where the values of $(q''_{\text{rod avg}}/q''_{\text{reactor avg}})$ are plotted against the number of rods having a power larger than shown by the local value of the curve. The dotted curve is a best-fit curve obtained from a regressive analysis of these data. The uncertainties in the calculated results are considered to be normally distributed over the total number of rods in the core. If the largest uncertainties are assigned to the rods having the largest local power, then the superposition of the uncertainty distribution on the best-fit curve results in the solid curve labeled as the worst case. This is obviously the most conservative distribution. We can express this distribution in terms of the predicted DNB flux. This is done in Fig. 5.10, where the rod-wise variation of $(q''_{\text{DNB}_{\text{predicted}}}/q'')$ at a 112% overpower condition is plotted as the additional ordinate scale. The ratio $(q''_{\text{DNB}_{\text{predicted}}}/q'')$ corresponds to our definition of DNBR$_{\text{des}}$.

The actual DNB ratio, defined by Eq. (5-38), can be rewritten as

$$\text{DNBR}_{\text{actual}} = \frac{q''_{\text{DNB}_{\text{predicted}}}}{q''_{\text{actual}}} \times \frac{q''_{\text{DNB}}}{q''_{\text{DNB}_{\text{predicted}}}} = \text{DNBR}_{\text{des}}/F^{\text{DNB}}. \quad (5\text{-}49)$$

Again, a failure may be considered to occur when DNBR$_{\text{actual}}$ is less than 1 or whenever $F^{\text{DNB}} \geqslant$ DNBR. We obtain the probability of this occurring by convoluting the distribution function for DNBR$_{\text{des}}$ (from Fig. 5.10) with that for F^{DNB}. The probability distribution for F^{DNB}, which was obtained from Tong's W-3 DNB correlation for a confidence level of 95% by the previously described procedure, is plotted as a function of the DNBR$_{\text{des}}$ in Fig. 5.11.

In the Brookwood reactor design, the DNB ratio in the hot channel

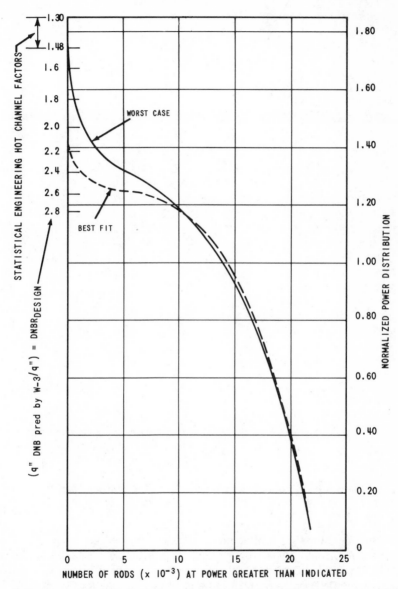

Fig. 5.10 Power distribution for Brookwood at 112% overpower. (From Ref. 22.)

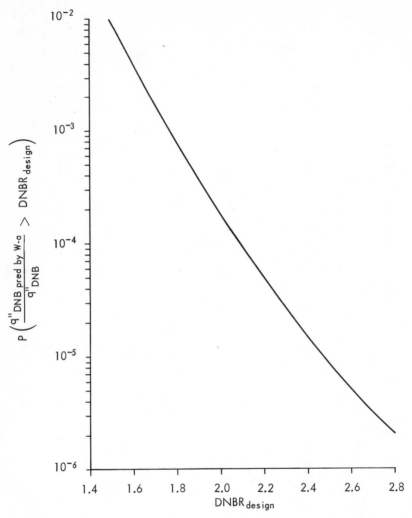

Fig. 5.11 Probability distribution curve for W-3 DNB correlation. (From Ref. 22.)

with the engineering hot-channel factors applied is 1.3 at the over-power conditions. The worst overpower situation is taken as 112% of nominal power. Omitting the engineering uncertainties results in an overpower DNB ratio of 1.48, as shown on the second ordinate of Fig. 5.10. To obtain the number of fuel rods that might possibly reach DNB, it is necessary only to convolve Fig. 5.10 with Fig. 5.11 in accordance with Eq. (5-49). The number of rods so obtained may be considered to be an index of the design reliability.

The actual convolution procedure can be demonstrated by a sample calculation. From Fig. 5.10, the number of rods that have $DNBR_{des}$ values between 1.48 and 1.49 is 29. From Fig. 5.11, the probability that F^{DNB} will be greater than a $DNBR_{des}$ value of 1.48 is 0.011. The product of 29 and 0.011 is 0.319 rods that might possibly reach DNB in this group of 29 rods. This process is continued group by group for the entire core, and the summation of the results of all groups gives 2.4 (see Table 5.4) as the number of rods that might possibly reach DNB in the core of the Brookwood reactor at the worst over-power condition.

The method described above is similar to the "synthesis method" of uncertainty analysis proposed by Fenech and Gueron.[23] However, in the "synthesis method," the fuel rods are divided into axial segments for which the failure probabilities are computed. The non-failure probability for the rod is the product of the non-failure probabilities for the individual segments. The influence of the number of axial segments chosen is taken into account by allowing for a greater variation in the enthalpy rise, at the axial location considered, for smaller numbers of segments.

5-4 PROTECTION AND MEASUREMENT INSTRUMENTATION

5-4.1 Reactor Protection

The basis for the design of the reactor protection system is contained in the Atomic Energy Commission's "General Design Criteria for Nuclear Construction Permits,"[24] which states, "The reactor core shall be designed to function throughout its design lifetime without exceeding acceptable fuel damage limits which have been stipulated and justified. The core design, together with reliable process decay and heat removal systems shall provide for this capability under all expected conditions of normal operation with appropriate margins for uncertainties and for transient situations which can be anticipated, including the effects of loss of power re-circulation in pumps, tripping of the turbine generator set, isolation of the reactor from the primary heat sink, and loss of all off-site power." This criterion is generally interpreted as meaning that failures due to exceeding the critical-heat flux or an excessive linear heat production must be avoided during any reasonably anticipated situation.

Following these guidelines, the revised Code of Federal Regulations[25] defines "safety limits" and "safety settings." "Safety limits are limits upon important process variables which are found to be necessary to reasonably protect the integrity of each of the physical

Table 5-4

Reliability Calculations for Brookwood Reactor

(1) DNBR$_{des}$	(2) No. of Rods In Group	(3) Probability of DNB Occurring	(4) Number of Rods Which Might Reach DNB (2) × (3)
1.48	29	0.011	0.3190
1.49	14	0.0097	0.1358
1.52	22	0.0075	0.1650
1.55	22	0.00562	0.1236
1.58	22	0.00448	0.0986
1.60	22	0.00370	0.0814
1.62	22	0.00315	0.0693
1.64	21	0.00270	0.0567
1.66	21	0.00236	0.0496
1.67	21	0.00212	0.0445
1.68	108	0.00190	0.2052
1.74	108	0.00123	0.1328
1.78	108	0.00087	0.0940
1.82	108	0.00066	0.0713
1.85	217	0.000526	0.1141
1.90	217	0.000352	0.0764
1.95	1 083	0.000250	0.2708
2.13	2 166	0.000070	0.1516
2.31	2 166	0.0000245	0.0531
2.44	2 166	0.0000116	0.0251
2.60	2 166	0.0000048	0.0104
2.86	10 830	0.00000147	0.0159
	21 659		2.3642 ≈ 2.4

Note: The second column lists the number of rods at the maximum overpower condition which from Fig. 5-10 have DNBR$_{des}$ values between consecutive values in the first column. The sum of the entries in this column is the total number of rods in the core: 21 659. The third column lists the probability from Fig. 5-11 of DNB occurring at the corresponding DNBR$_{des}$ value. The fourth column is obtained by taking the product of adjacent entries in Columns (2) and (3). This gives the number of rods for each group which might possibly reach DNB. The sum of the entries in this column is ≈2.4, which represents the total number of rods that might possibly reach DNB in the core of the Brookwood reactor.

barriers which guard against the uncontrolled release of radioactivity." The "maximum safety settings are settings for automatic protective devices related to variables on which safety limits have been placed. . . . A maximum safety setting shall be so chosen that automatic protective action will correct the most severe abnormal situation anticipated before a safety limit is exceeded." Thus, the safety limit on reactor power would be the power level at which operation is deemed to become unsafe, while the maximum safety setting would be the power level at which a trip is initiated. The maximum safety settings must take into account the measurement and instrument uncertainties associated with the process variables.

We may think of the reactor-protection system as a control system, which, in routine operation, remains an observer acting only if the reactor system reaches the limit of permissible operation (maximum safety setting). The following are the PWR abnormal operating conditions that usually will cause a reactor trip.[26]

1. High neutron flux level. High flux level indicates excessive power generation in the reactor. Coincident high flux level signals from two power range channels cause a trip.

2. High reactor start-up rate. Reactor start-up rate indication, computed by the start-up channels, gives the operator information on the rate of power change. High start-up rate signals from source range instrumentation actuate an alarm and a rod-stop circuit. High start-up rate signals from intermediate range channels actuate a rod-stop circuit to prevent further motion of the control rods and, if the start-up rate should continue to increase, initiate a trip signal.

3. Loss of reactor coolant flow. Trip is required upon loss of flow in one or more reactor coolant loops, or upon loss of power to one or more reactor coolant pumps. The need to trip on loss of flow in one loop is a function of the power level at the time of the accident and the number of loops in the plant. This protection is necessary to prevent excessive temperatures in core materials resulting from loss of flow.

4. Minimum DNBR trip. A reactor trip is provided to prevent reactor coolant conditions in the core that approach those at which the boiling crisis occurs. The set point for this trip is continuously calculated from the reactor power, coolant inlet temperatures, and pressurizer pressure. Figure 5.12 shows the safety limits[27] established for pressure, temperature, and

power at 100% flow in the San Onofre plant. The maximum safety settings are derived from these limits by proper allowance for instrument and measurement uncertainties.

5. Manual trip. Trip initiated by the reactor operator.

6. High water level in the pressurizer. High level in the pressurizer initiates trip to prevent filling the pressurizer and discharging water through the safety valves.

7. Initiation of safety injection operation. This trip provides a backup for the low-pressure trip (4).

8. Turbine-generator trip. Above approximately 10% power level, a turbine trip initiates a scram to prevent activation of the steam generator safety valve.

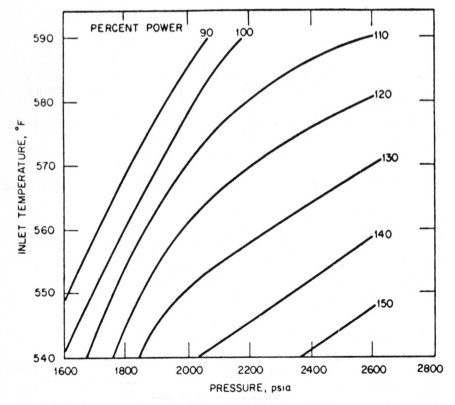

Fig. 5.12 Safety limits on pressure, temperature, and power at 100% nominal flow for San Onofre. (From *Nucl. Safety*, **9**, 153, 1968.)

9. Low steam generator water level. Redundant instrumentation
   is supplied to protect against loss of the steam generator
   inventory. Should this still occur, a reactor trip is indicated.

Figure 5.13 shows the relationship of the key thermal protection trips
and reactor operating conditions at 100% nominal flow.

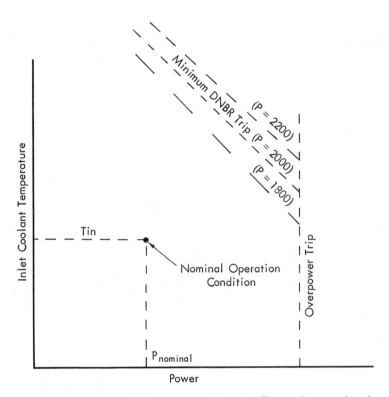

Fig. 5.13 Relationship of trip settings to flow and power level.

5-4.2 In-Core Instrumentation

The in-core instrumentation is used primarily to demonstrate the
power capability of a reactor. It has been generally found that the
measured power capability is higher than the design value; thus, in-
core instrumentation is not ordinarily required for safe operation but
has proved helpful in obtaining the "stretch" output of a number of
cores. A typical example is in the Yankee-Rowe plant, where in-core
instrumentation was extremely valuable in increasing the plant
capability from 392 to 600 MW(th).

The in-core instrumentation in the Yankee reactor[28] is shown in Fig. 5.14. The circles represent the thermocouple positions. There are 27 thermocouples inside the core: 19 are concentrated in one quadrant, 8 are located to check the symmetry of the flow and the power output. The crosses show the positions of the 22 flux wires in the core, again with 19 concentrated in one quadrant, and each of the remaining 3 located in one of the other quadrants to check the power tilt. The thermocouples and the flux wires are located at the centers of the fuel assemblies. The thermocouples, measuring the exit temperature of the coolant at the center of the assembly, are located at the exit nozzle in the upper-core support plate.

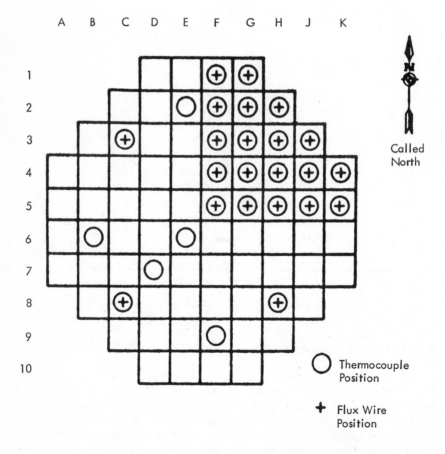

Fig. 5.14 Yankee in-core instrumentation.

The measured hot-channel factors are plotted against those predicted in Fig. 5.15. The ordinate indicates the hot-channel factor for enthalpy rise and the hot-spot factor for heat flux while the abscissa shows the control-rod group positions for various times during the life of the core. The comparison of the measured points (circles and squares) with the predicted values (solid lines) indicates good agreement.

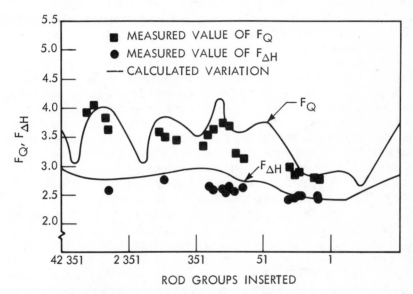

Fig. 5.15 Measured and predicted hot channel factors for enthalpy and heat flux. (From *Nucl. Eng. Design*, **6**, 301, 1967.)

5-5 TRANSIENT PERFORMANCE AND SAFEGUARDS ANALYSIS

5-5.1 Safety Criteria

In setting the "safety limits" and "maximum safety settings" described in Sect. 5-4.1, it is assumed that the transient causing a departure from normal reactor conditions will be such that proper action of the protection system will prevent any core damage. While this is possible for the most probable transients, we may postulate less likely, but more severe, accidents where it is not possible to prevent some damage.

The basic principle of safety-system design is that the potential magnitude of injury or damage should be considerably less for accidents that are likely than for those that have a low probability of occurrence. It is desirable to define sets of departures from normal operation that differ from set to set in the probability of their occurrence.[29]

Set I includes conditions that occur frequently or regularly in the course of normal operation, refueling, or maintenance; e.g., isolated rupture of a fuel element, load changes, approach to criticality, etc. It is required that the plant be designed such that the full range of these conditions can be handled without shutting the plant down manually or automatically.

Set II includes all faults that are not expected during normal plant operation but can reasonably be expected during the life of a particular plant. Good examples of such conditions are loss of power to reactor components (e.g., pumps) or control systems, loss of condensor cooling, loss of feedwater, inadvertant rod withdrawal, etc. Plant design must ensure that no such fault can cause others that are more serious or fuel damage in excess of that which may be normal in a rapid reactor shutdown. The conditions of this set correspond to those for which the "maximum safety settings" prevent the "safety limits" from being reached. It is consistent with the AEC's "General Design Criteria for Nuclear Plant Construction Permits."[24]

A third condition is comprised of departures from nominal conditions that are not expected to occur in the lifetime of any particular plant but may be expected to occur a few times in the nuclear power industry over a 30- to 40-year period. Such accidents as a minor loss of primary coolant, minor secondary steam break, or inadvertent boric-acid dilution would fall into this category. For such conditions, it is desired that the fault create no necessity for interruption or restriction of public use of the areas in the plant vicinity to which the public normally has access.

The fourth and final set is made up of those faults that are so improbable they are not expected to occur in the industry but whose consequences include the potential for serious public damage or injury. Thus, despite their low probability, safeguards must be provided. They represent the limiting case. In this category, the thermal designer would have to consider a major rupture of the primary or secondary system, ejection of the maximum worth control rod, or the consequences of movement of the fuel or structure. For these drastic conditions, the possibility of significant plant damage is accepted, but it is required that in the event of such a fault, accompanied by an independent loss of function of any engineered safeguard system, the off-site radioactivity dosage limitations of the Code of Federal

Regulations Section[25] 10 CFR 100 are not exceeded. This requirement is that stipulated for severe accidents in the AEC's "General Design Criteria for Nuclear Plant Construction Permits."[24]

The major accident situations which the thermal designer usually considers are: (a) the loss-of-flow accident due to pump power loss; (b) reactivity insertion; (c) the steam break accident due to a major rupture of the secondary system; and (d) the loss-of-coolant accident due to a major rupture of the primary system (may include rupture of a control rod housing and subsequent rod ejection). Since the loss-of-flow accident and most reactivity insertion accidents are considered as likely to occur, they are condition II situations, and the reactor system is required to respond without damage to the core. The remaining accidents are highly unlikely and are considered to fall under condition IV. The thermal designer must then determine what damage, if any, will occur under these situations.

5-5.2 Loss-of-Load Transient

A loss-of-load transient is quite likely during the life of a plant. The transient, therefore, falls into set II where the design criteria are that the transient cause no damage nor generate a worse fault.

A sudden reduction in the steam flow first causes a reduced rate of heat removal from the primary coolant. Heat addition in the reactor core remains constant initially and exceeds the rate of heat removal. This results in heat-up of the coolant and a pressurizer insurge: a flow of water from the loop into the pressurizer. The increased coolant temperature progresses around the loop, and, when it reaches the core, it decreases reactivity and, hence, power. The reduction in power may be to a level below that of the rate of heat removal. This may then lead to a pressurizer outsurge. The pressurizer heaters and sprays are used to maintain system pressure within the control band.

Analysis of these transients requires an accurate modeling of the pressurizer. Redfield and Margolis[30] devised a model of the pressurizer and loop based on the concept of two closed systems. One system contains the steam phase and that portion of the pressurizer liquid from which evaporation takes place or into which steam condenses. The other system is the remainder of the liquid phase. Mass- and energy-conservation equations are applied to each of the closed systems in order to derive heat- and mass-conservation equations for the gas and liquid phases, which are open systems. The heat- and mass-transfer rates are calculated assuming that heat transfer between the steam and liquid phases involves a desuperheating resistance[30] from the steam to the liquid interface and a resistance between the liquid interface and the bulk of the liquid in question. The resistance between the condensate and bulk of the spray drops is assumed negligible, but the resistance between the surface of the pressurizer liquid and condensate is obtained from experimental data. The rate of water evaporation from the steam-water interface is estimated on the basis of kinetic theory.

The Redfield-Margolis model has been compared with the results of loss-of-load tests in the Shippingport plant, and good agreement was obtained.[31] Computations based on a saturation line model or an isentropic model provide substantially poorer predictions.

5-5.3 Loss-of-Flow Accident (LOFA)

Simplified Analysis. In a loss-of-flow accident, the clad temperature will rise rapidly if the boiling crisis occurs immediately after the transient is initiated. If the boiling crisis can be postponed until after the reactor-power trip, the clad temperature increase is usually moderate. Thus, the time to the boiling crisis t_{crit} is a significant parameter in the LOFA analysis.

The determination of the coolant flow as a function of time is the first step in the analysis. If we make the conservative assumption that pump inertia is negligible, the head change across the pump may be considered to go immediately to zero and remain there. We may then determine the flow coast-down by equating the frictional retarding force in the loop to the change in momentum of the fluid. We then have

$$\frac{L\,\rho}{g_c}\frac{du}{dt} = -C_f\,\frac{\rho u^2}{2g_c} \quad , \tag{5-50}$$

where

L = total length of the loop

t = time

C_f = total pressure loss coefficient of the loop

u = effective flow velocity

ρ = average fluid density .

The above equation can be rewritten as

$$\frac{du}{dt} + Ku^2 = 0 \quad , \tag{5-51}$$

where

$K = C_f/2L$.

(For example, K equals 0.0893/ft for the Yankee-Rowe hot channel.)
The boundary conditions are

$$u = u_o, \quad \text{at} \quad t = 0 \quad . \tag{5-52}$$

Then, the solution of the differential equation is

$$\frac{u}{u_o} = \frac{1}{(Ku_ot + 1)} \quad . \tag{5-53}$$

The coolant enthalpy rise in a hot channel up to the length l_{crit}, at which the boiling crisis occurs, is

$$\Delta H_{crit} = \frac{4}{GD_e} \int_0^{l_{crit}} q''(z) \, dz \quad , \tag{5-54}$$

and

$$l_{crit} = \int_0^{t_{crit}} u \, dt \quad . \tag{5-55}$$

By combining Eqs. (5-53) through (5-55), Tong[32] obtained the relationship

$$t_{crit} + \frac{1}{Ku_o} = f\left(\frac{q''_{crit}}{De}\right), \tag{5-56}$$

where f indicates a functional relationship and

$$\frac{q''_{crit}}{De} \propto \frac{kW}{\text{liter of H}_2\text{O}} \quad . \tag{5-57}$$

The major contribution of this work is to point out that the time-to-boiling crisis depends strongly on the value of volumetric power density (kW/liter of H_2O) in the core.

Once the time at which the boiling crisis occurs is known, we may determine the rate at which the fuel cladding temperature rises. In the case of a UO_2 fuel rod, the thermal resistances and capacitances of the UO_2 pellet and the metallic clad can be lumped respectively for simplicity in calculations (see Chap. 2, Sec. 2-3.2). If we define

$$q'_2 = \theta / R_2 \quad , \tag{5-58}$$

we may rewrite Eq. (2-144) as

$$q'_n = C_1 C_2 R_1 R_2 \, q'_2 + (C_1 R_2 + C_2 R_2 + C_1 R_1) \, q'_2 + q'_2 \quad . \tag{5-59}$$

Hence the fuel rod transfer function is

$$\frac{q'_2(s)}{q'_n(s)} = \frac{1}{C_1 C_2 R_1 R_2 \, s^2 + (C_1 R_2 + C_2 R_2 + C_1 R_1) \, s + 1} \quad . \tag{5-60}$$

The effective time constant of a UO_2 fuel rod is different for various heat transfer mechanisms. The heat transfer coefficient to water, before DNB, is usually very high and the clad temperature is approximately equal to the water temperature. Thus, only the pellet capacitance is considered in a power transient. The resulting time constant is C_1R_1, which is approximately 8 sec for the Yankee-Rowe fuel rod. In case of a film boiling, the heat-transfer coefficient at rod surface is so low that R_2 approaches infinity. The time constant for transient heat transfer between the pellet and clad is $R_1C_1C_2/(C_1 + C_2)$, which is approximately 2.5 sec for the Yankee fuel rod.

To facilitate a parameter study of the fuel-rod transient behavior, these parameters were re-grouped by Tong,[32] who rearranged Eq. (2-144) and its boundary conditions Eq. (2-143) into

$$\frac{(T_{2,\max} - T_c)}{q_n'(0)} = Z \left(\frac{\beta_2}{\beta_1}\right)^{\beta_1/(\beta_1-\beta_2)} \times \left(\frac{Z}{Y}\right)^{\beta_2/(\beta_1-\beta_2)} + 0.22R_{2,fb} \quad , \quad (5\text{-}61)$$

where

$$Y = \left[R_{2,0} - R_{2,fb} - \frac{1}{\beta_2 A_c} \left(1 - \frac{R_{2,0}}{R_{2,fb}}\right)\right] \exp(\beta_1 \tau_1) + R_{2,fb}(1 - 0.22)$$

$$Z = \left[\frac{\beta_1}{\beta_2}(R_{2,0} - R_{2,fb}) - \frac{1}{\beta_2 A_c}\left(1 - \frac{R_{2,0}}{R_{2,fb}}\right)\right] \exp(\beta_2 \tau_1) + \frac{\beta_1}{\beta_2} R_{2,fb}$$

$$\times (1 - 0.22) \quad , \tag{5-62}$$

and

$$\tau_1 = t_1/r_1^2 \quad , \tag{5-63}$$

where

$t_1 = t_{\text{scram}} - t_{\text{DNB}}$
$r_1 = $ pellet radius
$\beta_1 = r_1^2 \alpha_1$
$\beta_2 = r_1^2 \alpha_2$
$A_c = C_2/r_1^2$
$0 = $ subscript indicating initial conditions
$f_b = $ subscript indicating film-boiling conditions

and α_1 and α_2 are the two roots of the homogeneous form of Eq. (2-136) as

$$C_1C_2R_1\alpha^2 + (C_1 + C_2 + C_1R_1/R_2)\alpha + 1/R_2 = 0 \quad . \tag{5-64}$$

It can be seen from Eq. (5-61) that the maximum clad temperature $(T_{2,\max})$ is a function of τ_1 and R_2 providing the physical properties of the pellet and clad and the steady-state power level $q_n'(0)$ are known. Now we can plot working curves to evaluate the influences of the thermal output of fuel rod, the pellet and rod sizes, the time interval between boiling crisis and effective scram, and the film-boiling heat-transfer coefficient on the maximum transient clad temperature in a loss-of-flow accident. In preparing the working curves shown in Fig. 5.16, the assumed physical parameters were:

c_1 of fuel $= 0.08$ Btu/(lb °F)
ρ_1 of fuel $= 635$ lb/ft^3

c_2 of clad = 0.16 Btu/(lb °F)

ρ_2 of clad = 474 lb/ft^3

k_1 = fuel thermal conductivity = 1.15 Btu/(h ft °F)

h_g = gap conductivity = 1000 Btu/(h ft^2 °F)

$h_{2,0}$ = steady-state heat-transfer coefficient = 5000 Btu/(h ft^2 °F)

$h_{2,fb}$ = heat-transfer coefficient in film boiling = 100 Btu/(h ft^2 °F)

Δr = clad thickness = 0.087 r_1.

The thermal resistance of the clad was neglected. Further, since the maximum clad temperature generally occurs within 10 sec from the instant power is lost, the coolant temperature can be taken as a constant and the decay bent during this period may be assumed constant at 0.22 $q_n'(O)$.

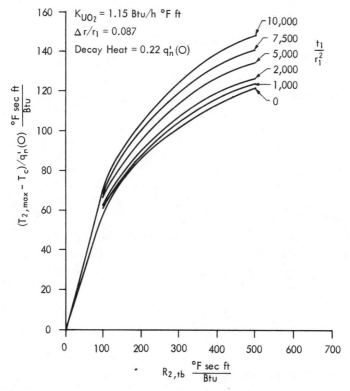

Fig. 5.16 Thermal transient parameters of a fuel rod. (From *Nucl. Sci. Eng.*, **9**, 306, 1959.)

Detailed Analysis. In many situations, the simplified analysis we have described will be adequate to demonstrate the safety of the system. However, in cores operating at high specific powers, the simplified approach may not be adequate, and the pump inertia must be considered to demonstrate the safety of the system. Numerical solutions to this problem have been presented by Arker and Lewis[33] and Boyd et al.[34] Burgreen[35] has considered the determination of coast-down flow when pump data are limited.

More recently, Fuls[36] has developed a numerical analysis and incorporated it into the FLOT computer code. The analysis requires that we know the flow through the pump at any instant. For a given pump, Fuls approximates the characteristic curves by

$$H/\omega^2 = (C_1)(F/\omega)(|F/\omega|) + C_2 \quad , \tag{5-65}$$

where

H = pump head, ft

F = volumetric flow through pump, ft^3/sec

ω = pump speed, rad/sec

C_1, C_2 = constants for given pump.

The absolute value of flow divided by speed provides an increasing negative pressure drop in case of reverse flow through the pump. To utilize Eq. (5-65), we must know the pump speed during the transient. This is obtained by applying Newton's Second Law to the pump to give

$$\Sigma T = \frac{d\omega}{dt}\left(\frac{I}{g_c}\right) \quad , \tag{5-66}$$

where

I = moment of inertia of the rotating parts, lb ft^2

ΣT = net torque rotating part, lb ft.

The major torques on the pump are the windage and bearing torques and the hydraulic torque on the impeller that arises as it imparts head to the fluid. For any given pump, the windage and bearing torques $T_{\omega b}$ can usually be described by

$$T_{\omega b} = C_3\left(\omega/\omega_s\right)^2 \quad , \tag{5-67}$$

where

C_3 = constant

ω_s = normal pump speed, rad/sec.

If the pump were 100% efficient, the hydraulic torque would be obtained by dividing the energy imparted to the fluid by the impeller

THERMAL AND HYDRAULIC PERFORMANCE

speed. In any real pump, the actual hydraulic torque is greater than we would calculate in this manner due to inefficiency in the transfer of energy to the fluid. These inefficiencies are taken as proportional to the square of the relative velocity between the impeller and the fluid. Thus, the total hydraulic torque T_h is given by

$$T_h = \frac{\rho FH}{\omega}\left(\frac{g}{g_c}\right) + C_4(\omega r - u)^2, \tag{5-68}$$

where

C_4 = constant for given pump

r = effective impeller radius, ft

u = fluid velocity, ft/sec.

Equation (5-66) then becomes

$$\frac{d\omega}{dt}\left(\frac{I}{g_c}\right) = -C_3(\omega/\omega_s)^2 - \frac{\rho FH}{\omega}\left(\frac{g}{g_c}\right) \oplus C_4(\omega r - u)^2. \tag{5-69}$$

The flow in a given loop is determined by rewriting Eq. (5-50) to allow for the pump head. If there is only one pump per loop, we may write for the j'th loop

$$\left(\frac{1}{g_c}\right)\frac{d}{dt}\left[\left(\frac{W'L'}{A'}\right)_R + \left(\frac{W'L'}{A'}\right)_L + \left(\frac{W'L'}{A'}\right)_{SG}\right] = -\left\{\left[\frac{C'}{\rho}\left(\frac{W'}{A'}\right)^{n_1}\right]_R\right.$$

$$\left. + \left[\frac{C'}{\rho}\left(\frac{W'}{A'}\right)^2\right]_L + \left[\frac{C'}{\rho}\left(\frac{W'}{A'}\right)^{n_2}\right]_{SG}\right\} + \rho H, \tag{5-70}$$

where

L' = axial length of component, ft

W' = mass flow through component, lb/sec

C' = pressure loss coefficients for individual components

A' = cross-sectional area of component, ft^2

and the subscript R refers to the reactor vessel, SG refers to the steam generator, and L refers to the loop. The exponents n_1 and n_2 allow a pressure-loss relationship other than one dependent on the square of the fluid velocity. By use of separate equations for each loop, transients in which only some of the pumps are lost may be considered. A set of continuity relationships must be written to relate the flows in the various components.

A finite difference method may now be used to solve the problem. Consider the simplest situation in which all pumps are lost simultaneously, and we can consider the entire system as if it were a single loop. Steady-state values for flow and pump speed are used to determine the rate at which the pump speed changes (Eq. 5-69). A short time interval is assumed, and the reduced head obtained from the pump is estimated from Eq. (5-65). The pump head is then used to obtain the change in flow over the time interval (Eq. 5-70). If desired, an average value of the original and reduced flow may then be used to reestimate the changes in pump speed, pump head, and loop flow. If the changes over the interval are within the desired limits, the calculation proceeds to the next time period using the reduced flow, speed, and head to estimate the new changes in conditions. The flow coastdown information obtained from this analysis would normally be used subsequently as input to a numerical analysis of the thermal behavior of the reactor fuel and coolant. A combined analysis of flow coastdown and thermal behavior is desirable.

The method of analysis discussed here can be used to determine the pump inertia that will ensure minimal temperature rises. This may be determined by a series of studies at varying pump inertia values.

5-5.4 Reactivity-Insertion and Steam-Break Accidents

In any reactivity-insertion accident, such as an uncontrolled rod withdrawal for a short time, a reasonable analysis requires consideration of the combined thermal-hydraulic-nuclear effects. A steam-break accident has many of the same characteristics. In the case of a rupture of a large steam line, there is an uncontrolled heat removal from the reactor, causing a rapid cooldown of the primary coolant system. This results in a reactivity addition that is compensated by boric-acid additions to the coolant. Check valves in the steam lines limit the steam blowdown to that from one steam generator.

A rod-withdrawal accident initiates a fast transient where an accurate representation of the reactivity feed-back effects is required. Redfield[37] has devised a coupled thermal-nuclear model, incorporated in the CHIC-KIN code, which considers the core to be represented by a single fuel element and associated coolant channel. The reactor is forced into transient conditions by either a reactivity insertion, or a coolant temperature or flow transient, or a system pressure transient.

CHIC-KIN assumes point reactor kinetics and solves the equations

$$\frac{dN}{dt} = \left(\frac{\delta k - \overline{\beta}}{l^*}\right) N + \frac{1}{l^*} \sum_{d=1}^{7} \overline{\beta}_d \, C_d$$

$$\frac{dC_d}{dt} = \lambda_d (N - C_d) \quad , \tag{5-71}$$

where

  N = neutron density

  $\overline{\beta_d}$ = effective neutron fraction, delayed neutron group d

  $$\overline{\beta} = \sum_{d=1}^{7} \overline{\beta_d}$$

  C_d = precursor concentration, delayed group d

  l^* = prompt neutron lifetime

  λ_d = decay constant, delayed neutron group d

and δk is defined by

$$\delta k = \delta k^\circ + \delta k(t) + \delta k_{TC} + \delta k_\rho + \delta k_{exp} + \delta k_{Doppler} \quad . \qquad (5\text{-}72)$$

The reactivity forcing functions are δk°, an initial step insertion, and $\delta k(t)$ a time-varying reactivity insertion. The feedback components are due to water temperature change (δk_{TC}), water density change (δk_ρ), fuel expansion (δk_{exp}), and fuel temperature change ($\delta k_{Doppler}$).

The total reactor power is assumed proportional to the neutron density N. The heat generation rate is assumed to be a separable function of space and time, with the spatial relationship preassigned. The heat conducted into the coolant is determined by an implicit solution of the heat conduction equations in finite difference form.

Coolant properties are obtained by simultaneous solutions of the equations of state and the conservation equations for mass, energy, and momentum. The momentum equation is put in its integral form in the manner described in Sec. 3-3.3. The coolant void fraction is computed on the basis of a homogeneous flow model.

Obenchain[38] has extended the CHIC-KIN model to consider several parallel coolant channels. Point kinetics are still assumed, but fuel and coolant conditions vary with radial channel location as well as axially. It is reported[39] that this revised model agreed very well with the results of reactivity transient studies of the SPERT program.

If a major steam break were to be accompanied by a stuck control rod, one would be concerned about local-flux distortion and the possibility of local damage. A point kinetics code cannot provide this information. Transient, three-dimensional flux codes with void feedback are not available. Fortunately, the reactivity transient initiated by a steam break is relatively slow. At any one time, the flux distribution is essentially that which would obtain in the steady state at the given reactor coolant conditions. Overall core conditions can thus be obtained from a simple transient computation, and these conditions may then be used as input to steady-state computation of the spatial-flux variation (e.g., by use of THUNDER[13]).

5-5.5 Loss-of-Coolant Accident (LOCA)

System Behavior. The most serious accident generally considered in the safeguards analysis is the hypothetical loss-of-coolant accident occasioned by the double-ended rupture of a main coolant pipe. If such an unlikely accident were to occur, the course of expected events would be:

1. Subcooled Blowdown. As described in Sect. 3-1.4, pressure waves are propagated through the system at sonic velocities. The system is rapidly depressurized until the vapor pressure of the coolant is reached. This period may be of the order of 5- to 50-msec long.

2. Saturated Blowdown. After the system pressure falls to the level of the coolant vapor pressure, steam voids are formed. The sonic velocity is drastically reduced, the pressure waves are damped out, and choked flow occurs at the break. The length of this period depends on the location and size of the break.

    During this period, the fuel rods are cooled by the fluid in the reactor core. Initially, high forced convection or nucleate-boiling heat-transfer coefficients prevail. As the fluid enthalpy increases, the boiling crisis may be reached leading to a marked reduction in core cooling. The clad temperature rise is reduced as the time between blowdown initiation and the boiling crisis is increased.

    The boiling crisis is generally predicted by means of one of the steady-state correlations described in Sec. 4-3.2. Since present indications are that the transient critical-heat flux is at least as high as the steady-state value, the procedure is conservative. Heat-transfer correlations suitable for use before and after the boiling crisis are indicated in Table 5.5.

3. Dry Period. As the blowdown proceeds, the inventory of the primary system decreases to the point where liquid, or rather the liquid-steam froth, falls below the top of the core. When the froth level is above the bottom of the core, the dry portion is cooled by steam generated in the lower region. When the froth level drops below the bottom of the core, the only core cooling is by radiation to the surrounding structure and by convection and radiation to the small amount of steam generated by froth contact with the vessel wall. Heat-transfer coefficients appropriate to radiation and convection to steam are indicated in Table 5.5.

Table 5-5

CORE COOLING HEAT TRANSFER CORRELATIONS

Process	Correlation	Typical Values	References
Nucleate boiling	$\Delta T_{sat} = 0.072 \, q''^{\,0.5} \, e^{-P/1260}$	$h = 50\,000$	Chap. 4, Ref. 21
Flow-film boiling	$h = 0.0193 \dfrac{k_{vf}}{D} \left(\dfrac{DG}{\mu_v}\right)_f^{0.80} \left(\dfrac{c_p \mu}{k}\right)_f^{1.23} \left(\dfrac{\rho_v}{\rho_b}\right)_f^{0.68} \left(\dfrac{\rho_v}{\rho_l}\right)^{0.068}$ $T_f = \frac{1}{2}(T_{wall} + T_{sat})$, $\rho_b = \alpha \rho_v + (1-\alpha)\rho_l$	$150 < h < 5000$	Chap. 4, Ref. 45
Pool-film boiling at high pressures	$h = 0.28 \left[\dfrac{k_v g \, \delta_v^3}{\nu_v^2} \left(\dfrac{\rho_l - \rho_v}{\rho_v}\right)\right]^{0.33}$	$150 < h < 300$	Chap. 4, Ref. 49
Pool-film boiling at low pressures	$h = 0.7 \left[\dfrac{k_v^3 \, \rho_v (\rho_L - \rho_v) \, g h_{lg}}{L \, \Delta T \, \mu_v}\right]^{0.25}$	$25 < h < 60$	Chap. 4, Refs. 50 and 51
Turbulent forced convection to steam	$h = 0.020 \dfrac{k}{De} (Re_b)^{0.8} (Pr)_b^{0.4} \left(\dfrac{T_b}{T_w}\right)^{0.5}$	$15 < h < 70$	Chap. 4, Ref. 48
Radiation to steam/water mixture	$h = \dfrac{\sigma(T_w^4 - T_b^4)}{\left(\dfrac{1}{\epsilon_1} + \dfrac{1}{\epsilon_2} - 1\right)(T_w - T_b)}$ $\epsilon_1 = \epsilon_{oxide} = 0.8 - 1.0$ $\epsilon_2 = \alpha \, \epsilon_{steam} + (1 - \alpha)\epsilon_{water}$ $= (1 - 0.8\alpha)$	$5 < h < 250$	Chap. 4, Ref. 53

4. Emergency Cooling Period. The emergency cooling system has
two functions. It attempts to maintain good core cooling in the
period immediately following the break when heat fluxes are
high. It then attempts to ensure that the core is re-covered, or
remains covered, so that the residual decay heat can be removed. The first of these functions is accomplished by injection
of coolant water from high-pressure accumulators when the
primary pressure falls to a predetermined level. The second
function is accomplished by high-flow pumps, which refill the
reactor vessel after the accumulator injection has stopped and
the system pressure has fallen further. By these means, the
length of time the high-power region of the core remains uncovered is minimized. During this phase of the accident, the
heat-transfer process observed depends on whether water is
injected from below or above the core. For bottom injection,
the flow distribution is rather even and the cooling is effective.
The heat-transfer mechanism is expected to have two stages:

- As the cold water first comes in contact with the fuel
  cladding, it will be exposed to the fuel-rod temperatures
  considerably in excess of the water-saturation temperature. Initially, the water will not be able to wet the surface, and thus pool-film boiling exists. The surface
  above this level will experience steam cooling.

- The water soon will be able to penetrate the steam film
  and nucleate boiling will result (rod is quenched).

Heat-transfer coefficient correlations for the flow regimes
encountered are given in Table 5.5. The complexity of the
situation can make it difficult to determine the applicable flow
regime; therefore, the results of empirical studies of the
reflooding region are sometimes relied upon. Farman et al.[40]
present their data, obtained from a single 0.422-in.-diam rod,
in terms of the average coefficient between flooding and quench.

A spray system is generally used for top injection. The flow
distribution may be expected to be nonuniform. In spray cooling, the maintenance of a cooling liquid film on the heating surface is of vital importance. Two mechanisms, sputtering and
flooding, can reduce the film cooling effectiveness considerably.

- The sputtering or Leidenfrost temperature is the temperature above which a water film is ejected from the heated
  surface. It has been observed in Sec. 4-3.3 that this
  temperature is about 50°F above saturation at 30 psia and
  250°F above saturation at 1000 psia.

- Flooding is a condition wherein the upward steam velocity
  is large enough to trip and stop the downward motion of

the liquid film. This phenomenon has been examined in a counter flow by Shires and Pickering.[41] The data could be correlated in terms of nondimensional flooding velocities V_g^+ and V_i^+, which are defined by

$$V_g^+ = \frac{V}{\sqrt{g\,D_e}}\sqrt{\frac{\rho_v}{\rho_l}} \qquad (5\text{-}73)$$

$$V_L^+ = \frac{V}{\sqrt{g\,D_e}} \quad , \qquad (5\text{-}74)$$

where V_g and V_L are the superficial gas and liquid velocities, and D_e is the equivalent diameter of the passage. The data for 7-rod and 37-rod bundles indicate:

$$\sqrt{V_g^+} + \sqrt{V_L^+} = 1.10 \quad . \qquad (5\text{-}75)$$

This equation was obtained by spraying the test rods with water before heat was applied to them. The flooding line as represented by Eq. (5-75) will be much lower if the fuel rod surface was originally red hot.

Estimation of Fuel Rod Temperature. In the preliminary design of the emergency-cooling system, it is often desirable to be able to estimate the total time the core hot spot can remain uncovered before clad melting begins. Clad and fuel temperatures can be calculated by the Laplace transformation of the lumped-parameter equations for the fuel rod developed in Chap. 2. Equations (2-133) and (2-134) can be written as

$$\Pi = \tau_1\,\frac{dT_1}{dt} + T_1 - T_2 \qquad (5\text{-}76)$$

$$\lambda(T_1 - T_2) = \tau_2\,\frac{dT_2}{dt} + T_2 - T_c \quad . \qquad (5\text{-}77)$$

It will be recollected that

T_1 = average pellet temperature

T_2 = average clad temperature

T_c = bulk coolant temperature

and other parameters are as defined previously. We define

$$\Pi = R_1 q_n' \qquad (5\text{-}78)$$

$$\lambda = R_2/R_1 \qquad (5\text{-}79)$$

$$\tau_1 = C_1 R_1 \qquad (5\text{-}80)$$

$$\tau_2 = C_2 R_2 \ . \tag{5-81}$$

Since the τ_1, τ_2, and λ are constants, the solution of Eq. (5-76) and (5-77) can be obtained by using a Laplace transformation

$$T_1(s) = \frac{\lambda\Pi(s) + (\tau_1 s + 1)T(s) + \lambda\tau_1 T_{1,0} + \tau_2(\tau_1 s + 1)T_{2,0}}{\tau_1\tau_2 s^2 + (\tau_1 + \tau_2 + \lambda\tau_1)s + 1} \tag{5-82}$$

$$T_2(s) = \frac{(\tau_2 s + 1 + \lambda)\Pi(s) + T(s) + (\tau_2 s + 1 + \lambda)\tau_1 T_{1,0} + \tau_2 T_{2,0}}{\tau_1\tau_2 s^2 + (\tau_1 + \tau_2 + \lambda\tau_1)s + 1}. \tag{5-83}$$

We solve for the above temperatures by letting

$$\Delta(s) = \tau_1\tau_2 s^2 + (\tau_1 + \tau_2 + \lambda\tau_1)s + 1 = (s + \alpha_1)(s + \alpha_2) \quad , \tag{5-84}$$

where α_1 and α_2 are the roots of the expression. The partial fraction expansion is then written as

$$T(s) = \frac{K_1}{(s - \alpha_1)} + \frac{K_2}{(s - \alpha_2)} \quad , \tag{5-85}$$

and the functions $T_1(t)$ and $T_2(t)$ are determined from the inverse transformation providing expressions for q_n^1 are available. Approximate expressions that may be used for the decay heat in the fuel are

$$\frac{q_n'}{q_{n,o}'} = 0.06e^{-0.0025} + 0.20e^{-0.1\prime}, \quad \text{for} \quad t \leqq 50 \text{ sec} \tag{5-86}$$

$$\frac{q'}{q_{n,o}'} = 0.132t^{-0.22}, \qquad\qquad \text{for} \quad 50 < t \leqq 1000 \text{ sec} \ . \tag{5-87}$$

An even simpler estimation of cladding temperature is possible when it may be assumed that the heat transfer between the hot spot and the neighboring "warm spot" is solely by radiation. The heat flux q'' can then be calculated as[42]

$$q_r'' = \frac{0.173 \times 10^{-8}[(T_{\text{hot}} + 460)^4 - (T_{\text{warm}} + 460)^4]}{(1/\epsilon_1 + A_1/(A_2\epsilon_2) - A_1/A_2)}, \tag{5-88}$$

where

ϵ_1 and ϵ_2 are the emissivities of the hot and warm rods

A_1 is the surface area of hot rod

A_2 is the equivalent area of neighboring warm rods.

For a quick estimation of the time for the first clad meltdown (i.e. $T_{\text{hot}} = 2550\ °\text{F}$ for stainless-steel clad), q_r'' can be assumed as equal to the heat flux of hot spot due to decay heat at the time t_1. The number of warm rods is usually large; therefore, it can be assumed they are heated by their own decay heat without being significantly affected by radiation from the other rods. We may then calculate the temperature of the clad at the warm spot at any given time t_1. When the temperature so calculated, T_{warm} equals that calculated from Eq. (5-88) with T_{hot} equal to the melting temperature; time t_1 corresponds to the beginning of clad melting. In this estimation, note that no steam cooling at the time of melting is considered, and the effect of any steam-cladding reaction is also ignored.

Detailed Calculations. The complex nature of the coolant blowdown and core heat-up phenomena have lead to the development of a number of calculational models. Waage[43] provides a good review of the techniques that were available in 1967.

In the subcooled and early saturated blowdown portions of the accident, the designer is concerned with the effect of the pressure pulses (water-hammer) on the core, reactor vessel structure, loop components, and supports. To obtain the forces acting around the system, a detailed hydraulic analysis is required. By solving the wave equations (Sec. 3-1.4) algebraically, Fabic[44] was able to develop a relatively rapid method for computing system behavior during subcooled blowdown. The solution procedure requires the assumption of a constant sonic velocity and therefore cannot be used once portions of the system fall below the saturation pressure. Since significant pressure waves may still exist, it is desirable to extend the analysis into the two-phase region. Fabic[44] has done this using the method of characteristics which has been outlined in Sec. 3-1.4. A similar procedure was followed by Goulding,[45] but Nahavandi,[46] on the other hand, chose to represent the system by a node-and-branch model (Sec. 3-1.4) and to integrate the resultant differential equations numerically.

Any of the techniques capable of following the water-hammer analysis into the two-phase region must provide a detailed representation of the reactor system. Therefore, such computations of system behavior, which cover more than a few hundred miliseconds of real time, become very expensive. However, in less than a few hundred milliseconds, the pressure pulses will generally be damped to levels that are no longer of concern. The designer is then concerned with determining the rate at which core temperatures are changing. To accomplish this, he needs an estimate of the froth level in the core and the steam-flow rate through any uncovered portion of the core. Margolis and Redfield[47] and Redfield and Murphy[48] have recognized that a much more approximate representation of the system may suffice for this purpose. In the very early portion of the accident, flow velocities are so high that a homogeneous model may be used to represent the steam-water mixture although this is not true as the accident progresses. During most of the accident the steam bubbles will be rising at a significant rate with respect to the liquid. Accordingly, in their FLASH model, the reactor system is represented by a series of control volumes; a typical control volume is shown in Fig. 5.17. A steam phase and steam-water mixture are both assumed to exist within each control volume, and steam bubbles

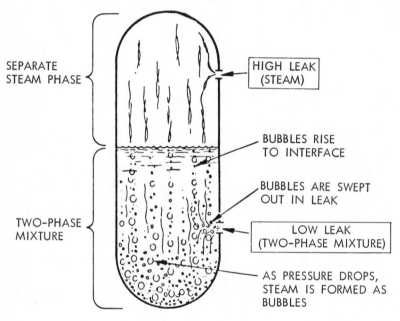

Fig. 5.17 FLASH representation of control volume. (From *Nucl. Appl.*, **6**, 127, 1969.)

are assumed to be created by bulk flashing of the liquid and then to rise. A mass balance on the steam trapped below the surface of the liquid is used to compute the height of the two-phase system. Initially, a constant bubble rise velocity of 2 ft/sec relative to the container was assumed, and the time t_B, required for a bubble to leave the froth in a given control volume, was

$$t_B = u_B/z_f \quad , \tag{5-89}$$

where u_B = bubble velocity (2 ft/sec) and z_f = height of froth. Redfield and Murphy[49] report that better agreement is obtained with experimental data when

$$t_B = u_B/z_l \quad , \tag{5-90}$$

where z_l = height of liquid only in the froth layer. The value of u_B remains at 2 ft/sec.

The connection of a series of control volumes to represent a simple reactor system is shown in Fig. 5.18. Flow between the control volumes is computed by application of the one-dimensional momentum equation. It will be observed that this computational

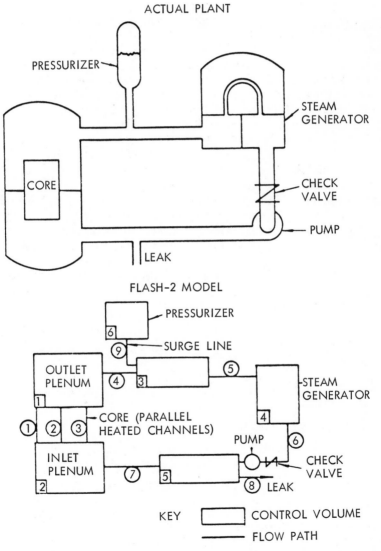

Fig. 5.18 FLASH representation of a single loop reactor plant. (From *Nucl. Appl.*, **6**, 127, 1969.)

procedure is another application of the node-and-branch approach. The model is capable of handling rod-ejection transients since point reactor kinetics, similar to those described for CHIC-KIN (Sec. 5-5.4) are included. The increase in fuel-element temperature is determined by considering the fuel to be a single axial section with a lumped-heat capacity.

In view of the simplified heat transfer approach, a model such as FLASH is generally not considered to provide a sufficiently detailed view of core behavior. The significant results of FLASH-type calculations, core-inlet flow and enthalpy as a function of time, are commonly used as input to a more detailed calculation of core temperatures. In the model of Walters et al.,[50] the core is considered to be made up of a series of annular rings, and it is further divided into axial segments, each of which may contain several node points. The temperatures of the node points are computed throughout the accident by an explicit numerical solution of the conduction equations (Sec. 2-3.1). Boundary conditions are the heat-generation rate and the heat-transfer conditions. The latter are determined from the inlet conditions and the heat transfer to the coolant that has taken place below the node considered. No allowance is made for any flow redistribution or mixing between channels.

When a portion of the core is uncovered, the heat generated in that region must include the heat obtained from any cladding-steam reaction. The reaction between zirconium and steam is of greatest concern. Under the usual conditions, the reaction rate is controlled by solid-state oxidation kinetics. The experimental data available have been described by Baker and Just[51] in terms of a parabolic rate law

$$W^2 = (33.3 \times 10^6\, t)\, \exp(-45\,000/RT) \quad , \qquad (5\text{-}91)$$

where

W = weight of zirconium oxidized, mg/cm^2

T = temperature of unoxidized zirconium, °K

t = time, sec

R = universal gas constant, 1.987 cal/mole °K.

This reaction rate can be related to the distance δ that the metal-metal oxide interface has moved from its original position by

$$d\delta/dt = (K/\delta)\, \exp(-45\,000/RT) \quad , \qquad (5\text{-}92)$$

where K = parabolic rate law constant (0.3937 cm^2/sec).

Walters et al.[50] observe that as the zirconium-water reaction proceeds, the gas in the upper portion of the core may become largely hydrogen. As the steam concentration is reduced, the diffusion of steam through the boundary layer adjacent to the reacting cladding may become the rate limiting step. When this occurs, we may write

$$d\delta/dt = k_c C_S (M_{zr}/2\rho_{zr}) \quad , \qquad (5\text{-}93)$$

where

k_c = mass transfer coefficient

C_S = concentration of steam in the flowing stream

M_{zr} = molecular weight of zirconium

ρ_{zr} = density of zirconium.

The value of k_c is obtained by employing the heat-mass transfer analogy. The reaction rate is then taken as the smaller of the values obtained by Eqs. (5-92) or (5-93).

Models similar to that of Walters[50] have been proposed by Iyer[52] and Cybulskis et al.[53]; however, in these models, the geometry considered is that of an assembly of fuel rods. Iyer[52] confines his consideration to a single channel, but Cybulskis et al.[53] consider coupled channels and allow for flow redistribution at the core inlet to maintain a constant pressure drop across the hot and average channel.

All the models for reactor-core heat transfer after the loss of coolant assume the basic core configuration remains intact; which implies that the emergency core cooling system operates properly. One may postulate the very unlikely coincidence of a loss-of-coolant accident followed by a failure of the emergency cooling system. In that hypothetical event, it would be impossible to prevent melting of the cladding and fuel. Some of the various core-melt models summarized by Fontana[54] predict that a molten mass of fuel and cladding would collect at the bottom of the reactor vessel. The molten material would displace any water below the vessel, and heat the concrete between it and the containment. Since concrete will not withstand the temperatures involved, suggestions have been made for use of a ceramic lined core catcher.[54] Zivi[55] has pointed out that the rate of penetration of the ceramic barrier is reduced by an order of magnitude if the core mass floats on the barrier. This can be achieved by use of an unenriched UO_2 barrier, which, Zivi computes, would prevent melt through of the containment vessel.

Comprehensive studies[56] of the loss-of-coolant accident have indicated that proper design and operation of the emergency core-cooling system can provide reasonable assurance that no core melt-down will occur. It was observed[56] that safeguards analyses assume major malfunctions despite great efforts at plant quality control, fail-safe features, and redundancy. Engineered safeguards are provided to keep the plant safe despite such failures. Next, these engineered safeguards are assumed to fail simultaneously with the accident they are expected to safeguard, and the consequences are determined. If additional means to rescue the situation can be found, these may be provided. The analysis then continues by assuming these to fail. Obviously, such a system of building a pyramid of failures can always be carried to the point where it would be impossible to cope with the highly artificial situation created. However, the likelihood of the situation arising becomes vanishingly small.

REFERENCES

1. C. M. FREIDRICH and H. W. GUILINGER, "CYGRO-2, a FORTRAN IV Computer for Stress Analysis and the Growth of Cylindrical Fuel Elements with Fission Gas Bubbles," USAEC Report WAPD-TM-547, Bettis Atomic Power Laboratory (1966).

2. B. W. LeTOURNEAU and R. E. GRIMBLE, "Engineering Hot Channel Factors for Nuclear Reactor Design," *Nucl. Sci. Eng.*, **1**, 359 (1956).

3. HAROLD CHELEMER and L. S. TONG, "Engineering Hot Channel Factors for Open Lattice Cores," *Nucleonics*, **20**, *9*, 68 (1962).

4. A. HALD, *Statistical Theory with Engineering Applications*, John Wiley & Sons, Inc., New York (1950).

5. D. B. OWEN, "Tables of Factors for One-Sided Tolerance Limits for a Normal Distribution," USAEC Report SCR-13, Scandia Corporation (April 1958).

6. W. E. ABBOTT, "Statistical Analysis of the Measurements from SELNI Fuel Assemblies," WCAP-3269-7, Westinghouse Atomic Power Division (1963).

7. G. HETSTRONI, "SCE Hydraulic Studies," WCAP-3269-8, Westinghouse Atomic Power Division (June 1964).

8. R. A. DEAN, "Mixing Vane Tests," WCAP-2678, Westinghouse Atomic Power Division (September 1964).

9. D. S. ROWE, "Gross Flow Mixing Between Parallel Flow Channels During Boiling, Part I, COBRA Computer Program," USAEC Report NBWL-371, Part 1, Pacific Northwest Laboratory (1967).

10. R. W. BOWRING, "HAMBO—A Computer Programme for the Subchannel Analysis of the Hydraulic and Burnout Characteristics of Rod Clusters, Part I," UKAE Report AEEW-R-524, Atomic Energy Establishment, Winfrith, England (1967).

11. J. WEISMAN, A. H. WENZEL, L. S. TONG, D. FITZSIMMONS, W. THORNE, and J. BATCH, "Experimental Determination of the Departure from Nucleate Boiling in Large Rod Bundles at High Pressures," *Chem. Eng. Prog. Symp. Ser.*, **64**, *82*, 114 (1968).

12. F. R. VAUGHAN, "The Effect of Multi-Pass Hydraulic Core Configurations in PWR Core 2," ASME Paper 62-HT-45 (1962).

13. G. H. MINTON, "Inter-relating Aspects of the Evolutionary Development of Larger Scale Digital Computers and Nuclear Power Reactors," Proceedings of International Conference on Utilization of Research Reactors and Reactor Mathematics and Computation, Mexico City, Report CNM-R-2, Centro Nucleare de Mexico, Mexico City (1967).

14. H. V. SMITH, "A Process Optimization Program for Nonlinear Optimization (POP II)," IBM Systems Research Institute, White Plains, New York, Project Report (1965).

15. J. WEISMAN, C. F. WOOD, and L. RIVLIN, "Optimal Design of Chemical Process Systems," *Chem. Eng. Prog. Symp. Ser.*, **61,** *55,* 50 (1965).

16. A. V. FIACCO and G. P. McCORMICK, *Nonlinear Programming—Sequential Unconstrained Minimization Techniques,* John Wiley & Sons, Inc., New York (1968).

17. G. HADLEY, *Nonlinear and Dynamic Programming,* Addison-Wesley Publishing Co., Reading, Massachusetts (1964).

18. W. I. ZANGWILL, *Nonlinear Programming*: *A Unified Approach,* Prentice Hall, New York (1969).

19. G. ANTOGNETTI, G. POZZI, J. D. De BRUYN, and G. Di COLA, "Statistical Methods for Hot Channel and Hot Spot Calculators," USAEC Euratom Report EUR-1702.e, Fiat Co., Turin, Italy (1964).

20. V. L. BUSINARO and G. P. POZZI, "A New Approach to Engineering Hot Channel and Hot Spot Statistical Analysis," USAEC Euratom Report EUR-1302.e, Fiat Co., Turin, Italy (1964).

21. L. S. TONG, "Heat Transfer in Water-Cooled Nuclear Reactors," *Nucl. Eng. Design,* **6,** 301 (1967).

22. Rochester Gas and Electric Corporation Brookwood Nuclear Station Unit No. 1, Third Supplement to: Preliminary Facility Description and Safety Analysis Report, AEC Docket 50-244, Exhibit D-3 (1966).

23. H. FENECH and H. M. GUERON, "The Synthesis Method of Uncertainty Analysis in Nuclear Reactor Thermal Design," *Nucl. Sci. Eng.,* **31,** 505 (1968).

24. "General Design Criteria for Nuclear Power Plant Construction Permits," U.S. Federal Register (July 11, 1967) and 10 CFR 50, Appendix A.

25. Code of Federal Regulations, Section 50.36(d) of 10 CFR 50. Licensing of Production and Utilization Facilities, U.S. Federal Register 31 (158)-10891 (1966).

26. "Zion Station—Preliminary Safety Analysis Report," Vol. II, Section 7.1.2, Commonwealth Edison Co., Chicago (1967).

27. O. J. ORTEGA and K. P. BASKIN, "Operating Experiences: San Onofre-PWR," *Nucl. Safety,* **9,** 153 (1968).

28. L. S. TONG, "Thermal Operating Performance of Nuclear Reactors," A panel discussion held at the Fifth National Heat Transfer Conference, Houston, Texas, August 1962, DAVID MILLER, Ed., p. 58, USAEC Report TID-7669.

29. "Supplementary Hazards Criteria," American Nuclear Society—American Standards Association, Nuclear Systems Engineering Subcommittee, Draft Report, American Nuclear Society, Hinsdale, Ill. (1968).

30. J. A. REDFIELD and S. G. MARGOLIS, "TOPS—A Fortran Program for Transient Thermodynamics of Pressurizers," USAEC Report WAPD-TM-545, Bettis Atomic Power Laboratory (1965).

31. J. A. REDFIELD, V. PRESCAP, and S. G. MARGOLIS, "Pressurizer Performance During Loss-of-Load Tests at Shippingport: Analysis and Test," *Nucl. Appl.*, **4**, 173 (1968).

32. L. S. TONG, "Simplified Calculation of Thermal Transient of a Uranium Dioxide Fuel Rod," *Nucl. Sci. Eng.*, **11**, 340 (1961).

33. A. J. ARKER and D. G. LEWIS, "Rapid Flow Transients in Closed Loops," USAEC Report TID-7529, Part 1 (1957). See also *Reactor Handbook, Engineering, Vol. IV*, S. McLAIN and J. H. MARTENS, Eds., pp. 135-139, Interscience Publishers, New York (1964).

34. G. M. BOYD, Jr., R. M. ROSSER, and B. B. CARDWELL, Jr., "Transient Flow Performance in a Multiloop Nuclear Reactor System," *Nucl. Sci. Eng.*, **9**, 442 (1961).

35. D. BURGREEN, "Flow Coastdown in a Loop After Pumping Power Cutoff," *Nucl. Sci. Eng.*, **6**, 306 (1959).

36. G. M. FULS, "FLOT-1: Flow Transient Analysis of a Pressurized Water Reactor During Flow Coastdown," USAEC Report WAPD-TM-428, Bettis Atomic Power Laboratory (1968).

37. J. A. REDFIELD, "CHIC-KIN: A Fortran Program for Intermediate and Fast Transients in a Water Moderated Reactor," USAEC Report WAPD-TM-479, Bettis Atomic Power Laboratory (1965).

38. C. F. OBENCHAIN, "PARET: A Program for the Analysis of Reactor Transients," Proceedings of International Conference on Utilization of Research Reactors and Reactor Mathematics and Computation, Mexico City, Report CNM-R-2, Centro Nucleare de Mexico, Mexico City (1967).

39. C. F. OBENCHAIN, "Thermal-Hydraulic Aspects of Nuclear Excursions," Paper presented at Second Joint Meeting American Institute of Chemical Engineers and Instituto de Ingeneros Quimicos de Puerto Rico, Tampa, Florida, A.I.Ch.E., New York (1968).

40. R. F. FARMAN, R. H. LEYSE, D. P. DOMINICUS, and J. O. CERMAK, "Bottom Flooding Heat-Transfer Results for Single Rod Tests," *Trans. Am. Nucl. Soc.*, **12**, 352 (1969).

41. G. L. SHIRES and A. R. PICKERING, "The Flooding Phenomenon in Counter Current Two-Phase Flow," University of Exeter Symposium, England (June 1965).

42. J. P. HOLMAN, *Heat Transfer*, 2nd ed., Equation 8-38, McGraw-Hill, New York (1963).

43. J. M. WAAGE, "Description of Calculational Methods and Digital-Computer Codes for Analyzing Coolant-Blowdown and Core-Heatup Phenomena," *Nucl. Safety*, **8**, 549 (1967).

44. S. FABIC, "Westinghouse Atomic Power Department Computer Program for Calculation of Fluid Pressure, Flow, and Density Transients During a Loss of Flow Accident," *Trans. Am. Nucl. Soc.*, **12**, 358 (1969).

45. H. GOULDING, "An Analytical Experimental Comparison of the Initial Response of High Enthalpy Water During Decompression," *Trans. Am. Nucl. Soc.*, **11**, 366 (1968).

46. A. NAHAVANDI, "Loss of Coolant Accident Analysis in Pressurized Water Reactors," *Nucl. Sci. Eng.*, **36**, 159 (1969).

47. S. G. MARGOLIS and J. A. REDFIELD, "FLASH: A Program for Digital Simulation of the Loss of Coolant Accident," USAEC Report WAPD-TM-534, Bettis Atomic Power Laboratory (1966).

48. J. A. REDFIELD and J. H. MURPHY, "The FLASH-2 Method for Loss of Coolant Analysis," *Nucl. Appl.*, **6**, 127 (1969).

49. J. A. REDFIELD and J. H. MURPHY, "Void Fraction and Residual Water Predictions During a Loss of Coolant Accident," *Trans. Am. Nucl. Soc.*, **11**, 686 (1968).

50. C. T. WALTERS, J. M. GENCO, and G. RAINES, "Heat Transfer Analysis in Loss-of-Coolant Accidents," *Nucl. Eng. Design*, **7**, 123 (1968).

51. L. J. BAKER and L. C. JUST, "Studies of Metal-Water Reactions at High Temperatures III—Experimental and Theoretical Studies of the Zirconium-Water Reaction," USAEC Report ANL-6548, Argonne National Laboratory (1962).

52. J. S. IYER, "ECCSA-I: A Digital Computer Program for Thermal and Hydraulic Analysis of Core Channels in the Event of a Nuclear Reactor Loss-of-Coolant Accident," USAEC Report BMI-1832, Battelle Memorial Institute (1968).

53. P. CYBULSKIS, W. A. CARBIENER, R. E. HOLMES, and R. A. CUDNIP, "Application of the ECCSA-4 and MUCHA Computer Codes to Emergency-Core-Cooling Analyses," *Trans. Am. Nucl. Soc.*, **12**, 353 (1969).

54. M. H. FONTANA, "Core Melt-Through as a Consequence of Failure of Emergency Core Cooling," *Nucl. Safety*, **9**, 14 (1968).

55. S. M. ZIVI, "A Passive Safety Device Against a Melt-Through Accident," *Nucl. Appl.*, **5**, 53 (1968).

56. W. K. ERGEN, L. BAKER, E. S. BECKJORD, A. P. BRAY, J. DIETRIC, S. LEVY, I. H. MANDIL, D. L. MORRISON, W. E. NYER, J. M. WAAGE, R. E. WASCHER, and T. R. WILSON, "Emergency Core Cooling," Report of Advisory Task Force on Power Reactor Emergency Cooling, U. S. Atomic Energy Commission, Washington, D. C. (1967).

Index